AN ELEMENTARY TREATISE

ON

CURVE TRACING

BY

PERCIVAL FROST, Sc.D., F.R.S.

FELLOW OF KING'S COLLEGE
FORMERLY FELLOW OF ST. JOHN'S COLLEGE, CAMBRIDGE

REVISED BY

R. J. T. BELL, M.A., D.Sc.

LECTURER IN MATHEMATICS, UNIVERSITY OF GLASGOW

FIFTH EDITION

CHELSEA PUBLISHING COMPANY
NEW YORK, N.Y.

THE PRESENT, FIFTH, EDITION IS A REPRINT OF THE
FOURTH EDITION, WITH A REARRANGEMENT OF PLATES

LIBRARY OF CONGRESS CATALOG CARD NUMBER 60-10348

FIRST EDITION, 1872
SECOND EDITION, 1892
THIRD EDITION, 1911
FOURTH EDITION, 1918
FIFTH EDITION, 1960

PRINTED IN THE UNITED STATES OF AMERICA

PREFACE

I DO not much like the idea of writing a preface, but I feel myself obliged to say a few words on the publication of what I have called a treatise, the term being very likely a misnomer.

Although my subject is Curve-tracing and not Curves, I am aware that some complete branches of this art are not alluded to at all.

The student might expect, in a treatise upon this subject, to find methods of drawing Polar Curves, Rolling Curves, Loci of Equations in Trilinear Coordinates, and Intrinsic Equations; he might also expect to find interesting Geometrical Loci discussed; these, and many other things immediately connected with the tracing of curves, have been deliberately omitted, for reasons which I consider good.

A treatise, if I had ventured upon it, at all comparable in exhaustive qualities with the excellent one of Salmon on Curves of Higher Orders, would have demanded, on the part of the student, far more extensive reading than I suppose him to possess; such a treatise would have required an advanced knowledge of Differential and Integral Calculus, of Higher Algebraical processes which do not appear in elementary treatises on Algebra, and of the science of projections, to understand which involves a familiarity with Solid Geometry, beyond the standard to which I have supposed the student to have attained.

My readers must not be disappointed if they do not meet with an historical survey of the researches which have been made in old times on modes of generation and properties of particular curves; and in modern times on the singularities of curves; such a survey would have been irrelevant to the object which I have proposed to myself.

I acknowledge myself, nevertheless, indebted to many of those old mathematicians for ideas, and especially to Cramer, for many curves which I have employed in illustrating points on which I have been engaged.

In cutting off so many vital parts of a complete treatise, I have to shew that I do not fall to the ground by sawing on the wrong side the branch on which I am sitting; I shall therefore explain, in as few words as I can, the objects which I have had in view in my work as it stands.

In order to make any rapid progress, in after years, in all the difficult subjects to which mathematical analysis is applied, it is absolutely necessary that, by some means or other, a student should, as early as possible, make himself familiar with all the ordinary instruments of his trade, such as he handles when he studies Algebra, Trigonometry, and Algebraical Geometry; his tastes may carry him with greater impetus in one direction than another, but he should remember that it is necessary to be strong all round, and even against the grain he should use efforts to avoid having weak points.

He must practise himself, while he is young and his mind flexible, in all sorts of analytical processes and geometrical artifices. The solution of a great number of equations may be looked upon as one of the best exercises of one sort of faculties, and familiarity with the Binomial Theorem and cognate subjects as essential, such as approximation to roots, expansion of a variety of functions in Algebra and Trigonometry, reversion of series, etc., accurate numerical calculations not being avoided.

I have reason to think that this kind of preliminary preparation for the study of the higher branches of mathematics has been much neglected in later years, and I am fortified in this opinion by observations made by Examiners of the greatest experience, who complain both of a want of power of work and of a want of individuality in the manner in which particular problems are attacked; this they attribute to defective early training and the omission of that practice which I have described as necessary.

Whether this practice has been neglected principally in consequence of the temptation to push forward to certain physical subjects, which have been recommended for the use of schools, I cannot say; but I have no doubt that the feeling of dignity acquired by entering upon the field of the Physical Sciences has enticed many a student from a course which, if pursued, would have enabled him to do in a few weeks what it has taken him many months to puzzle over.

If there is time for a student not only to attend to the dry work of polishing, but also to make himself acquainted with a little Mechanics and Hydrostatics, he should by all means do so; but everyone who has examined in public schools knows how little time there is for the study of Mathematics, and how sensible the mathematical masters are of the insufficiency of this time. Looking, therefore, upon the total amount of energy as nearly constant, I should have no hesitation in reserving for some future time the study of the Physical Sciences, which will not eventually suffer; whereas, to attempt after a certain age to acquire ease in mathematical operations is like a grown man trying to learn the violin.

Having, then, a distinct feeling of the absolute necessity of developing skill and power—I will not add cunning—and, at the same time, being perfectly sensible in what dry places the poor spirit of a student has been condemned to wander in the performance of his duty, I have selected the subject of this work in order to relieve him in the dull work involved in his preparation for climbing heights, by taking him along a very pleasant path, on which he may exercise in an agreeable way all his mathematical limbs, and, if he keeps his eyes open, may see a variety of things which it will be useful to have observed when his real work begins.

For the subject, which I have chosen with this object in view, presents so many faces, pointing in directions towards which the mind of the intended mathematician has to radiate, that it would be difficult to find another which, with a very limited extent of reading, combines, to the same extent, so many valuable hints of methods of calculations to be employed hereafter, with so much pleasure in its present use.

For example, the subject of Graphical Calculations is coming more into use every day, and is applied with success to many difficult problems in Statics, Engineering, and Crystallography; hints of this the student will find in the practical solution of divers equations and in the determination of the number of their real roots, which are obtained by graphical methods with great facility.

Again, the methods of successive approximations which are employed in Optics and Astronomy are illustrated in the process of finding asymptotes and approximations to the forms of curves at a finite distance.

The comparison of large and small quantities of different orders of magnitude contains the staple of many of the most important applications of Mathematical Analysis; the Lunar and Planetary Theories depending almost entirely upon such considerations of relative magnitude.

The habit of looking towards an infinite distance, and discussing what takes place there, will render less startling a multitude of conceptions having in them a tendency to produce a feeling of vagueness, such, for instance, as the treatment of the mechanical effect of a couple as synonymous with that of an infinitely small force acting at an infinitely great distance.

As an important point, I would mention the tentative character of the inverse problem in which the form of a curve being given, its equation is investigated; the kind of uncertainty which will remain on the mind on account of defective estimation of magnitudes; and the necessity of a selection of what may appear the best of many possible solutions; all this will prepare the student for the disappointment which, having perhaps a wrong notion of what is meant by calling mathematics an exact science, he will feel in the conflict of theories by which it is attempted to reconcile the results of experiment in such subjects as Heat, Light, Electricity, and Molecular action generally; for an instance of this I may refer to the battle of philosophers about the direction of vibration of the ether in Plane Polarization.

The very uncertainty which exists in these subjects, the necessary balancing of evidence, and the difficulty of making up the mind as to what is to be believed, place such subjects, in the opinion of one at least of our greatest philosophers, among the best for the training of the intellect.

Looked upon as a special preparation for a special subject, I hope that my treatise may be considered useful in having given clear ideas, when the student enters upon the systematic treatment of the properties of curves; especially since the classification of curves according to degrees, and the subdivision of curves of the same degree into species is now being taken in hand by some eminent mathematicians.

With regard to the rejection of methods supplied by the Differential Calculus, I may observe that since the equations whose loci are investigated are rational equations, and never rise to a high degree, little would have been gained by the employment of such methods, since the Binomial Theorem is sufficient for all my purposes, and as ready in its application; independently of the consideration that I suppose myself to be instructing a student whose reading has been confined to very narrow limits.

As to the last chapter on Inverse Methods I trust that it will be looked upon as only a sketch. I have no doubt that the subject of it is capable of considerable perfection, and I shall be glad to have commenced, however defectively, so instructive a study.

To save the student trouble I may observe that I have
used, as sufficiently near approximations in estimating their
values, $\sqrt{3}=\frac{7}{4}$, $\sqrt{5}=\frac{9}{4}$, $\sqrt{7}=\frac{8}{3}$, $\sqrt{6}=\frac{5}{2}$, $\sqrt{10}=\frac{16}{5}$; and,
with a view to the graphical solution of equations, I should
advise him to practise himself in drawing a good parabola
and in tracing readily the hyperbola from the equation
$xy=ax+by+c$ for a variety of values of a, b, c.

I may mention here that I have used the symbol (α, β)
for ' a point whose coordinates are α and β '; and instead of
speaking of a curve as ' the locus of the equation, $f(x, y)=0$,'
or as ' represented by the equation,' I have called it simply
the curve $f(x, y)=0$.

For obvious reasons I have represented the fraction $\frac{a}{b}$
by a/b, also $\equiv$ is used for ' is equivalent to.'

In concluding this preface, or apology, I desire to say
that I have read, with much advantage, some notes on
Newton's enunciation of Lines of the Third Order by
C. R. M. Talbot; and that I am indebted for some valuable
hints to the late Professor Clifford; but, especially, I must
acknowledge myself in the highest degree indebted to two
gentlemen, Mr. H. G. Seth Smith and Mr. G. L. Rives, of
Trinity College, for their extreme kindness in guarding me
against errors, when I was preparing my first edition. The
nature of the subject rendered it extremely difficult to avoid
mistakes; and, although very great pains have been taken to
give correct drawings of the large number of curves which
have been discussed, I am aware that in this edition there
is still much that is open to censure.

CAMBRIDGE, *January*, 1892.

PREFACE TO REVISED EDITION

THE present edition of Frost's *Curve Tracing* does not differ from previous editions except in places where alterations were necessary to remove ambiguities or to correct mistakes. No effort has been spared to detect errors in the analysis as well as in the diagrams, and it is hoped that this edition will be found to be comparatively free from inaccuracies.

In the forty-five years that have elapsed since the book was first published, graphical work has taken an increasingly prominent place in mathematical instruction; so that to the modern student a few parts of the work may appear to be very elementary. The reader of moderate mathematical attainments will, however, always find in its perusal much that is interesting and instructive, while there is no other book that contains in such compact form the detailed discussion and the diagrams of so many beautiful curves.

To facilitate the use of the volume as a work of reference, a classified list of the curves and an index have been added.

R. J. T. B.

GLASGOW, *November*, 1917.

CONTENTS

CHAPTER I.

INTRODUCTORY THEOREMS.   DEFINITIONS.   TRACING BY POINTS.
SYMMETRY.

ARTS.		PAGE
3–4	Theorems for working - - - - - - - - -	2
5	Definitions - - - - - - - - - -	5
6	Curves traced by points - - - - - - - -	6
7	Symmetry - - - - - - - - - -	7
	Examples I. - - - - - -	8

CHAPTER II.

ORDERS OF SMALL QUANTITIES.   FORMS OF PARABOLIC CURVES NEAR THE
ORIGIN.   CUSPS.   TANGENTS TO CURVES.   CURVATURE.

		PAGE
9–10	Orders of small quantities - - - - - - -	9
11–12	Standards of vanishing quantities - - - - -	10
13–14	Graphic construction of parabolic curves - - - -	12
15	Tracing of $y^m = cx^n$ near the origin - - - - -	13
16	Shape at any point - - - - - - - -	14
17	Example of a point of inflexion - - - - -	15
18	Algebraical representation of a cusp - - - - -	15
19–20	Tangent to a curve - - - - - - - -	16
21	Measure of curvature - - - - - - - -	17
22	Circle of curvature - - - - - - - -	18
	Examples II. - - - - - -	18

CHAPTER III.

FORMS OF PARABOLIC CURVES AT AN INFINITE DISTANCE.   EXAMPLES OF
TRACING CURVES.   TRIGONOMETRICAL CURVES.   ILLUSTRATIONS OF
THEORY OF EQUATIONS.   RULES FOR APPROXIMATION.

26–28	Forms of parabolic curves at a great distance from the origin	20
29–31	Examples of finding a tangent to a curve, where it is parallel to an axis, and the position of a point of inflexion -	21

ARTS.		PAGE
32–33	Examples of tracing curves in which y can be expressed in terms of x explicitly - - - - - - -	22
35–38	Curves representing changes of trigometrical functions -	28
39–41	Illustrations of theory of equations - - - -	29
42–45	Condition for a point of inflexion - - - -	31
47–49	Graphic solution of equations - - - - -	32
51	Working formulæ for approximation - - - -	33
52	Illustrations of methods of approximation - - -	34
	Examples III. - - - - -	36

CHAPTER IV.

FORMS OF CURVES IN THE NEIGHBOURHOOD OF THE ORIGIN. SIMPLE
TANGENTS. DIRECTION AND AMOUNT OF CURVATURE. MULTIPLE POINTS
OF TWO BRANCHES. CURVATURE OF BRANCHES AT MULTIPLE POINTS.
MULTIPLE POINTS OF HIGHER ORDERS.

54	Forms of curves near the origin - - - - -	39
55–57	Simple tangent - - - - - - -	39
58–60, 62	Conic of curvature - - - - - -	40
60, 61	Circle and diameter of curvature - - - -	41
63	Examples of curvature - - - - - -	42
64	Tangent to $u_1 + u_1v_1 + u_3 + \ldots = 0$ - - - -	44
66	Tangents to multiple points of two branches - -	45
67–69	Form of $v_1w_1 + u_3 + \ldots = 0$ - - - -	45
70, 71	,, $v_1w_1 + u_4 + \ldots = 0$ - - - -	48
72, 73	,, $v_1w_1 + v_1v_2 + u_4 + \ldots = 0$ - - -	49
74, 75	,, $v_1^2 + u_3 + \ldots = 0$ - - - -	51
76, 77	,, $v_1^2 + v_1v_2 + u_4 + \ldots = 0$ - - -	51
78, 79	,, $v_1^2 + w_1^2 + u_3 + \ldots = 0$ - - -	53
80, 81	Curvature of branches at multiple points - - -	54
82, 83	Multiple points of higher orders - - - -	54
	Examples IV. - - - - -	56

CHAPTER V.

FORMS OF BRANCHES WHOSE TANGENTS AT THE ORIGIN ARE THE
COORDINATE AXES.

84–88	Forms when x and y are of different orders of magnitude -	58
89	Tentative methods - - - - - - -	61
90	Rules for rejecting terms - - - - - -	61
91	Worked examples - - - - - - -	62
	Examples V. - - - - -	66

CHAPTER VI.

ASYMPTOTES.   POINTS OF INTERSECTION AT AN INFINITE DISTANCE.
ASYMPTOTES PARALLEL TO THE AXES.

ARTS.		PAGE
94, 95	Rectilinear and curvilinear asymptotes	68
96–98	Intersection of curves with their asymptotes	69
99–102	Comparison of singular asymptotes with tangents at points of inflexion and multiple points at a finite distance	71
103, 104	Worked example	73
106, 107	Determination of asymptotes by points of intersection at an infinite distance	74
107–110	Worked examples	74
112	Method by approximation	79
113	Cases of x alone infinite	80
114	Side on which the curve lies	80
115, 116	Varieties in the determination of asymptotes which are parallel to the axes	81
117	Examples of asymptotes	82
	Examples VI.	87

CHAPTER VII.

ASYMPTOTES NOT PARALLEL TO THE AXES.   ASYMPTOTES TO HOMOGENEOUS
CURVES.

119	Simple examples of asymptotes not parallel to the axes	88
120	Illustration by multiple points at a finite distance	90
121	General statement of the method of finding by approximation those asymptotes which are not parallel to either axis	90
122–124	Side on which the curve lies	91
125	Case of a parabolic asymptote	92
126	Investigation of a proper parabolic asymptote	93
127	Examples of parabolic asymptotes	93
128–130	Parallel rectilinear asymptotes	95
131	Direct method of expansion	97
132	Observations relating to the side on which the curve lies	97
134	Homogeneous curves and their asymptotes	100
	Examples VII.	106

CHAPTER VIII.

CURVILINEAR ASYMPTOTES.

136–138	Infinite branches when x and y are not of the same order of magnitude	109
	Examples VIII.	115

CONTENTS

CHAPTER IX.

THE ANALYTICAL TRIANGLE. PROPERTIES OF THE ANALYTICAL
TRIANGLE.

ARTS.   PAGE
140–143   Newton's parallelogram and De Gua's triangle   -   -   - 117
144   Modified form in which the triangle is employed in this
          work   -   -   -   -   -   -   -   -   -   -   - 119
145–147   Statement and proof of properties of the triangle   -   - 119
148   Examples of the use of the triangle   -   -   -   -   - 122
                            Examples IX.   -   -   -   -   - 131

CHAPTER X.

SINGULAR POINTS. DIVISION INTO COMPARTMENTS. SPECIAL CURVE OF
THE FOURTH DEGREE.

157–160   Degeneration of curves of the form $y^m = cx^n$ -   -   - 135
161, 162 General conditions for singular points -   -   -   - 137
163   Examples of singular points   -   -   -   -   -   - 138
164–166   Assistance derived from compartments   -   -   -   - 143
167, 168 Methods of detecting isolated portions of a curve   -   - 149
170–192   Symmetrical curve of the fourth degree of the form
          $(y^2 \mp x^2)\{(\tfrac{1}{2}y - 1)^2 \mp x^2\} + \mu(y + a) = 0$ -   -   -   - 152
                            Examples X.   -   -   -   -   - 165

CHAPTER XI.

SYSTEMATIC TRACING OF CURVES. REPEATING CURVES.

194   Rules for systematic tracing   -   -   -   -   -   - 167
195–197   Worked examples   -   -   -   -   -   -   -   - 168
199–202   Class of repeating curves   -   -   -   -   -   - 177
                            Examples XI.   -   -   -   -   - 184

CHAPTER XII.

INVERSE PROCESS. DETERMINATION OF THE EQUATION OF A
GIVEN CURVE.

210–212   Difficulties of the inverse process -   -   -   -   - 186
213–215   First steps towards the solution of the problem -   -   - 187
217–222   Method of making use of the analytical triangle -   -   - 193
223   Use of the rule of signs   -   -   -   -   -   - 195
225   Examples of use of rule of signs -   -   -   -   - 195
226–231   Use of partial curves and compartments   -   -   -   - 200
                            Examples XII.   -   -   -   - 202

          CLASSIFIED LIST OF THE CURVES DISCUSSED   -   -   - 203

          INDEX   -   -   -   -   -   -   -   -   -   -   - 209

AN ELEMENTARY TREATISE ON CURVE TRACING.

CHAPTER I.

INTRODUCTORY THEOREMS. DEFINITIONS. TRACING BY POINTS. SYMMETRY.

PLATE
I.

1. In order to understand this work on the tracing of curves whose equations are given in Cartesian coordinates, all that is required of the student is that he shall know the ordinary rules of Algebra as far as the Binomial theorem, the fundamental theorems of the Theory of Equations, and the general methods employed in Algebraical Geometry.

Since my object is neither to arrange the curves into classes, nor to shew systematically by what transitions one curve can be transformed into another by gradual changes of constants, nor to investigate properties of the curves, except incidentally, it will not be necessary to have much knowledge of what is called Higher Algebra, nor of Algebraical Geometry of a higher kind than that which simply relates to the Conic Sections.

It would be some advantage to have read the first section of Newton's Principia, but I hope that questions concerning limits and curvature will be made clear independently of such reading.

2. There are many reasons why at this point of his mathematical studies a student should have his attention directed to this subject, in a general way, without any

PLATE
I.

attempt to do for curves of higher degrees what has been done so completely for curves of the second degree.

He will, for example, find himself better able to appreciate the illustrations which are used to make clear many theorems of the Differential Calculus, Theory of Equations, etc.; he will have definite ideas of the relative magnitudes of small quantities, and of infinitely great quantities : and especially he will become skilled in making correct approximations to the values of quantities which cannot be found exactly, to any degree of accuracy which may be required.

And, at the same time, I hope that he will have much to interest him in the great variety which this application of Algebra to Geometry will open out to him.

INTRODUCTORY THEOREMS.

3. In order to prevent interruption in the course of the work as much as possible, I shall call attention to a few propositions with which some of my readers may not be familiar.

(1) If α, β, ... be the n values, real or imaginary, called roots, which make $f(x)$, any rational or integral function of x, vanish, then $f(x)$ will be indentically equal to

$$a(x-\alpha)(x-\beta) \ldots \text{ to } n \text{ factors,}$$

supposing a to be the coefficient of the highest power of x in $f(x)$; consequently, the coefficient of x^{n-1} in $f(x)/a$ is the sum of the n roots with their signs changed, that of x^{n-2} is the sum of the products taken two together, and so on.

(2) If $F(x, y)$ denote a homogeneous function of n dimensions of the form $ay^n + bxy^{n-1} + \ldots + gx^r y^{n-r} + \ldots + px^n$, and m_1, m_2 ... be the n roots of $at^n + bt^{n-1} + \ldots + p = 0$, $F(x, y)$ will be identical with $a(y - m_1 x)(y - m_2 x) \ldots$, and the equation $F(x, y) = 0$ will represent n straight lines, real or imaginary, passing through the origin.

If we write y^2 for y, $F(x, y^2)$ will be a homogeneous function of x and y^2, and will represent a series of parabolas, corresponding to the n values of $y^2 : x$.

PLATE
I.

(3) If $f(x, y)$ and $\phi(x, y)$ be homogeneous functions of x and y, each of n dimensions, and $x/l = y/m = r$, then

$$\frac{f(x, y)}{\phi(x, y)} \equiv \frac{ax^n + bx^{n-1}y + \ldots + ky^n}{\alpha x^n + \beta x^{n-1}y + \ldots + \kappa y^n} = \frac{f(l, m)}{\phi(l, m)}.$$

(4) In order to shew what is the form of a curve, whose equation is given, in the neighbourhood of any point (α, β), it is convenient to obtain an equation for which the origin is (α, β) and the direction of the axes the same as before; this transformation is effected by substituting $\alpha + \xi$ and $\beta + \eta$ for x and y. Since the equations with which we have to deal are never of a very high degree, this can be done, in particular cases, as easily by common algebraical methods as by any other; but, for the sake of general statements, it is well to notice the law of formation of the coefficients in the expansion of $f(x + \xi)$, where $f(x)$ is a rational integral function of x. This law is given by the differential calculus, but for the student who is not acquainted with that calculus, the law, in the case we are considering, may be established as follows:

Suppose gx^r to be one of the terms of $f(x)$, then the coefficients of ξ, $\frac{1}{2}\xi^2$, $\frac{1}{6}\xi^3 \ldots$ in $g(x + \xi)^r$, given by the binomial theorem, are grx^{r-1}, $gr(r-1)x^{r-2}$, $gr(r-1)(r-2)x^{r-3} \ldots$ and similarly for each term of $f(x)$; hence, if $f'(x)$ be the coefficient of ξ, $f'(x)$ is obtained from $f(x)$ by multiplying each term by the index of the power of x in it, and then diminishing the index by unity. The coefficient of $\frac{1}{2}\xi^2$ is obtained from $f'(x)$ in the same way as $f'(x)$ from $f(x)$, and is written $f''(x)$, and so on, whence

$$f(x + \xi) = f(x) + f'(x)\,\xi + \tfrac{1}{2}f''(x)\,\xi^2 + \ldots.$$

(5) If $u \equiv u_n + u_{n-1} + \ldots + u_s + \ldots + u_1 + u_0$, where $u_s(s < n)$ is a rational homogeneous function of the sth degree, the curve $u = 0$ (i) and the straight line $lx + my = 1$ (ii) intersect in n points, real or imaginary. For, the values of x and y being the same at every point of intersection, we may eliminate x or y between (i) and (ii), and the resulting equation, being of the nth degree, will have n roots; or

PLATE
I.

we may make the equation (i) homogeneous, by means of (ii), obtaining

$$u_n + u_{n-1}(lx+my) + \dots + u_0(lx+my)^n = 0,$$

which, by the theorem (2), represents n straight lines through the origin. Any other combination of the two equations gives rise to a curve which passes through the n points of intersection. An application of this theorem shews that, when we have tried to trace a curve, if we see that some straight lines could be drawn which would cut the curve in more points than the degree of the curve, there must have been something wrong in the work.

4. The following examples serve to illustrate the theorems given above.

Ex. 1. Suppose we wish to find the form of the curve

$$2y + x^3 - 6x + 5 \equiv 2y + (x-1)(x^2+x-5) = 0$$

in the neighbourhood of $(1, 0)$, for x we write $1+\xi$, ξ being the abscissa with a new origin $(1, 0)$; then $2y = 3\xi - 3\xi^2 - \xi^3$. Considering points which correspond to numerically small values of ξ, as, for instance, $\xi = \frac{1}{10}$, the three terms in the value of y being then in the ratio $1 : \frac{1}{10} : \frac{1}{300}$, $y = \frac{3}{2}(\xi - \xi^2)$ very nearly. The curve is therefore below the line $y = \frac{3}{2}\xi$, whether ξ be $+$ or $-$, and more and more nearly coincides with it as ξ diminishes and ultimately vanishes. The shape near $(1, 0)$ is given by fig. 1.

Fig. 1.

Ex. 2. Consider the curve $x^3 + y^3 - 3axy = 0$, and let the three points in which it is intersected by a straight line $lx + my = 1$ be P, Q, R. By the theorem (5) the three radii OP, OQ, OR are given by $x^3 + y^3 - 3axy(lx+my) = 0$ (i), so that if θ, ϕ, ψ be the inclinations of these lines to Ox, $\tan\theta \tan\phi \tan\psi = -1$.

If $l = m$, the inclination of one of the radii, suppose OP, will be $135°$, and since $\tan\phi = \cot\psi$, OQ and OR will be equally inclined to Ox and Oy. For the shape of the curve, see fig. 2, Plate v.

DEFINITIONS.

PLATE
I.

5. The following definitions are required :

A point of inflexion is a point at which the tangent to the curve cuts the curve, so that the curve bends as in the figure.

Fig. 2.

A multiple point is a point in a curve through which more than one distinct branch passes ; a multiple point may be double, triple, etc., as in the figures.

Figs. 3, 4.

A point of osculation is a multiple point through which two branches pass which have a common tangent at that point.

Fig. 5.

A cusp is a point at which two branches of a curve touch, but through which they do not pass.

A cusp of the first species, called a *ceratoid* cusp, is one in which the branches lie on opposite sides of the common tangent.

Fig. 6.

A cusp of the second species, called a *ramphoid* cusp, is one in which the branches lie on the same side.

Fig. 7.

A conjugate point is an isolated point, whose coordinates satisfy the equation, but through which no branches pass, such as a circle or ellipse would become if the diameter or axes were made indefinitely small.

All these points are called *Singular Points.*

An *asymptote* of a curve is a line towards which the curve finally approaches, as we recede from the origin to an infinite distance, and from which the distance of points on the curve becomes less than any assignable quantity.

An *asymptote* may be either curvilinear or rectilinear.

When a rectilinear asymptote is meant, this condition of indefinite approach is supposed to hold in every case.

A proper curvilinear asymptote satisfies the same condition, but it is usual, for want of a better term, to call any curve, which serves as a guide to the direction of the flexure in an infinite branch, an asymptotic curve.

TRACING BY POINTS.

PLATE
I.

6. The most rudimentary way of tracing curves is to map down a number of points whose coordinates satisfy the equation of a curve, the points being taken in some order, and the number so large that no branch may escape; if there be a doubt how to fill up any of the intervening spaces, more points must be interpolated.

Ex. 1. Take the curve $y = x(x^2 - 1)$.

When $\quad x = 0, \quad \frac{1}{4}, \quad \frac{1}{2}, \quad \frac{3}{4}, 1, \quad \frac{5}{4}, \quad \frac{3}{2}, \quad \frac{7}{4}, \quad 2,$

$\qquad 64y = 0, \ -15, \ -24, \ -21, \ 0, \ 45, \ 120, \ 231, \ 384.$

If the sign of x be changed, that of y will be changed, the magnitudes being unaltered.

Fig. 8. If these points be mapped down as in the figure, a rough picture of the curve can be drawn without investigating the exact angles at which the curve cuts the axes, or the exact points at which the tangent to the curve is parallel to the axis of x, which we shall see is somewhere between $x = \frac{1}{2}$ and $\frac{3}{4}$, say about $\frac{5}{8}$.

Ex. 2. Again, take the curve $x^4 - 3axy^2 + 2ay^3 = 0$. Although we cannot solve the equation with regard to x or y, we can obtain a number of points by assuming $y = zx$, whence $x = (3 - 2z)z^2a$.

When

$\quad z = 0, \quad \frac{1}{4}, \quad \frac{1}{2}, \quad \frac{3}{4}, \quad 1, \quad \frac{5}{4}, \frac{3}{2}, \qquad \frac{7}{4}, \qquad 2,$

$32x = 0, \ 5a, \ 16a, \ 27a, \ 32a, \ 25a, \ 0, \ -49a, \ -128a,$

$32y = 0, \ \frac{5}{4}a, \ 8a, \ \frac{81}{4}a, \ 32a, \ \frac{125}{4}a, \ 0, \ -\frac{343}{4}a, \ -256a,$

$\quad z = \qquad \frac{5}{2}, \qquad 3, \quad -\frac{1}{4}, \quad -\frac{1}{2}, \qquad -1, \qquad -2,$

$32x = \ -400a, \ -864a, \ 7a, \ 32a, \ 160a, \ 896a,$

$32y = -1000a, \ -2592a, \ -\frac{7}{4}a, \ -16a, \ -160a, \ -1792a.$

Fig. 9. The points are mapped in the figure as far as space will allow.

To obtain a dubious part of the curve near the origin, it would be sufficient to interpolate two more values in the neighbourhood of $z = \frac{3}{2}$,

PLATE
I.

thus, if $\quad z = \frac{3}{2} - \frac{1}{8} = \frac{11}{8}, \quad x = \frac{121}{256}a, \ y = \frac{11}{8}x,$

if $\quad z = \frac{3}{2} + \frac{1}{8} = \frac{13}{8}, \quad x = -\frac{169}{256}a, \ y = \frac{13}{8}x,$

and to notice that z, which is $\tan POx$, diminishes as x changes from $-\frac{169}{256}a$ to $\frac{121}{256}a$.

In this manner it would be possible to give a very exact representation of the locus of many equations, within the limits of the paper, if we did not care for the trouble of interpolating values when the direction of the curve was at all doubtful.

The main object of a work on tracing curves must be to point out a variety of considerations which will relieve the student from a great deal of this labour, and enable him to indicate generally the peculiarities of a curve, its changes of direction and curvature, the interlacing of its branches, etc., while he can always for any particular purpose have recourse to more exact determination of special parts of the curve.

SYMMETRY OF A CURVE.

7. One of the first considerations is the symmetry of a curve with respect to certain lines or points, by means of which the labour is reduced one-half at once.

The principal kinds of symmetry arising from the form of the equation are as follows:

(1) If the rationalised equation of the curve involve only even powers of y, as $y^4 - b^2y^2 + ay^2x - cx^3 = 0$, the curve will be symmetrical with respect to the axis of $\overset{\circ}{x}$, for, if (x, y) be a point in the curve, $(x, -y)$ will also be in the curve. The figure will be the same as if a plane mirror were placed perpendicular to the paper on the axis of x.

If the equation involve only even powers of x, there will be symmetry with respect to Oy.

(2) If the equation be not altered when $-x$ and $-y$ are written for x and y, as when $x^4 - a^2xy + b^2y^2 = 0$, this shews that, when P is a point on the curve, and PO is joined, and produced to P', making $P'O = PO$, P' is also a point on the curve. In other words, O is a centre of the curve, and

Fig. 10.

PLATE
I.

the curve is symmetrical in opposite quadrants; so that, if yOx contained any part of the curve, and the figure were turned in its own plane through two right angles, it would overlie another portion of itself as it was in the original position.

(3) If the equation be unaltered when x and y are interchanged, as when $x^5 - 2a^3x^2 + 5a^3xy - 2a^3y^2 + y^5 = 0$, for every point $P(x, y)$ on the curve there will be a point $Q(y, x)$ also on the curve, so that the curve will be symmetrical with respect to a line bisecting the angle yOx, as in the figure.

Fig. 11.

Similarly, if $(-y, -x)$ may be substituted for (x, y) without altering the equation, as in $x^3 - 3axy - y^3 = 0$, this would shew symmetry with respect to a line bisecting the angle of $x'Oy$.

(4) There are other kinds of symmetry, but it is scarcely worth the trouble of looking out for them except as tests of the tracing. Thus, the substitution of $-x$ for y and y for x, may not alter the equation, as in $x^4 + a^2xy - y^4 = 0$. Such a curve would evidently shew no change of form if it were turned through a right angle in its plane.

Fig. 12.

Examples I.

1. Employ the method given in (5), Art. **3,** to prove the following :

(1) If a tangent to a circle whose equation is
$$x^2 + y^2 = a^2b^2/(a^2 + b^2)$$
meet an ellipse, whose equation is $x^2/a^2 + y^2/b^2 = 1$, in P and Q, prove that PQ will subtend a right angle at the centre of the ellipse.

(2) The equation of a hyperbola is
$$xy - 2x - 3y + 5 = 0.$$
Shew that the two chords which pass through (0, 2), and subtend a right angle at the origin, are inclined to Ox at angles 135° and $\cot^{-1}5$.

2. Construct the loci of the following equations :

     (1) $y^4 - 3axy^2 + 2a^2x^2 = 0.$ (2) $x^4 - a^2x^2 + 2a^2xy - a^2y^2 = 0.$

3. Trace the curves whose equations are given below, by means of particular points :

     (1) $y = x - 2x^2 + x^3.$ (2) $x^3 + y^3 - 3axy = 0.$ (3) $y^3 = x^2(x - a).$

CHAPTER II.

ORDERS OF SMALL QUANTITIES. FORMS OF PARABOLIC CURVES NEAR THE ORIGIN. CUSPS. TANGENTS TO CURVES. CURVATURE.

PLATE I.

8. IF the student has taken the trouble to trace one or two curves by points, he will at once appreciate the advantage which it would be to him to have at every point the direction of the curve and that of its bend, as well as the point itself; for he would obtain a much more accurate representation of the curve with far fewer points.

The first thing I shall endeavour to make clear is the way to determine the shape of a curve in the neighbourhood of a point through which it passes; and since, by transformation, every point at a finite distance can be made a new origin of coordinates, it will be sufficient to discuss the form of any curve in the neighbourhood of the origin in cases in which it passes through it.

The form of the curve at points at an infinite distance will be discussed hereafter.

ORDERS OF SMALL QUANTITIES.

9. In handling this subject we are obliged to distinguish accurately such expressions as small, very small, infinitely small, vanishing, ultimately vanishing, large, infinitely large quantities, and to speak of things being equal, nearly equal, and so on; a few words may be useful to those who have not been in the way of dealing with variable quantities, which, although they vanish simultaneously, do not tend necessarily to equality though they both be zero.

PLATE
I.

10. Finite quantities are said to be exactly equal when their difference is nothing.

Finite variable quantities become equal when their difference vanishes.

But it is evident that this is not a proper definition of equality of magnitudes which are themselves vanishing quantities. For, $2x$ is as truly double of x, when x is indefinitely small, as two inches are double of one, and yet the difference x vanishes. Hence the necessity of another definition.

Variable quantities are said to become equal, when their difference vanishes compared with either of them.

We may add that quantities are nearly equal, when the ratio of their difference to either of them is small.

11. Now, with regard to great and small things, it must be remembered that no quantity is absolutely small or great, but only so with reference to some unit either expressed or implied in the nature of the subject.

In measuring a degree, four yards would be a very large error, while in sweeping for the lost end of the Atlantic cable a couple of hundred yards was thought a small error in the supposed position.

In ancient times eight minutes was a small error in an astronomical observation; in modern times eight seconds is enormous.

Thus, when a unit has been determined in any subject in which a calculation is to be made, we must ask what is considered small—is it to be a tenth or a hundredth of the unit, or what other fraction ?

Just as the unit of measurement was arbitrary, so the standard of smallness must be selected before the idea of what is small can be made definite for purposes of calculation.

Again, something more definite must be determined upon than the degrees of smallness or largeness expressed by the vague terms, very small or very large, extremely small or minute.

PLATE I.

For this purpose, having fixed upon what we determine to consider small, we introduce the terms small quantities of the second, third, etc. orders; the small quantities of the second order having the same ratio to those of the first order as those standard small quantities have to the unit employed.

Thus, in the Lunar Theory, fractions varying between $\frac{1}{12}$ and $\frac{1}{20}$ are called small compared with unity, $(\frac{1}{12})^2$ a small fraction of the second order, and so on, and complete calculations of the motion of the moon have been made to the sixth or seventh orders of small quantities.

If α be the fraction of the unit which is taken as the standard of smallness, and the exact value of u in terms of α be $a+b\alpha+c\alpha^2+\ldots$ to any number of terms, then

$$b\alpha+c\alpha^2+\ldots < \frac{k\alpha}{1-\alpha},$$

where k is the greatest of the magnitudes $b, c, \ldots$. Thus a differs from u by a quantity of the first order, and a is called the first approximation; similarly $a+b\alpha$ is called the second approximation, etc.; these approximations imply that $k\alpha : a$ is of the same order as α, which circumstance must guide us in the selection of the standard.

It follows that whatever be the coefficients, still supposed finite, α can always be taken so small that a, $a+b\alpha$, ... are first, second, etc. approximations to the value of u, to any degree of accuracy.

12. When a variable quantity is supposed capable of being diminished until it becomes less than any assignable quantity, it is called a vanishing quantity, and if it be taken as the standard, finite multiples of its square, cube, etc. are called vanishing quantities of the second, third, etc. orders; so that, if $u_1, u_2, u_3, \ldots$ be vanishing quantities of the first, second, third, etc. orders, the ratio $u_{n+1} : u_n$ is of the first order, $u_3 : u_1$ of the second, and so on; and if $v : u$ be a vanishing quantity, v is said to be of a higher order than u.

PLATE
I.

13. A graphic notion of the closeness of the approximations mentioned above will be obtained by tracing the curves $y = x^2$, $y = x^3$, $y = x^4$, ..., called parabolic curves, from $x = 0$ to $x = 1$, using the same coordinate axes for all the curves, so that the relative magnitudes of the ordinates of the different curves, corresponding to any small value of x which we choose, may be seen, if x be not chosen too small, and conceived from the general run of the curves, if x be chosen extremely small. The ordinates of these will be magnitudes of the second, third, ... orders, the standard being the chosen value of x. In the figure, $OA = AB$ is taken as the unit, and $Oa = \frac{1}{2}$, $Ob = \frac{1}{4}$, $Oc = \frac{1}{8}$.

Fig. 13.

The ordinates for the lines $y = x$, x^2, x^3, ...

corresponding to a, are $a\alpha_1$, $a\alpha_2$, $a\alpha_3$, $a\alpha_4$...
.........………....…..b, are $b\beta_1$, $b\beta_2$, $b\beta_3$,...
...............……….....c, are $c\gamma_1$, $c\gamma_2$,....

Each of the ordinates $a\alpha$ is $\frac{1}{2}$ of the preceding, each of $b\beta$ is $\frac{1}{4}$ of the preceding, each of $c\gamma$ is $\frac{1}{8}$ of the preceding, and the ordinates, corresponding to $Od = \frac{3}{4}$, have been constructed in order to guide to the general forms of the curves, five of which are placed in the figure.

We observe that, with a value of $x = \frac{1}{2}$, the ordinate of $y = x^6$ is very small, while, for $x = \frac{1}{4}$, we can distinguish neither the curve $y = x^5$ nor $y = x^6$, and for $x = \frac{1}{8}$, $y = x^4$ is not distinguishable from the corresponding point in the line of abscissæ. If we take an abscissa $Og = \frac{1}{4} Oc$ or $\frac{1}{32}$, a length which is sufficiently visible, all the curves are coincident as far as we can see by our diagram.

Some idea can thus be formed of the nature of the approximations to $a + bx + cx^2 + ...$ when x is excessively small.

14. I have traced these curves by setting off particular points within the limits proposed, because in cases of this simplicity, the method shews sufficiently that there are no sinuosities, and it is easy to follow the form in the mind's eye up to any value of x however small. It should be observed that the reason why all the curves touch the axis of x at the origin is because y is of a higher order than x.

If we trace the curves for negative values of x, it will be seen that those with odd powers will occupy the opposite quadrant $x'Oy'$, as $O\beta_3'$, $O\alpha_5'$, and those with even powers will be symmetrical with respect to the axis of y, as $O\beta_2'$, $O\alpha_4'$.

Fig. 13.

If we trace beyond $x=1$, the ordinate of $y=x^4$ becomes greater than that of $y=x^3$, and all the curves diverge very rapidly from one another as x increases, and very soon spread beyond the range of the paper.

It may also be seen what the form of such a curve as $y^3=x^7$ would be, for, in the quadrant xOy, it is intermediate between $y=x^2$ and $y=x^3$, and is symmetrical in opposite quadrants, since for every point (x, y) there is a point $(-x, -y)$.

It is not sufficient to consider the curve $y^2=x^3$ as lying between $y=x$ and $y=x^2$, we must also observe that it touches the axis of x, and is symmetrical with respect to that axis, also that no part lies on the negative side of Oy, since a negative x gives impossible values of y. The curve has a cusp of the first species, or ceratoid cusp, at the origin, and the shape is as in fig. 6, turned through a right angle.

15. The importance of knowing the shapes of curves whose equations are of the form $y^m=cx^n$ in the neighbourhood of the origin, will be seen hereafter; the student should exercise himself in drawing the forms for different values of m and n, as part of the machinery for tracing curves with facility; and also, in order to realise directly what is the relation among quantities of different orders of magnitude, two curves should be drawn with the same coordinate axes, and placed in their proper positions with reference to their degrees of closeness to the axis which they touch.

PLATE
I.

All curves, whose equations are of the form $y^m = cx^n$, in which m and n are unequal, are called *parabolic curves.*

When m and n are both even, the locus of the equation is two distinct parabolic curves.

The arguments by which the forms in the neighbourhood of the origin are determined will pass through the mind very rapidly in the following form, with very little practice :

(1) Take the case in which m is odd, and n is even, and less than m, and c is positive.

$-x$ written for x does not alter the equation; therefore the curve is symmetrical with respect to Oy.

x is small compared with y, therefore the curve touches the axis of y at O, hence the shape is the ceratoid cusp as in the figure ⅄.

When n is greater than m, the curve touches the axis of x at O, and the shape is ⊣⊢.

(2) Take the case in which m and n are both odd integers.

If we wrote $-x$ and $-y$ for x and y, the equation would not be altered, hence the curve is symmetrical in opposite quadrants, or the origin is a centre, bisecting all chords through it.

When n is greater than m, the curve touches the axis of x, since y is smaller compared with x, and the shape is ⤳ when c is positive, ⤨ when c is negative.

16. If we now consider the fact that $ax^n + bx^r + cx^s + ...,$ in which $n < r < s ...,$ differs from ax^n, $ax^n + bx^r$, ..., by a difference which ultimately vanishes compared with itself, when x is indefinitely diminished, *or* that the ratio of the difference to itself may be made as small as we please by diminishing x, we shall be able to assign the direction taken by a curve in the neighbourhood of any particular point, by transferring the origin to that point.

Thus, if the equation of the curve be $y^3 = x^4$, to find the tangent at the point $(1, 1)$, let $x = 1 + \xi,$ $y = 1 + \eta,$ then

PLATE
I.

$(1+\eta)^3 = (1+\xi)^4$, or $3\eta = 4\xi - 3\eta^2 + 4\xi^2 + \ldots$, and the part of the curve which is very near the new origin is sufficiently represented by $3\eta = 4\xi$, which is therefore the equation of the tangent.

In the different curves, discussed in Art. **13**, it can in this way be shewn that the tangents to the curves at B will, if produced, meet the axis of x at distances from A equal to $\frac{1}{2}, \frac{1}{3}, \frac{1}{4}, \frac{1}{5}, \frac{1}{6}$ respectively.

17. The equation of the tangent at any point is thus easily found, and the next approximation gives the direction in which the curve bends from the tangent.

Thus, for the curve $y = x + x^3$, $y = x$ is the tangent at the origin; let the ordinates MQ and $M'Q'$, at small distances from the origin O, meet the tangent at O in P, P'; if $OM = x$, $PQ = (x + x^3) - x = x^3$ will be the distance of Q from the tangent, measured in the direction Oy, and will change sign with x, so that $P'Q'$ must be measured downwards.

Fig. 14.

Hence, the curve lies above on the positive and below on the negative side of the origin, which is a point of inflexion.

CUSPS.

18. The following examples will shew how certain peculiar forms of curves, such as cusps and points of inflexion, arise from fractional indices occurring in the equations of the curves, when y is expressed explicitly in terms of x, or vice versâ.

(1) $$\mathbf{y} = 1 + \mathbf{x} + 2(\mathbf{x} - 1)^2 + 3(\mathbf{x} - 1)^{\frac{5}{2}},$$
near the point $(1, 2)$ let $y = 2 + \eta$, $x = 1 + \xi$,
then $$\eta = \xi + 2\xi^2 + 3\xi^{\frac{5}{2}}.$$

The first approximation gives $\eta = \xi$, so that, if $OM = 1$, $MP = 2$, the curve coincides with the line $Q'PQ$ nearly, which is therefore the tangent at P, and $\angle QP\xi = 45°$.

Fig. 15.

The second approximation is $\eta = \xi + 2\xi^2$, therefore $2\xi^2$ being added to the ordinates of $Q'PQ$, the curve more nearly coincides with the dotted line $R'PR$, where $RQ = R'Q' = 2\xi^2$, which is a parabola, whose diameter through P is $MP\eta$.

PLATE
I.

The term added in the next approximation $3\xi^{\frac{5}{2}}$ is impossible when ξ is negative, and has two values equal and of opposite signs when ξ is positive, thus the form is SPS', where $RS = RS' = 3\xi^{\frac{5}{2}}$ is small compared with RQ, if ξ be taken very small. Hence, at P there is a *ramphoid cusp*.

Fig. 16.

(2) If the fractional index had been $\frac{7}{3}$, the form would have been SPS', in the next figure, since $3\xi^{\frac{7}{3}}$ only changes sign when ξ becomes negative.

(3) If the fractional index be $\frac{3}{2}$, the terms must be re-arranged in the order $\eta = \xi + 3\xi^{\frac{3}{2}} + 2\xi^2$. The second approxi-

Fig. 17.

mation would give the form RPR', and the third would not be perceptibly different, since RS, $R'S'$ are small compared with QR or QR', and the only difference is, that the branch PS is further from PQ than PR, and PS' nearer than PR'; there is therefore at P a *ceratoid cusp*.

(4) If $\frac{1}{2}$ be the fractional index, $\eta = 3\xi^{\frac{1}{2}} + \xi + 2\xi^2$, the curve is nearly the form of $\eta = 3\xi^{\frac{1}{2}}$, or $9\xi = \eta^2$.

(5) If $\frac{2}{3}$ be the fractional index, $\eta = 3\xi^{\frac{2}{3}} + \xi + 2\xi^2$, then $\eta = 3\xi^{\frac{2}{3}}$ nearly, ξ is small compared with η, and η remains the same if ξ changes its sign, hence the shape of the curve is that of the first figure given in Art. **15** (1).

TANGENTS.

19. At this point I think that the student, who has not read Newton's Lemmas, should be introduced to the notion of limits, as applied to the theory of tangents and the curvature of curves.

Two variable magnitudes whose variations depend upon that of a quantity which is supposed to diminish until it vanishes, are said to be *ultimately* equal, when the ratio of their difference to either of them vanishes, as the quantity upon which they depend vanishes.

The *limit* of a variable magnitude is that fixed quantity to which it is *ultimately* equal, when the variable on which it depends vanishes.

PLATE
I.

This includes the case of a variable, upon which the variation of the magnitude depends, increasing until it becomes infinite, because the reciprocal of such a variable diminishes until it vanishes, and the magnitude may equally be considered to depend on the reciprocal as a variable.

20. If OP be any curve passing through the origin of coordinates, OT the tangent at O, and x, y the coordinates of any point P, $\tan POM = y/x$. As OP diminishes, and ultimately vanishes, the angle POT ultimately vanishes, and $\tan TOM = \tan POM$ ultimately, $=$ limit of y/x, when x and y vanish simultaneously.

The gradual diminution and ultimate evanescence of the angle POT may be seen by comparison with the curve *Fig. 18.* Oa_2B in Art. **13**, in which, if Oa_2, $O\beta_2$, $O\gamma_2$ be joined, the angles a_2OA, β_2OA, γ_2OA exhibit the continual diminution of the angle between the chord and tangent.

For the curve of sines, $y = \sin x$, since the limit of $\sin x/x = 1$ when x vanishes, the unit being the unit of circular measure, the tangent at the origin is inclined at $45°$ to the axis of x.

Similarly, the tangent of the angle which the tangent at any point (a, b) of a curve makes with Ox, is the limit of $(y - b)/(x - a)$, when $x - a$ and $y - b$ vanish, which they do simultaneously.

CURVATURE.

PLATE
II.

21. The only curve whose curvature is the same at every point is the circle, and the smaller the circle the greater is its curvature. Hence, the reciprocal of the diameter is taken as the measure of the curvature of a circle.

Suppose two circles have a common tangent AQ at A, *Fig. 1.* and diameters AB, Ab through A. QPp, perpendicular to the tangent AQ, meets the circles in P, p, and PM, pm are perpendicular to AB. Then

$$AM . MB = PM^2 = pm^2 = Am . mb \, ;$$

therefore

$$PQ . MB = pQ . mb \, ; \quad \text{or} \quad PQ : pQ :: mb : MB.$$

PLATE
II.

If AQ be made to diminish indefinitely, PQ and pQ will measure the deflection from the tangent, and the limit of the ratio $PQ : pQ$ will be $Ab : AB$, or equal to the ratio of the curvatures of the circles.

22. Any two curves AP, Ap, which have a common tangent at A, have the same curvature if $PQ = pQ$ ultimately.

If, therefore, a circle be drawn touching a curve at any point A, and its magnitude be such that $PQ = pQ$ ultimately, the circle has the same curvature as the curve at that point, and the curvature of that circle is the measure of the curvature of the curve at that point; the circle is called *the circle of curvature*, and its diameter *the diameter of curvature*.

Fig. 2.

23. No arc of any other circle can be drawn which lies, near the point of contact, between the curve and the circle determined above; for, if possible, let an arc lie between them, cutting pPQ in p', then Qp' is intermediate in magnitude to QP and Qp which are ultimately equal, hence Qp' is ultimately equal to Qp, and the diameters of the two circles, being the limits of $AQ^2/p'Q$ and AQ^2/pQ, are equal.

Fig. 2.

24. Since, for a circle, AQ^2/pQ is finite when the circle is of finite radius, it follows that when, at any point of a curve, AQ^2/PQ ultimately vanishes, or becomes indefinitely great, there is no finite circle which has the same curvature.

A curve has finite curvature at A, whenever AQ^2/PQ is ultimately finite, when AQ vanishes.

25. The diameter of curvature of a curve at A is the limit of either AQ^2/PQ or AP^2/PQ, since $AP^2 = AQ^2 + PQ^2 = AQ^2$ ultimately.

Examples II.

Find the forms, near the origin, of the curves whose equations are

(1) $a^3y^2 = x^5$.   (2) $y^4 = ax^3$.

(3) $y^7 = a^2x^5$.   (4) $a^2x^3 = y^5$.

(5) $y = x + x^4$.   (6) $y^2 = x^2 + x^3$.

(7) Find the tangent to the curve (2) at the point (a, a).

PLATE
II.

Find the form of the cusps at the given points on the following
curves :

(8) $(y-x)^2=x^3$ at the origin.

(9) $y-2=x^2+x^{\frac{7}{2}}$ at the point $(0, 2)$.

(10) $(2y+x+1)^2=4(1-x)^3$ at the point $(1, -1)$.

(11) $x^{\frac{2}{3}}+y^{\frac{2}{3}}=c^{\frac{2}{3}}$ at the points where it meets the axes.

(12) $a^4y^2=(x^2-a^2)^3$ at the points $(\pm a, 0)$.

Find the diameters of curvature at the origin for the curves

(13) $y^2=4ax.$ (14) $y^2=2mx+nx^2.$

(15) $ay(x-a)=(x-2a)x^2.$

CHAPTER III.

FORMS OF PARABOLIC CURVES AT AN INFINITE
DISTANCE. EXAMPLES OF TRACING CURVES.
TRIGONOMETRICAL CURVES. ILLUSTRATIONS
OF THEORY OF EQUATIONS. RULES FOR
APPROXIMATION.

FORMS OF PARABOLIC CURVES AT AN INFINITE DISTANCE.

PLATE
II.

26. In the last chapter the form of the parabolic curves, which are the loci of the equations of the form $y^m = x^n$, was examined only between the limits $x = 0$ and $x = 1$; in this chapter I shall consider the relative positions of the curves, and the way in which the curves bend, when $x > 1$.

Fig. 3.

For this purpose draw lines parallel to Oy, intersecting Ox at A_1, A_2, A_3, ..., where $OA_1 = 1$, $OA_2 = 2$, $OA_3 = 3$, etc.

All the curves $y = x^2$, x^3, ... pass through B, where $A_1 B = 1$, and the tangents of the angles, which they make at B with the axis of x, are 2, 3, 4, ...

On the line passing through A_2, measure distances

$$A_2 P_2 = 4, \quad A_2 P_3 = 8, \quad A_2 P_4 = 16, \ldots.$$

On that through A_3, measure $A_3 Q_2 = 9$, $A_3 Q_3 = 27, \ldots$

.... A_4, ... $A_4 R_2 = 16$, $A_4 R_3 = 64, \ldots.$

$$OBP_2 Q_2 R_2 \ldots \text{ is the curve } y = x^2,$$
$$OBP_3 Q_3 \ldots\ldots\ldots\ldots\ldots\ldots y = x^3,$$
$$OBP_4 Q_4 \ldots\ldots\ldots\ldots\ldots\ldots y = x^4,$$

....

27. The forms of these curves shew that their curvatures rapidly diminish after the point (1, 1) although the curves remain convex to the axis of x, and it is only by

PLATE
II.

a strong effort of the imagination that it is possible to conceive what becomes of the curves, when x is made of any considerable magnitude.

We shall, in the investigation of the forms of curves, have to consider their general shapes at a great distance from the origin, and it will be readily seen from the results obtained here, that it would be impossible to represent on paper the proper proportions of the different parts of such curves; we are therefore obliged to content ourselves by indicating the direction of the bending of the curves at a great distance, leaving to the imagination what would become of the branches if extended in the proper proportion, on the same principle as in a raised map of a mountainous district, like that of Flintoft in Keswick, it is found to give a better idea of the form of the country to take a scale for the vertical heights differing very materially from the scale of horizontal distances.

28. The form of curves such as $y^2 = x^3$, in which the order of y is a fraction between 1 and 2, may be conceived by measuring, as ordinates, the approximate distances $A_2\pi = 2\frac{4}{5}$, $A_3\kappa = 5\frac{1}{5}$, $A_4\rho = 8$, $A_5\sigma = 11\frac{1}{5}$, $A_6\tau = 14\frac{5}{7}$, and $A_7\upsilon = 18\frac{1}{2}$, and drawing a curve touching the axis of x at the origin, passing through B and the points π, κ, ρ, σ, τ, υ, and making at B an angle $\tan^{-1}\frac{3}{2}$ with the axis of x.

It will be seen that such a curve opens out more rapidly than the former curves as x increases, and near the origin leaves the axis of x more rapidly than those curves do.

The figure which represents this curve in the more distant points is necessarily constructed with an unit too small to give an idea of the form near the origin.

The shape of this curve, called the semicubical parabola, within the limits $x = 0$ and $x = 1$, is BOB', touching the lines BC, $B'C$ at B and B', where $OC = \frac{1}{3}OA$.

Fig. 4.

29. To illustrate the use which it is intended to make of the forms of these curves near the origin and at a great distance from it, I shall trace the curve $y = x^2 + x^3$.

PLATE
II.

Fig. 5.

Near the origin the approximate form of the curve is that of $y = x^2$; and, when x is very great, of $y = x^3$, whose general form is that of the dotted curve; again when $x = -1$, $y = 0$, and if $x = -1 + \xi$, then $y = \xi(1-\xi)^2$; therefore, neglecting powers of ξ above the first near this point, $y = \xi = x + 1$ is the tangent.

30. Although the Differential Calculus gives some advantages towards obtaining the particular points which appear in the form of the curve, yet it is not difficult to obtain them by the ordinary processes of Algebra.

For example, we observe in the figure a maximum ordinate near a, where the curve is parallel to the axis of x; if (α, β) be any point on the curve, let $x = \alpha + \xi$, $y = \beta + \eta$, then $\beta + \eta = (\alpha + \xi)^2 + (\alpha + \xi)^3$ and $\beta = \alpha^2 + \alpha^3$; therefore

$$\eta = (2\alpha + 3\alpha^2)\xi + (1 + 3\alpha)\xi^2 + \xi^3 \quad \ldots\ldots\ldots\ldots(1)$$

is the equation referred to axes through a, and

$$\eta = (2\alpha + 3\alpha^2)\xi$$

is the tangent, which is parallel to the axis of x, if $\alpha = -\frac{2}{3}$ and $\beta = \frac{4}{27}$.

31. Again, there is a point of inflexion near b. If (α, β) be this point of inflexion, since the curve must lie on opposite sides of the tangent at b, the term in (1) which involves ξ^2 must disappear; therefore $3\alpha + 1 = 0$, hence, the point of inflexion is $(-\frac{1}{3}, \frac{2}{27})$. The equation, referred to b as origin, will be $\eta = -\frac{1}{3}\xi + \xi^3$, where η is $>$ or $<-\frac{1}{3}\xi$, according as ξ is positive or negative, and the inclination of the tangent to Ox' is $\cot^{-1}3$.

EXAMPLES OF TRACING.

32. At this stage it will be useful to trace some curves in which the abscissa and ordinates are not involved with one another in any complicated manner, so that the methods already given are sufficient.

In such cases it will be seen, that there is rarely any necessity to enter minutely into the question of the direc-

PLATE
II.

tion of flexure from the tangent at any particular point, but the general run of the curve can be obtained by a small number of points and directions of tangents, combined with the consideration that a straight line cannot intersect the curve in more points than the greatest sum of the indices of x and y in any term.

Thus, it is impossible that there should be a point of inflexion or a cusp in a curve of the second degree; two cusps, or a multiple point of three branches, in a curve of the third degree.

Again, considering that a rectilinear asymptote to a curve is a straight line which joins two points at least at an infinite distance, it follows that a curve of the third degree may meet the asymptote at a finite distance in one point, and no more, one of nth degree in $n-2$ points, and no more.

Ex. 1. $\qquad\qquad$ $y = x(x^2 - 1)$.

If $-x$ and $-y$ be written for x and y, the equation is not altered; therefore the curve is symmetrical in opposite quadrants, or the origin is a centre, Art. **7** (2).

The principal points to examine are $(0, 0)$ and $(1, 0)$; $\qquad$ Fig. 6. near the origin, since $y = -x + x^3$, the curve is above the tangent when x is positive, and below when negative; to find the shape near $(1, 0)$ let $x = 1 + \xi$, then $y = 2\xi + 3\xi^2 + \dots$; near (∞, ∞), $y = x^3$, represented by the dotted line in the figure.

Ex. 2. $\qquad\qquad$ $cy^2 = x(x^2 + ax + b)$.

This curve is symmetrical with respect to Ox, it meets the axis of x at the origin, and where $x^2 + ax + b = 0$, and passes off to infinity in the form of $cy^2 = x^3$; the shape near the origin is $cy^2 = bx$.

$\quad$ i. When $x^2 + ax + b \equiv (x - \alpha)(x - \beta)$, $\alpha < \beta$,
$$\text{near } (\alpha, 0), \ cy^2 = \alpha(\alpha - \beta)\xi,$$
$$\dots\dots (\beta, 0), \ cy^2 = \beta(\beta - \alpha)\xi.$$

In the figure the dotted oval is the position of the oval $\qquad$ Fig. 7. when α is negative.

PLATE II.

Fig. 8.

ii. When $x^2 + ax + b \equiv (x-\alpha)^2$, near $(\alpha, 0)$, $cy^2 = \alpha\xi^2$.

iii. When $x^2 + ax + b \equiv (x-\alpha)^2 + \beta^2$.

One figure is drawn when $\alpha > \beta\sqrt{3}$, and one when $\alpha < \beta\sqrt{3}$, these limits being found from the values of x where the tangents are parallel to Ox, which are given by $3x^2 - 4\alpha x + \alpha^2 + \beta^2 = 0$. When a and b vanish, all these curves degenerate into the asymptotic curve, viz. the semi-cubical parabola, $cy^2 = x^3$.

It is useful to consider this degeneration, because it explains how it may have happened that, when $y = 0$, there were three values of x equal to 0, in the curve $cy^2 = x^3$, as, for instance, this curve may be considered as the limit of fig. 9 when the portion $ba'aO$ becomes condensed into the origin, and a line between ab and $b'a'$ contains three coincident points. It is interesting to see how the curve gradually changes from any of the forms figs. 7, 8, 10 until it assumes the final form of the asymptotic curve.

We may also see how the theory of equations assists us in drawing the curve in proper proportions. Thus, for any value of y the three values of x have their algebraical sum the same, so that if nab be a tangent at a, parallel to Ox, and the curve cuts the axis of x in α, β, $2n\alpha + n\beta = O\alpha + O\beta$; hence if am, br be ordinates at a, b, $Om + \beta r = m\alpha$, and when α, β coincide, $bn = 2\alpha m$.

Fig. 7.

If nab, $n'a'b'$ be two tangents parallel to Ox, the distance between b and b' measured parallel to Ox is double the distance between a and a'.

Fig. 9.

Ex. 3.
$$y = a \frac{(x-a)(x-3a)}{x(x-2a)}.$$

If
$x = 0,$	$y = \infty,$
$x < a,$	y is negative,
$x = a,$	$y = 0,$
$a < x < 2a,$	y is positive,
$x = 2a,$	$y = \infty,$
$2a < x < 3a,$	y is negative,

PLATE
II.

$$x = 3a, \qquad y = 0,$$

$$x > 3a, \qquad y \text{ is positive},$$

$$x = \infty, \qquad y = a,$$

$$\text{near } (a, 0), \quad y = a\frac{(x-a)(-2a)}{a(-a)} = 2(x-a),$$

$$\dots\dots (3a, 0), \quad y = a\frac{2a(x-3a)}{3a^2} = \tfrac{2}{3}(x-3a),$$

when x is negative, y is positive; for the form, see the figure. Fig. 11.

Ex. 4. $\qquad\qquad y^2 = a^2\dfrac{(x-a)(x-3a)}{x(x-2a)}.$

The curve is symmetrical with respect to Ox, and writing in the tabulation given above, y impossible, for y negative, y real, for y positive, and $x = \infty$, $y = \pm a$,

$$\text{near } (a, 0), \quad y^2 = 2a(x-a),$$

$$\dots\dots (3a, 0), \quad y^2 = \tfrac{2}{3}a(x-3a),$$

we have the form given in the figure. Fig. 12.

Ex. 5. $\qquad\qquad (y^2-1)y = (x^2-4)x.$

Since $-x$, $-y$ for x, y do not alter the equation, the curve is symmetrical in opposite quadrants; hence, it is only necessary to examine the form for positive values of x.

When $\qquad\quad x = 0, \quad y = 0,\ 1,\ -1,$

$$x < 2, \quad y < -1, \text{ or } 0 < y < 1,$$

$$x = 2, \quad y = 0,\ 1,\ -1,$$

$$x > 2, \quad -1 < y < 0, \text{ or } y > 1,$$

$$x = \infty, \quad y = \infty;$$

$$\text{near } (0, 0), \quad y = 4x,$$

$$(0, 1), \quad 2(y-1) = -4x,$$

$$(0, -1),\ 2(y+1) = -4x,$$

$$(2, 0), \quad -y = 8(x-2),$$

$$(2, 1), \quad 2(y-1) = 8(x-2),$$

$$(2, -1),\ 2(y+1) = 8(x-2);$$

near (∞, ∞), $y = x$, which meets the curve only at the origin, and at two points at an infinite distance. Fig. 13.

PLATE
II.

Ex. 6. $y(y-1)(y-2)=x(x^2-1)(x-2)$.

The equation becomes more symmetrical by transferring the origin to the point $(\frac{1}{2}, 1)$, viz. $y(y^2-1)=(x^2-\frac{9}{4})(x^2-\frac{1}{4})$; the curve is then symmetrical with respect to Oy.

When $\quad x=0, \qquad y(y^2-1)=\frac{9}{16}$,

$\qquad\qquad x<\frac{1}{2}, \qquad -1<y<0,$ or $y>1$,

$\qquad\qquad x=\frac{1}{2}, \qquad y=0,$ or ± 1,

$\qquad\qquad \frac{1}{2}<x<\frac{3}{2},\ y<-1,$ or $0<y<1$,

$\qquad\qquad x=\frac{3}{2}, \qquad y=0,$ or ± 1,

$\qquad\qquad x>\frac{3}{2}, \qquad -1<y<0,$ or $y>1$,

$\qquad\qquad x=\infty, \qquad y=\infty$;

y near 0, or ± 1, gives $y(y^2-1)=-y$, or $2(y\mp 1)$,

x near $\frac{1}{2}$, or $\frac{3}{2}$, gives $(x^2-\frac{9}{4})(x^2-\frac{1}{4})=-2(x-\frac{1}{2})$, or $6(x-\frac{3}{2})$; from which the tangents can be found at $(\frac{1}{2}, 0)$, $(\frac{1}{2}, \pm 1)$, $(\frac{3}{2}, 0)$, $(\frac{3}{2}, \pm 1)$; also near (∞, ∞), $y^3=x^4$.

The tangents are parallel to Oy, where $y=\pm\frac{1}{3}\sqrt{3}$, and to Ox, where $x=\pm\frac{1}{2}\sqrt{5}$ and 0.

Fig. 14.   This curve affords another illustration of the manner in which we may suppose a curve, whose equation is $y^3=x^4$, to be drawn in order that, when $x=0$, there may be three zero values of y, and, when $y=0$, four zero values of x, since, by conceiving the unit of measurement to become very small compared with the size of the paper, the undulating part may be made as small as we please.

33. The following curve is given as an example by almost all the writers on the differential calculus, and deserves to be considered carefully as to the points which we have at present discussed :

$$y^4-96a^2y^2+100a^2x^2-x^4=0,$$

or $\ y^2=48a^2\pm\sqrt{\{(x-8a)(x-6a)(x+6a)(x+8a)\}}$.

Since the curve is symmetrical with respect to both axes, it need only be traced in the angle xOy.

When $\ x=0,\ y=0\ $ or $\ a\sqrt{(96)}=a10\sqrt{(1-\frac{1}{25})}=(10-\frac{1}{5})a$ nearly; when $y=0$, $x=0$ or $10a$,

$x < 6a$, y is real,

$x = 6a$, $y = a\sqrt{(49-1)} = a(7 - \frac{1}{14})$ nearly,

$8a > x > 6a$, y is impossible,

$x = 8a$, $y = a(7 - \frac{1}{14})$ nearly,

$x = \infty$, $y = \infty$;

near $(0, 0)$, $x^2 = \frac{24}{25}y^2$, $\therefore$ $x = \pm(1 - \frac{1}{50})y$ nearly;

near $\{0, a\sqrt{(96)}\}$, let $y = a\sqrt{(96)} + \eta$, then, retaining only the principal terms,

$x^2 = -4a\sqrt{(24)}\frac{24}{25}\eta = -20a(1 - \frac{1}{25})^{\frac{3}{2}}\eta = -(19 - \frac{1}{5})a\eta$;

near $(10a, 0)$, let $x = 10a + \xi$,

then $y^2 = -(1 - \frac{1}{25})^{-1}20a\xi = -(21 - \frac{1}{5})a\xi$ nearly;

taking $\{6a, \sqrt{(48)}a\}$, and $\{8a, \sqrt{(48)}a\}$, as new origins the approximate equations are $\eta^2 = -\frac{7}{4}a\xi$ and $\eta^2 = \frac{7}{3}a\xi$;

near (∞, ∞), $y = \pm x$. Of the four points in which each of these lines meets the curve, two only are at a finite distance, therefore two must be at an infinite distance, or each of the lines is an asymptote.

At A and D in the figure the latera recta of the approximate parabolas are a little less than $19a$ and $21a$ respectively; at B and C they are $\frac{7}{4}a$ and $\frac{7}{3}a$, the vertices being at equal distances from Ox. The tangents at the origin are very nearly coincident with the asymptotes.   Fig. 15.

GRAPHIC REPRESENTATION OF VARIATIONS IN THE MAGNITUDE OF FUNCTIONS.

34. One of the most useful applications of curves is to represent to the eye the changes which take place in any quantity in consequence of changes in a variable upon which the quantity depends; everybody is familiar with the curves representing the changes in the barometer and thermometer during the course of a day or month, in which the height of the barometer and degree of the thermometer, taken as ordinates, are functions of the time, taken as abscissa; also with isothermal lines; and, in terrestrial magnetism, with isoclinal and isodynamic lines.

PLATE
II.

It is in fact much easier to follow the variations of the magnitude of ordinates to a curve, than to gather the same information from a table of numbers.

35. The changes of magnitude of the trigonometrical functions may be represented by taking each function for an ordinate of a curve, of which the angle is the abscissa, represented in any measure. Suppose x to be the circular measure of an angle, and we wish to trace $y = \sin x$.

Since $\sin(\pi - x) = \sin x$, the curve is the same backwards from π, as forwards from 0; $\sin(\pi + x) = -\sin x$, therefore, if the curve be traced for any portion extending over a distance π, measured on Ox, the curve is of the same form, but on the opposite side of Ox, for the distance π on either side.

When $x = 0$, $y = 0$; $x = \tfrac{1}{6}\pi$, $y = \tfrac{1}{2}$; $x = \tfrac{1}{2}\pi$, $y = 1$; near the origin $y = x$ for a first approximation,

near $x = \tfrac{1}{2}\pi$, if $x = \tfrac{1}{2}\pi + \xi$, $y = \cos\xi = 1 - \tfrac{1}{2}\xi^2$,

or the curve is ultimately a parabola, with axis perpendicular to Ox, and latus rectum 2.

Fig. 16.   The figure is called the curve of sines.

36. Here it is seen from the symmetry described above, that there is a point of inflexion at the origin, and therefore at the points where $x = \pi$, 2π, ..., so that it is unnecessary to find in this case the deflexion from the tangent, which would have been shewn by making the next approximation to the value of y, for which $y = x - \tfrac{1}{6}x^3$.

37. Again, if $y = \tan x$, then, since

$$\tan(\pi + x) = \tan x, \quad \text{and} \quad \tan(\pi - x) = -\tan x,$$

the curve repeats itself after every interval of π; and the curve is the same in form forwards from $x = 0$, and backwards from $x = \pi$, but on the opposite side of Ox.

When $x = 0$, $y = 0$; $x = \tfrac{1}{4}\pi$, $y = 1$; $x = \tfrac{1}{2}\pi$, $y = \infty$;

Fig. 17.   and near the origin $y = x$.

PLATE
II.

38. The figures for the other common trigonometrical functions can easily be drawn. The figures are given separately for **y** = **sec x** and **y** = **cot x**.

Figs. 18, 19.

The curves for **y** = **cos x** and **y** = **vers x** are the same as for $y = \sin x$, the origin being different. For the former, $O'y'$ is the axis of y, for the latter, $O''x''$, $O''y''$ are the axes.

Fig. 16.

39. Many of the properties of the Theory of Equations, which will be useful in the theory of curves, may be shewn simply by means of curves.

Let $f(x) = 0$ be the equation, the properties of whose roots are required, $f(x)$ being a rational integral function of x of the nth degree.

Consider the curve $y = f(x)$, for every value of x, there is only one value of y; for every value of x, which is a real root of the equation, the curve crosses the axis of x.

If $f(x)$ be divisible by $(x-a)^r$, there will be r coincident points where $x = a$.

When x is very large, $y = x^n$ is a curve whose form determines the direction of the given curve at a distance from the origin great compared with unity, being that of the dotted lines in the figures, drawn with n even or odd; the curve meets the asymptotic curve generally in $n-1$ points at a finite distance, real or imaginary, given by an equation of the form $px^{n-1} + qx^{n-2} + \ldots = 0$.

Figs. 20, 21.

40. The auxiliary equation, $f'(x) = 0$, is found by writing $x + \xi$ for x in $f(x)$, and equating the coefficient of ξ to 0.

By Art. **3** (4), $f(x+\xi) = f(x) + f'(x)\xi + \frac{1}{2}f''(x)\xi^2 + \ldots$, hence, for the form of the curve at any point $\{\alpha, f(\alpha)\}$,

$$y = f(\alpha) + f'(\alpha)\xi + \frac{1}{2}f''(\alpha)\xi^2 + \frac{1}{6}f'''(\alpha)\xi^3 + \ldots;$$

$$\therefore \ y = f(\alpha) + f'(\alpha)\xi \text{ is the equation of the tangent.}$$

The tangent is therefore parallel to the axis of x at every point for which $f'(\alpha) = 0$, *i.e.* for every value of x, which is a root of the auxiliary equation $f'(x) = 0$.

Now, it is obvious from the manner in which the curve must be drawn, that between every two distinct points in which the curve meets the axis of x, there must be an odd number of bends, from or towards Ox, and therefore an odd number of points in which the curve must run parallel to the axis of x, where two bends must be supposed to coincide in the case of an ordinary point of inflexion, so that between every two roots of the equation $f(x)=0$ there is an odd number of roots of $f'(x)=0$.

Whence it may be deduced that, if $f(x)=0$ have two roots each equal to a, a will also be a root of $f'(x)=0$; which is also obvious, either from the fact that the axis of x joins two points which are ultimately coincident, or from the analysis, because $y=f(x)=(x-a)^2\phi(x)$; therefore near $(a, 0)$, if $x=a+\xi$, $y=\xi^2 . \phi(a)$ will be the first approximation, and this curve obviously touches the axis of x.

41. Other properties can be deduced immediately from the curve.

(1) If two values of x give values of $f(x)$ affected with opposite signs, an odd number of real roots of $f(x)=0$ must lie between these values.

(2) Every equation of an even degree must have an even number of real roots, or none, since the curve terminates in both directions on the same side of the axis Ox.

(3) Every equation of an odd degree must have at least one real root of the sign contrary to that of the last term.

For the curve cuts the axis of y on the positive or negative side, as the last term is positive or negative; if positive, it must cut the axis of x in the negative direction, since the curve goes off to infinity in the angle $x'Oy'$, and vice versâ.

(4) Every equation of an even degree with the last term negative must have two real roots of opposite signs. For the curve cuts Oy in the negative side and must cross Ox twice, on opposite sides of O.

(5) Every function of x, which equated to zero forms an equation with no real root, must be invariable in sign.

42. To find a point of inflexion in the curve $y = f(x)$.

Let (α, β) be a point of inflexion, transfer the origin to this point, by writing $\alpha + \xi$, $\beta + \eta$, for x, y, and expand,

$$\therefore \beta + \eta = f(\alpha) + f'(\alpha)\xi + \tfrac{1}{2}f''(\alpha)\xi^2 + \tfrac{1}{6}f'''(\alpha)\xi^3 + \dots,$$

and $\beta = f(\alpha)$, (α, β) being a point on the curve. Hence $\eta = f'(\alpha)\xi$ is the tangent, and, in the curve, the value of $\eta - f'(\alpha)\xi$, being the difference of the ordinates for the curve and tangent, must change sign when ξ changes sign; therefore $f''(\alpha) = 0$ when α is the abscissa of a point of inflexion.

43. If $f''(\alpha)$ be not $= 0$, the curve has a parabolic form.

$f''(\alpha) = 0$ is a necessary, though not a sufficient condition for a point of inflexion, the sufficient condition is, that the first term in $\eta - f'(\alpha)\xi$ shall be of an odd degree in ξ.

44. Since in Art. **3** (4), it is shewn that $f''(x)$ is derived from $f'(x)$ in the same manner as $f'(x)$ from $f(x)$, if the curve $y = f'(x)$ be traced, and the values of x found, corresponding to which the curve runs parallel to Ox, the corresponding ordinates, produced if necessary, will pass through the points of inflexion of $y = f(x)$.

By this consideration, and from the fact that the curve $y = f'(x)$ cuts the axis of x at points corresponding to the values of x for which the original curve is parallel to Ox, it is easy to give its general form.

Part of the curve is traced by a fainter line in the figure, in which it may be observed, that when $f(x)$ is increasing with x, $f'(x)$ positive, and vice versâ. *Fig. 21.*

45. The necessary condition for a point of inflexion may also be obtained thus.

If ϕ be the inclination to Ox of the tangent at a point where $x = \alpha$, $\tan \phi = f'(\alpha)$; now, in passing through a point of inflexion, ϕ first increases and afterwards diminishes, or vice versâ, hence, if ξ be diminished sufficiently

$$f'(\alpha - \xi) \gtrless f'(\alpha) \lessgtr f'(\alpha + \xi),$$

so that $f'(\alpha + \xi) - f'(\alpha)$ has the same sign, whether ξ is positive or negative; hence the first term in the expansion

PLATE
III.
must involve an even power of ξ, which is impossible unless $f''(\alpha) = 0$.

46. As an example, take the curve

$$y = x(x-1)(x^2-1) \equiv x^4 - x^3 - x^2 + x.$$

The tangents are parallel to the axis of x, where

$4x^3 - 3x^2 - 2x + 1 = 0$, or $x = 1$, $x = \frac{3}{8}$, or $-\frac{5}{8}$ nearly; there may be points of inflexion, where $12x^2 - 6x - 2 = 0$, which gives $x = \frac{1}{12}\{ \pm \sqrt{(33)} + 3\} = \frac{35}{48}$, or $-\frac{11}{48}$ very nearly. The fainter line is the curve $y = f'(x)$ of Art. **44**, whose maximum and minimum ordinates pass through the points

Fig. 1. of inflexion of the given curve.

47. The nature of the roots of an equation can be frequently discovered by the use of the intersection of simple curves; an example or two will be sufficient to shew the method.

Consider the cubic $x^3 - qx + r = 0$, the roots of the equation are the abscissæ of the points of intersection of

$$y = x^2 \ldots(1) \quad \text{and} \quad x(q - y) = r \ldots(2).$$

Fig. 2. The figures, denoted by 1, 2, 3, shew how the hyperbola (2), which remains of constant magnitude if r be constant, changes its position, as q increases from some negative value, moving along the axis of y as an asymptote, its lower branch at first not cutting the parabola at all, then touching it, and afterwards cutting it in two points, its higher branch in every position cutting the parabola once. When the two curves touch at (α, β), since the point of contact bisects the part of the common tangent cut off by the asymptotes, $2\beta = q - \beta$, $\therefore \beta = \frac{1}{3}q = \alpha^2$, and $r = \alpha(q - \beta) = \frac{2}{3}q\alpha$, $\therefore \frac{1}{4}r^2 = (\frac{1}{3}q)^3$ is the condition for equal roots.

48. Another way of solving would be to consider the roots as the abscissæ of the points of intersection of the curve, $y = x^3$ with the straight line $y - qx + r = 0$.

The straight line always meets the curve in one real point, and, as q increases, it turns round until it touches it,

PLATE
III.

in which case two roots are equal, and afterwards it inter-sects in two more real points.

The equation of the tangent at (α, β) is $y - \beta = 3\alpha^2(x - \alpha)$, or $y = 3\alpha^2 x - 2\alpha^3$, ∴ if $y - qx + r = 0$ be a tangent, $3\alpha^2 = q$, $2\alpha^3 = r$, and $(\tfrac{1}{2}r)^2 = (\tfrac{1}{3}q)^3$.

49. The roots of $x^4 + qx^2 + rx + s = 0$ are given by the points of intersection of two parabolas
$$y = x^2, \quad \text{and} \quad y^2 + qy + rx + s = 0.$$

The figure shews how the cases of real or impossible or equal roots may arise, from the relative positions of the parabolas, 1, 2, 3 and 4, drawn for negative values of r and $4s - q^2$, q being positive for 1 and 2, negative for 3 and 4.

Fig. 3.

50. In the course of this work, many examples will occur of the practical advantage of this method of deter-mining the number of real roots of an equation, as well as of roughly fixing their values.

RULES FOR APPROXIMATION.

51. When we wish to approximate to the value of a quantity, of which the exact relation to another quantity, which may be considered very small, is expressed by a given equation, the following method is very simple in application.

Let y be given in terms of α, by means of the equation
$$y = a + \alpha f_1(y) + \alpha^2 f_2(y) + \alpha^3 f_3(y) + \ldots\ldots,$$
where α may be considered very small, and the functions do not involve α explicitly.

The first approximation, when α is neglected, is $y = a$; suppose the next approximate values of y, when α^2, α^3, α^4, ..., are neglected, to be y_1, y_2, y_3, ... respectively; we observe that any one of the functions $f(y)$ may be written
$$f\{a + \alpha f_1(y) + \alpha^2 f_2(y) + \ldots\}$$
$$\equiv f(a) + f'(a)\{\alpha f_1(y) + \ldots\} + \tfrac{1}{2}f''(a)\{\alpha f_1(y) + \ldots\}^2 + \ldots,$$
hence, since in y_1 α^2 is neglected, $y_1 = a + \alpha f_1(a)$;

PLATE III.

when α^3 is neglected, y_2 is obtained from

$$a + \alpha f_1(y_1) + \alpha^2 f_2(a);$$

neglecting α^4, y_3 is obtained from

$$y = a + \alpha f_1(y_2) + \alpha^2 f_2(y_1) + \alpha^3 f_3(a);$$

this will be found quite sufficient to shew the general method to be adopted in approximating.

52. In the following examples I have proceeded to many terms in order to shew that there is no great difficulty in working on the plan of the last article.

Ex. 1. *To expand* **tan x** *in ascending powers of x.*
By Gregory's series,

$$x = \tan x - \tfrac{1}{3}\tan^3 x + \tfrac{1}{5}\tan^5 x - \tfrac{1}{7}\tan^7 x + \ldots;$$
$$\therefore \ \tan x = x + \tfrac{1}{3}\tan^3 x - \tfrac{1}{5}\tan^5 x + \tfrac{1}{7}\tan^7 x - \ldots.$$

First and second approximations,

$$\tan x = x, \quad \text{and} \quad \tan x = x + \tfrac{1}{3}x^3.$$

Third, $\tan x = x + \tfrac{1}{3}(x + \tfrac{1}{3}x^3)^3 - \tfrac{1}{5}x^5 = x + \tfrac{1}{3}x^3 + (\tfrac{1}{3} - \tfrac{1}{5})x^5.$

Fourth, $\tan x = x + \tfrac{1}{3}(x + \tfrac{1}{3}x^3 + \tfrac{2}{15}x^5)^3 - \tfrac{1}{5}(x + \tfrac{1}{3}x^3)^5 + \tfrac{1}{7}x^7$
$= x + \tfrac{1}{3}x^3\{1 + x^2 + \tfrac{2}{5}x^4 + \tfrac{1}{3}(x^2 + \tfrac{2}{5}x^4)^2\} - \tfrac{1}{5}x^5(1 + \tfrac{5}{3}x^2) + \tfrac{1}{7}x^7$
$= x + \tfrac{1}{3}x^3 + \tfrac{2}{15}x^5 + \tfrac{17}{315}x^7.$

Ex. 2. *To expand* $r = a(1 - e\cos u)$ *in ascending powers of e, as far as* e^3, *where* $u = m + e\sin u$, *and e is a small proper fraction.*

For the first and second approximations,
$u = m$ and $u = m + e\sin m$, $\therefore \sin u = \sin m + \cos m \cdot e\sin m$;
for the third,

$$u = m + e\sin m + e^2\sin m\cos m = m + \alpha, \text{ suppose};$$
$$\therefore \ \cos u = \cos m(1 - \tfrac{1}{2}\alpha^2) - \alpha\sin m$$
$$= \cos m - (e\sin m + e^2\sin m\cos m)\sin m - \tfrac{1}{2}e^2\sin^2 m\cos m$$
$$= \cos m - e\sin^2 m - \tfrac{3}{2}e^2\sin^2 m\cos m;$$
$$\therefore \ r = a(1 - e\cos m + e^2\sin^2 m + \tfrac{3}{2}e^3\sin^2 m\cos m).$$

Ex. 3. To find y in ascending powers of x, when

$$6x^7 - 2x^5y^2 - a^3x^2y^2 + 4a^3x^3y + 2a^5x^2 - 3a^5xy + a^5y^2 = 0,$$
or $\quad a^5(y - x)(y - 2x) + a^3x^2(4xy - y^2) - 2x^5(y^2 - 3x^2) = 0,$
y being of the same order as x.

The first approximation gives

$$(y-x)(y-2x)=0 \, ;$$
$$\therefore \ y=x, \quad \text{or} \quad 2x.$$

(i) Commencing with $y=x$ for the second approximation,

$$y = x - \frac{4a^3x^3y - a^3x^2y^2}{a^5(y-2x)}$$

$$= x + \frac{3x^3}{a^2}.$$

For the third, $y = x - \dfrac{1}{a^2} \cdot \dfrac{4x^3y - x^2y^2}{y-2x} - \dfrac{6x^7 - 2x^5y^2}{a^5(y-2x)}$

$$= x + \frac{x^3}{a^2} \cdot \frac{4\left(1 + \dfrac{3x^2}{a^2}\right) - \left(1 + \dfrac{3x^2}{a^2}\right)^2}{1 - \dfrac{3x^2}{a^2}} + \frac{4x^6}{a^5}$$

$$= x + \frac{x^3}{a^2}\left(3 + \frac{6x^2}{a^2}\right)\left(1 + \frac{3x^2}{a^2}\right) + \frac{4x^6}{a^5}$$

$$= x + \frac{3x^3}{a^2} + \frac{15x^5}{a^4} + \frac{4x^6}{a^5}.$$

(ii) Commencing with $y = 2x$ for the second approximation,

$$y = 2x - \frac{1}{a^2}\frac{x^2y(4x-y)}{y-x}$$

$$= 2x - \frac{4x^3}{a^2}.$$

For the third,

$$y = 2x - \frac{1}{a^2}\frac{x^2\{4x^2 - (y-2x)^2\}}{y-x} - \frac{2x^5(3x^2 - y^2)}{a^5(y-x)}$$

$$= 2x - \frac{1}{a^2}\frac{x^2 \cdot 4x^2}{x\left(1 - \dfrac{4x^2}{a^2}\right)} + \frac{2x^6}{a^5}$$

$$= 2x - \frac{4x^3}{a^2} - \frac{16x^5}{a^4} + \frac{2x^6}{a^5}.$$

Ex. 4.   *To approximate to the solutions of the equation* **tan x = x**, *the unit being the unit of circular measure.*

Draw the curve $y = \tan x$, and let the tangent at O, $y = x$, meet the curve in $\ldots P'$, O, P, $Q, \ldots$, fig. 17, plate II.

The figure shews that, since the branches of the curve are all similar, the abscissæ of the points P, Q, R, etc. are nearer and nearer to the values $\frac{3}{2}\pi$, $\frac{5}{2}\pi$, $\frac{7}{2}\pi$, etc.

Let $x = \frac{1}{2}(2n+1)\pi - z$, where n is any positive integer, and z is a small quantity, then, by substituting in the given equation, $\tan(n\pi + \frac{1}{2}\pi - z) = n\pi + \frac{1}{2}\pi - z$.

For $n\pi + \frac{1}{2}\pi$ write α^{-1}, then α is small, since its greatest value, when $n=1$, is $(\frac{3}{2}\pi)^{-1} = \frac{7}{33}$ nearly; $\therefore \cot z = \alpha^{-1} - z$.

By Gregory's series, since $\tan z = \alpha(1 - \alpha z)^{-1}$,

$$z = \alpha(1-\alpha z)^{-1} - \tfrac{1}{3}\alpha^3(1-\alpha z)^{-3} + \tfrac{1}{5}\alpha^5(1-\alpha z)^{-5} - \ldots;$$

the first approximation gives $z = \alpha$; the second gives

$$z = \alpha(1 + \alpha z) - \tfrac{1}{3}\alpha^3, \text{ or } z = \alpha + \tfrac{2}{3}\alpha^3;$$

the third gives $z = \alpha(1 + \alpha z + \alpha^2 z^2) - \tfrac{1}{3}\alpha^3(1 + 3\alpha z) + \tfrac{1}{5}\alpha^5$

$$= \alpha + \alpha^2(\alpha + \tfrac{2}{3}\alpha^3) + \alpha^5 - \tfrac{1}{3}\alpha^3 - \alpha^5 + \tfrac{1}{5}\alpha^5 = \alpha + \tfrac{2}{3}\alpha^3 + \tfrac{13}{15}\alpha^5.$$

The solutions are 0, and $\pm(\alpha^{-1} - \alpha - \tfrac{2}{3}\alpha^3 - \tfrac{13}{15}\alpha^5 - \ldots)$, in which $\alpha^{-1} = \frac{3}{2}\pi$, $\frac{5}{2}\pi$, $\frac{7}{2}\pi$, ... successively; the first of these values gives $x = 257° 27' 17''$, the error introduced by omitting the fourth term being little more than $1' 17''$.

Examples III.

1. Shew that the tangent to the curve $y = x(x^2 - y)$ is parallel to Ox at the point $(-\frac{3}{2}, \frac{27}{4})$, and cuts the curve again where $x = 3$.

2. Shew that the distance between the two tangents to the curve $y = x(x^2 - 1)$, drawn parallel to the axis of x, is $\frac{4}{9}\sqrt{3}$.

3. Find the shape of the curve $y^2 - 2y = x^4 - x^2$ at the points of intersection with Ox, and at an infinite distance.

4. Shew that, if the form of the oval part of the curve
$$y^2 = x(x-1)(x-2)$$
be represented near the two vertices by two parabolas, having their axes coincident with Ox, the latus rectum of one is double that of the other.

5. Shew that, in the case of Art. 32, Ex. 2, iii., when $\alpha = \beta\sqrt{3}$, the form of the curve is like fig. 10, plate II., with the tangents at the points of inflexion parallel to Ox.

Trace the curves :   **6.** $y^2 = x^3 - x^5$.   **7.** $y^5 = (x^2 - 1)^2$.

8. $y^6 = (x-1)^3 x$.   **9.** $y^3 = (x-1)x^4$.   **10.** $y^2 - y = x^3 - x^2$.

11. Shew that there are points of inflexion at $(2, -16)$, $(4, 0)$ in the curve $y = x^4 - 12x^3 + 48x^2 - 64x$.

PLATE
III.

12. Find the point of inflexion in the curve
$$y^2 = x\{(x-1)^2 + \tfrac{1}{4}\}.$$

13. Trace the curve $xy^2 = (x-a)(x-b)^2$, for $b \gtreqless a$.

14. Shew by a curve the changes of sign and magnitude of
$$\sin x - \sin 2x.$$

15. Trace the curve $y = \sin x + \sin 2x - \sin 3x$.

16. Trace the curve $y = mx + c \sin \dfrac{\pi x}{a}$, when ma is greater than, equal to, or less than πc, and shew that the sum of the cotangents of the angles, at which the curve cuts any two ordinates whose distance apart is a, is constant.

17. Trace the curve $xy^2 - 2yx + y - 1 = 0$, and employ it to shew that there is only one real root of the equation
$$x^7 - 2x^4 + x^3 - 1 = 0.$$

18. Prove that there cannot be more than three real roots of the equation $x^7 - a^5x^2 + c^7 = 0$, if c be positive, nor more than one if c be negative.

19. Find, by means of two curves, properties of the roots of the equations
$$x^4 - 15a^3x + 14a^4 = 0, \quad \text{and} \quad x^5 - 2a^2x^3 + 3a^5 = 0.$$

20. Expand y in ascending powers of x, for three terms, when x is small, in the case of the two curves
$$x^3 + y^3 - 3axy = 0, \quad \text{and} \quad x^4 - 3xy^2 + 2y^3 = 0.$$

21. Solve the equation $\cos \theta = \theta$ approximately, having given that $\cos \alpha = \alpha + \beta$, when β is a small quantity.

22. Approximate to the solutions of the equation $4x \tan x = \pi$, in which the unit is the unit of circular measure.

CHAPTER IV.

FORMS OF CURVES IN THE NEIGHBOURHOOD OF THE ORIGIN. SIMPLE TANGENTS. DIRECTION AND AMOUNT OF CURVATURE. MULTIPLE POINTS OF TWO BRANCHES. CURVATURE OF BRANCHES AT MULTIPLE POINTS. MULTIPLE POINTS OF HIGHER ORDERS.

PLATE
III.

53. IN this and the following chapter I intend to discuss the forms of curves at particular points at a finite distance, when their equations are of a more complicated form.

For this purpose, it will be sufficient, as has already been mentioned, to consider the forms in the neighbourhood of the origin, since by transformation of coordinates, any point may be made the origin.

In order to trace a curve, we must know, at all points which have any peculiarity, the tangent, the side of the tangent on which the curve lies, and, in some cases, the rapidity with which the curve deflects itself from the tangent, *i.e.* the degree of curvature.

Although, in a great many cases the direction in which the curve bends from the tangent at any particular point may appear from consideration of other known portions of the curve, we must be in possession of methods of determining this when required, however troublesome the operation may be.

In illustrating these methods, I have given the forms of many of the curves throughout, although it has at present been shewn only very generally how the infinite branches can be determined. The student should, at all events,

PLATE
III.

obtain the directions of the curves at particular points, deferring the complete tracing until the chapter on asymptotes has been read. I have, however, avoided, as much as possible, any complicated forms of infinite branches.

FORMS OF CURVES NEAR THE ORIGIN.

54. Consider then, when a curve passes through the origin, and a point P, (x, y), is taken near the origin, on the branch which passes through it, that, as P is supposed to move towards O, x and y at some stage must diminish together, and that they ultimately vanish simultaneously.

One of the three following cases must therefore occur, as P describes the last small arc of the curve.

(1) x and y may be of the same order of small quantities.

(2) x may be small compared with y, in other words, $x : y$ may be a small ratio which ultimately vanishes.

(3) y may be small compared with x.

I think it best to consider these cases separately, and I shall in this chapter examine the cases in which x and y are of the same order of small magnitudes, so that an expression like $ax^2 + bxy + cy^2$ has every term of the second order, and is itself of the second order; we may observe that $ax^2 + bxy + cy^3 + dx^2y^2$ is also of the second order, if a, b, c, d be finite quantities.

SIMPLE TANGENT.

55. Let the equation of a curve, supposed rationalized, be arranged in a series of homogeneous functions of x and y, in the form
$$u_1 + u_2 + u_3 \ldots = 0,$$

where u_s denotes a homogeneous function of s dimensions in x and y; so that there being no term independent of x and y, the curve considered passes through the origin.

56. Consider first the case in which u_1, the function of the first degree, exists, and let $u_1 \equiv ax + by$, and at present

PLATE
III.

consider a and b to be finite quantities. Then $u_1 = 0$ is the first approximation to the relation which must exist between x and y for the part of the curve near the origin, for the whole equation may be written

$$a(1+\alpha)x + b(1+\beta)y = 0,$$

where, by diminishing x and y, α and β may be made as small as we please. Thus, for $ax + by + cx^2 + dxy + ey^2 = 0$ we may write

$$a\left(1 + \frac{cx+dy}{a}\right)x + b\left(1 + \frac{ey}{b}\right)y = 0.$$

Hence $u_1 = 0$ is the tangent to the curve at the origin.

57. It can be shewn as follows that no straight line can be drawn, which, near the origin, lies so close to the curve as $u_1 = 0$. For, if (x, y) be any point in the curve, the distance of this point from $u_1 = 0$ is

$$\frac{ax+by}{\sqrt{a^2+b^2}} = -\frac{u_2 + u_3 + \ldots}{\sqrt{a^2+b^2}},$$

which is of the second order of small quantities, whereas the distance from any other line $lx + my = 0$ is $\dfrac{lx+my}{\sqrt{l^2+m^2}}$, which is of the first order.

DIRECTION AND AMOUNT OF CURVATURE.

58. The next step is to discover in what direction the curve bends after leaving the point of contact; for this purpose we proceed to the next approximation, by taking into account the terms of the next order; the form of the curve is *generally* given more nearly by $u_1 + u_2 = 0$, the equation of a conic, if the coefficients in u_2 are not all zero.

At present we shall not consider the case in which this conic is two straight lines, in which case it will be seen that $u_1 + u_2 = 0$ is not the next approximation.

Such a conic may be called a conic of curvature, since it has the same curvature as the given curve in the neighbourhood of the origin.

PLATE
III.

59. The proof that the two curves have the same curvature may be given thus.

Let OT be the tangent $u_1 = 0$, OP' the conic $u_1 + u_2 = 0$, Fig. 4. and OP the curve $u_1 + u_2 + u_3 + \ldots = 0$.

Draw TPP' perpendicular to OT, and let (x, y), (x', y') be the points P, P'; it may be shewn, as in Art. **57**, that

$$PT : P'T = u_2 + u_3 + \ldots : u_2',$$

and since $x/y = b/(-a) = x'/y'$ ultimately, $u_2 : u_2'$ is a ratio of equality ultimately; therefore PT and $P'T$ are ultimately equal, which is the test of the curvature being the same.

60. That there is an infinite number of conics which have the property of coinciding with the curve to within quantities of the third order, may be seen as follows.

$u_1 = -u_2 - u_3 \ldots$ is a quantity of the second order for all points on the curve near the origin; therefore $u_1(\lambda x + \mu y)$ is of the third order, λ, μ being any constants arbitrarily chosen,

$$\therefore \quad u_1 + u_2 + (\lambda x + \mu y)u_1 = 0 \ldots\ldots\ldots\ldots\ldots(1)$$

is a conic which differs from the curve by a quantity of the third order. The particular conic which is the circle of curvature can be found by giving proper values to λ, μ in (1). If $u_2 \equiv cx^2 + dxy + ey^2$, then for a circle we have

$$\lambda b + \mu a + d = 0 \quad \text{and} \quad \lambda a + c = \mu b + e = \rho, \text{ say}.$$

Hence

$$b\frac{\rho - c}{a} + a\frac{\rho - e}{b} + d = 0 \quad \text{and} \quad \rho = \frac{b^2 c - abd + a^2 e}{a^2 + b^2}.$$

The equation of the circle is therefore

$$x^2 + y^2 + \frac{ax + by}{\rho} = 0,$$

and the radius $= \dfrac{\sqrt{a^2 + b^2}}{2\rho} = \dfrac{(a^2 + b^2)^{\frac{3}{2}}}{2(b^2 c - abd + a^2 e)}.$

61. The diameter of curvature may also be found directly by the method of Art. **25** without previously finding the equation of the circle.

PLATE
III.

Fig. 4.

For
$$PT = \frac{\pm u_1}{\sqrt{a^2 + b^2}} = \frac{\mp u_2 + \dots}{\sqrt{a^2 + b^2}},$$

and the diameter of curvature

$$= \mathrm{Lt}\, \frac{OP^2}{PT} = \mathrm{Lt}\, \frac{\pm (x^2 + y^2)\sqrt{a^2 + b^2}}{u_2}$$

$$= \frac{\pm (a^2 + b^2)^{\frac{3}{2}}}{b^2 c - abd + a^2 e}, \quad (\text{Art. } \mathbf{3}, 3),$$

since $\dfrac{x}{b} = \dfrac{y}{-a}$ ultimately.

62. If u_2 does not appear in the equation, u_1, instead of being of the second, is of the third order. Thus there is no conic of curvature, since the deflection from the tangent for the curve is infinitely less than that for any conic which can be drawn with the same tangent, the deflection for a conic being of the second order.

Compare the curves $O\alpha_2 B$, and $O\alpha_3 B$ in fig. 13, Plate I.

The approximate curve $u_1 + u_3 = 0$ has a point of inflexion at O, since the perpendicular from (x, y) on $u_1 = 0$, which varies as u_3, changes sign as (x, y) passes through the origin.

63. The following examples will shew how to apply the methods given above.

Ex. 1. *To find the tangent to the curve* $\mathbf{y}^r = \mathbf{x}^s$ *at the point* $(1, 1)$.

For x and y write $1 + \xi$ and $1 + \eta$, and arrange in homogeneous functions; the first term is $r\eta - s\xi$, which gives the equation of the tangent $r(y - 1) = s(x - 1)$. The radius of curvature at $(1, 1)$ is $(r^2 + s^2)^{\frac{3}{2}} / rs(r \sim s)$.

Ex. 2. *To find the tangents to the curve* $\mathbf{y} = \dfrac{(\mathbf{x}-1)(\mathbf{x}-3)}{\mathbf{x}-2}$ *at the points* $(1, 0)$, $(3, 0)$.

For x write $1 + \xi$; the first approximation gives

$$y = \xi \frac{1 - 3}{1 - 2} = 2\xi,$$

or $y = 2(x-1)$ is the equation of the first tangent;

similarly $y = 2(x-3)$ represents the second tangent.

Ex. 3. *To find the tangent and circle of curvature at a point (α, β) of the curve $\mathbf{a}x^2 + \mathbf{b}y^2 = 1$.*

For x, y write $\alpha + \xi$, $\beta + \eta$,

then $a(\alpha + \xi)^2 + b(\beta + \eta)^2 = 1$, and $a\alpha^2 + b\beta^2 = 1$,

$$\therefore \ 2(a\alpha\xi + b\beta\eta) + a\xi^2 + b\eta^2 = 0,$$

whence $a\alpha\xi + b\beta\eta = 0$ gives the tangent referred to the new axes.

Since, near the origin, $a\alpha\xi + b\beta\eta$ is of the second order,

$$2(a\alpha\xi + b\beta\eta) + a\xi^2 + b\eta^2 - (a\alpha\xi + b\beta\eta)(\lambda\xi + \mu\eta) = 0$$

is a curve which differs from the given curve by a quantity of the third order, and this is a circle if λ, μ satisfy

$$a(1 - \alpha\lambda) = b(1 - \beta\mu) = \rho, \quad \text{and} \quad a\alpha\mu + b\beta\lambda = 0,$$

whence $(a^2\alpha^2 + b^2\beta^2)\rho = ab(a\alpha^2 + b\beta^2) = ab,$

and the equation of the circle of curvature becomes

$$ab(\xi^2 + \eta^2) + (a^2\alpha^2 + b^2\beta^2)(2a\alpha\xi + 2b\beta\eta) = 0, \ \ldots\ldots(1)$$

the square of whose radius is $(a^2\alpha^2 + b^2\beta^2)^3/a^2b^2$.

For the centre of the circle of curvature (1),

$$\xi = -\frac{(a^2\alpha^2 + b^2\beta^2)\alpha}{b},$$

therefore, if (x, y) be the centre referred to the original axes,

$$x = \alpha + \xi = (a\alpha^2 + b\beta^2)\alpha - \frac{(a^2\alpha^2 + b^2\beta^2)\alpha}{b}$$

$$= \frac{a(b-a)\alpha^3}{b}.$$

Similarly $y = \dfrac{b(a-b)\beta^3}{a}.$

Hence, substituting in $a\alpha^2 + b\beta^2 = 1$,

$$\left(\frac{x}{\sqrt{a}}\right)^{\frac{2}{3}} + \left(\frac{y}{\sqrt{b}}\right)^{\frac{2}{3}} = \left(\frac{a-b}{ab}\right)^{\frac{2}{3}},$$

which is the locus of the centre of curvature.

Ex. 4. *To find the diameter of the circle of curvature at the point* (a, b) *of the curve* $\mathbf{y}(\mathbf{b}^2 - \mathbf{y}^2) = \mathbf{x}^2(\mathbf{a} - \mathbf{x})$.

Let $x = a + \xi$, $y = b + \eta$, then

$$(b + \eta)(2b\eta + \eta^2) = (a + \xi)^2 \xi,$$

or $\qquad 2b^2\eta - a^2\xi + 3b\eta^2 - 2a\xi^2 + \eta^3 - \xi^3 = 0 \,;$

whence, as in Art. **61**, the diameter of curvature

$$= \mathrm{Lt} \frac{(\xi^2 + \eta^2)\sqrt{(a^4 + 4b^4)}}{2a\xi^2 \sim 3b\eta^2}$$

$$= \frac{(a^4 + 4b^4)^{\frac{3}{2}}}{ab(8b^3 \sim 3a^3)}, \ \text{ since } \frac{\xi}{\eta} = \frac{2b^2}{a^2} \text{ ultimately.}$$

Cor. If $3a^3 = 8b^3$ the diameter is infinite.

In this case $2b^2\eta - a^2\xi = 0$ is true to quantities of the third order; therefore the approximation up to ξ^3 is

$$2b^2\eta = a^2\xi + \left(1 - \frac{a^6}{8b^6}\right)\xi^3 = a^2\xi + \tfrac{1}{9}\xi^3,$$

shewing that (a, b) is a point of inflexion.

64. The preceding is the general case of a simple tangent; we can proceed by a similar method of approximation, when singularities occur in the forms of the functions succeeding u_1.

It will be sufficient to take, as an instance, the case mentioned above, Art. **58**, in which the conic $u_1 + u_2 = 0$ becomes two straight lines, which happens when $u_2 \equiv u_1 v_1$.

In this case, the equation of the curve being

$$u_1 + u_1 v_1 + u_3 + \ldots = 0,$$

the tangent to the curve is $u_1 = 0$, and the next approximation to the form of the curve near the origin is given by

$$u_1 + u_3/(1 + v_1) = 0 \quad \text{or} \quad u_1 + u_3 = 0,$$

shewing that the distance of a point in the curve from the tangent, which varies as u_1, is ultimately of the third order, and, consequently, that $u_1 v_1$ is of the fourth order; thus, for points in the branch through the origin, u_3 ranks before u_2, shewing, as was stated in Art. **58**, that $u_1 + u_2 = 0$ is not the next approximation.

PLATE
III.

Since u_3 changes sign, as (x, y) passes through the origin, the curve has generally a point of inflexion at the origin.

65. Take, as an example of such a form of u_2, the curve

$$a^3(y+x) - 2a^2x(y+x) + x^4 = 0.$$

The approximate form of the branch through the origin is given by

$$a^3(y+x) + x^4 = 0,$$

which shews that the curve bends towards the negative ends of Ox and Oy, and that its distance from the tangent is of the fourth order.

It may be shewn that it cuts the axis of x at four points, by the discussion of the equation in the form

$$a^2(2x - a)y = x(x - a)(x^2 + ax - a^2),$$

and that the angles of inclination to Ox at the points of section are $\pm 45°$ and $\pm \tan^{-1}\sqrt{5}$.

The asymptotes are $2x = a$ and $2a^2y = x^3$. These considerations are sufficient for the general shape given in the figure.

Fig. 5.

MULTIPLE POINT OF TWO BRANCHES.

66. I proceed next to the case of two branches through the origin. Such points occur when the rationalized equation commences with a function of the second degree, thus

$$u_2 + u_3 + u_4 + \ldots = 0,$$

in which u_2 may be of the form I. v_1w_1, II. $v_1{}^2$, III. $v_1{}^2 + w_1{}^2$.

I. $u_2 \equiv v_1w_1$.

67. The tangents to the curve at the origin are given by $v_1 = 0$ and $w_1 = 0$. If $v_1 \equiv ax + by$, the next approximation for the branch touching $v_1 = 0$, is obtained from $v_1 + u_3/w_1 = 0$, in the form $v_1 + Ax^2 = 0$, by writing $-ax/b$ for y in the fraction u_3/w_1, which is generally the simplest method; or, since $v_1 + \dfrac{u_3}{w_1} \equiv v_1 + \dfrac{u_3}{w_1x^2}x^2$, and so A is the limit of $\dfrac{u_3}{w_1x^2}$, the numerator and denominator of which are each homogeneous functions of the third degree, the value is given by writing b for x and $-a$ for y, Art. **3** (3).

PLATE
III.

68. We may observe that the curve $v_1 + Ax^2 = 0$ is a parabola whose axis is parallel to Oy; it is easy to shew how an approximate parabolic form may be found having its axis parallel to any given line $mx + ny = 0$, for $\dfrac{u_3}{w_1}$ may be written $\dfrac{u_3}{w_1(mx+ny)^2}(mx+ny)^2$, which gives for the approximation $B(mx+ny)^2$, where B is to be found by Art. **3** (3) as A was in the last article.

If $m = -b$, $n = a$, the approximate parabola will have its vertex at the origin.

69. Take for examples the investigation of the forms of the following curves near the origin.

   Ex. 1. $\mathbf{x^2(y-b) = y^2(x-a),}$ $\mathbf{a > b.}$

The first approximation gives $ay^2 - bx^2 = 0$, and hence the tangents at the origin are $y\sqrt{a} = \pm x\sqrt{b}$.

The second approximation for the branch whose tangent is $y\sqrt{a} = x\sqrt{b}$, comes from

$$y\sqrt{a} - x\sqrt{b} + \frac{xy(x-y)}{y\sqrt{a}+x\sqrt{b}} = 0$$

giving by either of the methods of Art. **67**, neglecting powers of x above the square,

$$y\sqrt{a} - x\sqrt{b} + \frac{\sqrt{a}-\sqrt{b}}{2a}x^2 = 0\;;$$

changing the sign of $\sqrt{b}$, for the other branch we have

$$y\sqrt{a} + x\sqrt{b} + \frac{\sqrt{a}+\sqrt{b}}{2a}x^2 = 0.$$

Fig. 6.   The figure shews how each branch bends.

   Ex. 2. $\mathbf{a^2(x^2 - y^2) + 2axy^2 + ay^3 - x^4 - x^2y^2 = 0.}$

The tangents at the origin are $y = \pm x$. For the next approximation, retaining only the parts of the given equation which give rise to terms of the second order, the forms of the two branches are given by

$$y = x + \frac{2xy^2 + y^3}{a(y+x)} = x + \frac{3x^2}{2a},$$

$$y = -x + \frac{2xy^2 + y^3}{a(y-x)} = -x - \frac{x^2}{2a}.$$

Both branches bend towards the negative end of the axis of x.

Ex. 3. $$x^4 - y^4 - a^2x^2 + b^2y^2 = 0.$$

For the direction of flexure from $by = ax$,

$$by - ax = \frac{y^4 - x^4}{by + ax} = \frac{x^3(a^4 - b^4)}{2ab^4}.$$

For the flexure from $by = -ax$,

$$by + ax = \frac{y^4 - x^4}{by - ax} = \frac{-x^3(a^4 - b^4)}{2ab^4}.$$

Writing $100a^2$ for a^2 and $96a^2$ for b^2, we obtain the equation discussed in Art. **33**, and Plate II., fig. 15, shews the form of the curve for the above values of a and b.

Ex. 4. $$y^4 - 2a^2y^2 + 2a^2x^2 - 3ax^3 + x^4 = 0,$$
or $$y^2(2a^2 - y^2) = x^2(x - a)(x - 2a).$$

The curve is symmetrical with respect to Ox.

Near $(0, 0)$, $$y^2 = x^2 - \frac{3x^3}{2a},$$

$$\therefore \; y = \pm x\left(1 - \frac{3x}{2a}\right)^{\frac{1}{2}} = \pm x\left(1 - \frac{3x}{4a}\right)$$

near $(a, 0)$, $2a^2y^2 = -a^3\xi$, or $y^2 = -\frac{1}{2}a\xi$;

near $(2a, 0)$, $2a^2y^2 = 4a^3\xi$, or $y^2 = 2a\xi$;

near $(0, a\sqrt{2})$, $-2a^2 . 2\sqrt{2}a\eta = 2a^2x^2$, or $x^2 = -2\sqrt{2}a\eta$;

near $(a, a\sqrt{2})$, $-2a^2 . 2\sqrt{2}a\eta = -a^3\xi$, or $\eta = \frac{1}{8}\sqrt{2}\xi$;

near $(2a, a\sqrt{2})$, $-2a^2 . 2\sqrt{2}a\eta = 4a^3\xi$, or $\eta = -\frac{1}{2}\sqrt{2}\xi$.

To find where the curve is parallel to the axis of x, let (α, β) be such a point, and consider that if $x = \alpha + \xi$ and $y = \beta + \eta$, the resulting equation in ξ, η represents a curve passing through the origin and touching the axis of ξ, so that η vanishes compared with ξ near the point of contact.

The substitution in the proposed equation gives, near (α, β),

$$(4a^2\alpha - 9a\alpha^2 + 4\alpha^3)\xi + P\eta + Q\xi^2 + \ldots = 0,$$

since $$\beta^4 - 2a^2\beta^2 + 2a^2\alpha^2 - 3a\alpha^3 + \alpha^4 = 0;$$

PLATE
III.

therefore, making ξ very small,

$$4a^2\alpha - 9a\alpha^2 + 4\alpha^3 = 0,$$

whence $\alpha = 0$ and $\frac{1}{8}\{9 \pm \sqrt(17)\}a$, or $\frac{13}{8}a$ and $\frac{5}{8}a$ nearly; these values give the position of the points required, viz. a, c, b and b', symmetrically placed on opposite sides of Ox.

Similarly, the curve is parallel to Oy, where

$$4y^3 - 4a^2y = 0, \quad \text{or} \quad y = 0 \text{ and } y = \pm a,$$

Fig. 7.   when $y = a$, $x^4 - 3ax^3 + 2a^2x^2 - a^4 = 0.$

The values of x are the abscissæ of the points of intersection of $x^2 = ay$ ....(1)

and $y(y - 3x + 2a) = a^2.$ ....(2)

If the parabola (1) and the hyperbola (2) be constructed, it will be seen that, since the parabola cuts the asymptote $y - 3x + 2a = 0$ at the points where $x = a$ and $2a$, the points

Fig. 8.   of intersection, p and q, have for their abscissæ a small negative value and a positive value a little greater than $2a$, and that these are the only points of intersection. The

Fig. 7.   points so determined are the points e, e', and f, f', in the curve.

The student may also find the solutions of the biquadratic by the intersections of $ay = x^2$ and $y(x - a)(x - 2a) = a^3$.

70. If there be no functions of the third order, the equation of the curve being $v_1w_1 + u_4 + \ldots = 0$, the next approximation to $v_1 = 0$ may be obtained from $v_1 + u_4/w_1 = 0$ in the form $v_1 + Bx^3 = 0$, which expresses that the distance of a point of that branch from the tangent changes sign as we pass through the point of contact, or that there is a point of inflexion.

71. Take, as an example, the curve $\mathbf{a^2(x^2 - y^2) + x^4 + y^4 = 0}$. The curve is symmetrical with respect to both axes, and meets the axis of y where $y = \pm a$.

The branch, whose tangent is $y = x$, has the approximate form of $y = x + x^3/a^2$.

Near $(0, a)$, since the equation can be written

$$(a^2 + x^2)x^2 + y^2(y^2 - a^2) = 0,$$

PLATE
III.

if we write $a+\eta$ for y, we have the parabolic form,

$$x^2+2a\eta=0, \quad \rightarrow\kern-0.6em\prec.$$

A nearer approximation is $x^2+\eta^2+2a\eta=0$, which shews
that the radius of curvature is a. The dotted line in the Fig. 9.
figure is the circle of curvature at the points $(0, \pm a)$.

72. When v_1 is a factor of u_2 and u_3, the equation being

$$v_1 w_1 + v_1 v_2 + u_4 + \ldots = 0,$$

the form of the branch, whose tangent is $v_1=0$, is given by

$$v_1 + \frac{u_4}{w_1+v_2} = 0,$$

and therefore by

$$v_1 + \frac{u_4}{w_1} = 0 \quad \text{or} \quad v_1 + A x^3 = 0 ;$$

whence, as in Art. **70**, this branch has a point of inflexion.
In this case, v_1 being of the third order, $v_1 v_2$ is of the fifth
and therefore ranks after u_4.

73. The following curves will serve as examples:

Ex. 1. $\quad a^2(x+2y)(y-2x) - a(y-2x)x^2 + y^4 = 0.$

The direction of flexure from the tangent $y-2x=0$,
obtained from

$$y - 2x + \frac{y^4}{a^2(x+2y)} = 0,$$

by making $y=2x$ in the smaller term, is given by

$$y - 2x + \frac{16x^3}{5a^2} = 0.$$

For the other branch, whose tangent is $x+2y=0$, the
flexure is given by that of the parabola $a(x+2y)=x^2$.

The curve cuts the axis of x where $x=a$; if $x=a+\xi$,
since, when y^2 is rejected, the equation becomes

$$-3a^2 xy - ax^2 y + 2ax^2(x-a) = 0,$$

the tangent at this point is $2y=\xi$.

To obtain some idea of the size of the loop, which joins
the ends of the branches in xOy, put $x=y$. Then

$$x = y = \tfrac{1}{2}(\pm\surd(13)-1)a = 1\cdot3a, \quad \text{or} \quad -2\cdot3a \text{ nearly.}$$

PLATE
III.

Fig. 10.

The guiding asymptote is $2ax^3 + y^4 = 0$, and, since the next most important term is $-ayx^2$, the numerical value of y, for large values of x, is greater in the curve than in the asymptote when y is $+$, and less when y is $-$, so that both branches lie above the asymptote; the curve cuts the lower branch in two points, only one of which is given in the figure.

The calculation of the direction of flexure of the branches at the multiple point might have been avoided, as remarked in Art. **53**, by observing that $y - 2x = 0$ does not meet the curve except at the origin, consequently there are three consecutive points in the tangent, and therefore a point of inflexion; and that $x + 2y = 0$ meets it again at the point $(-40a,\ 20a)$, too far to be represented in the figure.

Ex. 2. $a^3(y^2 - x^2) - 2a^2(y^3 + x^3) + ay^4 + x^5 = 0.$

The tangents to the branches through the origin are $y = \pm x$, and the next approximations are

$$a(y - x) - 2x^2 = 0, \quad a^2(y + x) - \tfrac{1}{2}x^3 = 0.$$

The equation may be written in the form

$$ay^2(y - a)^2 = x^2(x + a)(a^2 + ax - x^2),$$

or $a\{(y - \tfrac{1}{2}a)^2 - \tfrac{1}{4}a^2\}^2 = x^2(x + a)(x + 2a\sin 18°)(2a\sin 54° - x),$

the curve is therefore symmetrical with respect to the line $y = \tfrac{1}{2}a$, and y is impossible, if $x > 2a\sin 54°$, or between $-2a\sin 18°$ and $-a$. The forms, where $x = -a, -2a\sin 18°$, and $2a\sin 54°$, are common parabolas.

Fig. 11. The infinite branch is of the form $x^5 + a(y - \tfrac{1}{2}a)^4 = 0$.

We may illustrate the method of Art. **47** in approximating to the position of the points of intersection of the curve with the line $y = \tfrac{1}{2}a$, given by the equation

$$x^5 - 2a^2x^3 - a^3x^2 + \tfrac{1}{16}a^5 = 0.$$

The values of x are the abscissæ of the points of intersection of the curves

$$a^2y = x^3, \quad \text{and} \quad x^2(y - a) - 2a^2y + \tfrac{1}{16}a^3 = 0,$$

the asymptotes of the latter are $y = a$, and $x = \pm a\sqrt{2}$.

PLATE
III.

Fig. 12.

The first curve is the dotted curve, the asymptotes of the second are omitted. The letters m, n, r determine the position of M, N, R in the figure of the given curve.

$$\text{II. } u_2 \equiv v_1^2.$$

74. The second case, when $u_2 \equiv v_1^2$, in which there are two coincident tangents, gives, generally, as the approximate form, $v_1^2 + u_3 = 0$; hence, if A be the value of u_3/x^3 when b, $-a$ are written for x and y, $v_1^2 + Ax^3 = 0$; therefore if A be finite, *i.e.* unless v_1 be a factor of u_3,

$$ax + by = \pm(-Ax^3)^{\frac{1}{2}};$$

so that, generally, when u_3 exists, this curve has a ceratoid cusp at the origin [see Art. **18** (3)].

75. An example of this form occurs in the curve

$$(ax - by)^2 - ax^2y - y^4 = 0.$$

Near the origin, $(ax - by)^2 - \dfrac{a^2x^3}{b} = 0$, or $by = ax \pm \dfrac{ax^{\frac{3}{2}}}{b^{\frac{1}{2}}}$;

near the points, $(0, \pm b)$, $\mp 2ab^2x \mp b^2 . 2b\eta = 0$, or $b\eta + ax = 0$;

where $y = a$, $x = \infty$, or $-(a^2 - b^2)/2b$.

If x and y be both very large, $ax^2 + y^3 = 0$, which meets the curve where $x = -b^3/a^2$. The figure is drawn for $a > b$.

Fig. 13.

76. When v_1 is a factor of u_3, we have to obtain the approximate form from $v_1^2 + v_1v_2 + u_4 = 0$; in which case

$$(v_1 + \tfrac{1}{2}v_2)^2 = \tfrac{1}{4}v_2^2 - u_4, \quad \text{or} \quad v_1 = -\tfrac{1}{2}v_2 \pm Bx^2 = (C \pm B)x^2.$$

If B be impossible, the origin is a conjugate point.

If B be real and different from zero, each of the branches is parabolic, the curvatures being different.

If $B = 0$, or $4u_4 = v_2^2$, the form must be found from the next approximation, viz.

$$(v_1 + \tfrac{1}{2}v_2)^2 + u_5 = 0, \quad \text{or} \quad v_1 + \tfrac{1}{2}v_2 = Dx^{\frac{5}{2}},$$

which shews, as in Art. **18** (1), that there is a ramphoid cusp at the origin.

PLATE
III.

77. The following examples will illustrate these forms:

Ex. 1. $\qquad (x-y)^2 - (x-y)x^2 - \tfrac{1}{3}x^4 - \tfrac{1}{9}y^4 = 0.$

Near the origin $\quad x - y = \tfrac{4}{3}x^2,$ or $\quad -\tfrac{1}{3}x^2;$

where $\qquad\qquad y = 0, \quad x^2 - x^3 - \tfrac{1}{3}x^4 = 0, \ldots\ldots\ldots\ldots\ldots\ldots$(i)

$\qquad\qquad \therefore \quad x = \tfrac{4}{5} \quad$ and $\quad -3\tfrac{4}{5}$ nearly ;

near the points $(0, \pm 3)$, if $y = \pm 3 + \eta$, it can then be shewn
that $\qquad\qquad \eta = -x + \tfrac{1}{6}x^2 \quad$ and $\quad \eta = -x + \tfrac{5}{6}x^2,$

so that the curve bends upwards at both the points where
the curve meets Oy, which, for the upper point, is contrary
to what one would have expected without calculation.

The tangent $y + x = 3$, it will be found, meets the curve
at points where $x = \tfrac{15}{16}$ and $-2\tfrac{7}{16}$ nearly.

To obtain a good idea of the size of the curve, observe
that $x = -y$ meets it where $x = -y = \tfrac{3}{2}$ or -6. We can
shew that the tangents at these points are $3\eta + 13\xi = 0$, and
$3\eta = 7\xi.$

Fig. 14.

The directions of the curve, at the points where the curve
intersects the axis of x, are deduced from a curious property
of the curve, which may be shewn as follows:

Let the curve be cut by a line $x + y = \alpha$, then the lines
joining the origin with the four points of intersection are
given by the homogeneous equation

$$(x^2 - y^2)^2 - \alpha x^2(x^2 - y^2) - \tfrac{1}{3}\alpha^2 x^4 - \tfrac{1}{9}\alpha^2 y^4 = 0,$$

or $\qquad (1 - \alpha - \tfrac{1}{3}\alpha^2)x^4 - (2 - \alpha)x^2 y^2 + (1 - \tfrac{1}{9}\alpha^2)y^4 = 0 \ldots\ldots$(ii)

When all four points are real, these lines form two pairs,
equally inclined to the axes; if two only are real, the two
lines are equally inclined to the axes.

Hence, a pair are coincident at each of the points of
intersection with the axis of x; this appears directly from
equation (ii), since $y^2 = 0$ when $1 - \alpha - \tfrac{1}{3}\alpha^2 = 0$, which makes
$y + x = \alpha$ satisfied by the points given in (i).

The same property shews that there is a double tangent
parallel to $x + y = 0$, touching at a, b, so that Oa, Ob, are
equally inclined to Oy.

PLATE
III.
___

Ex. 2. $2(x-y-\frac{2}{3}x^2)^2+(x+y)y^4-y^6-x^6=0$.

Near $(0, 0)$,

$$(x-y-\tfrac{2}{3}x^2)^2+x^5=0, \quad \text{or} \quad y=x-\tfrac{2}{3}x^2\pm(-x)^{\frac{5}{2}},$$

so that there is a ramphoid cusp at the origin.

Where $y=0$, $x^2=0$ and $2(1-\frac{2}{3}x)^2-x^4=0$,

$$\therefore\ x^2\pm\tfrac{2}{3}\sqrt{2}x+\tfrac{2}{9}=\tfrac{2}{9}\pm\sqrt{2}=\tfrac{1}{9}(2\pm13) \text{ nearly},$$

$\therefore\ x+\frac{1}{3}\sqrt{2}=\pm\frac{1}{3}\sqrt{(15)}$,   or $x='8$ and $-1'8$ nearly.

Where $x=0$, $2y^2+y^5-y^6=0$,

$\therefore\ y^2=0$ and $y^4-y^3-2=0$,   or $y=-1$ or $\frac{3}{2}$ nearly;

where $x=y$, $\frac{8}{9}x^4+2x^5-2x^6=0$; $\therefore\ x=\frac{4}{9}$ or $-\frac{1}{3}$;

where $x=-y$,   each $=1'1$ or $-1'8$ nearly.   Fig. 15.

III. $u_2\equiv v_1{}^2+w_1{}^2$.

78. The third case, when u_2 is of the form $v_1{}^2+w_1{}^2$ gives a conjugate point, since the first approximation has $v_1=0$, $w_1=0$, as the only solutions.

79. Take the following curve as an example:

$$a^2(x^2+y^2)-2a(x-y)^3+x^4+y^4=0.$$

There is a conjugate point at the origin.

To trace the curve, observe that $-x$ for y and $-y$ for x do not alter the equation, hence the curve is symmetrical with respect to the line $x+y=0$, which cuts the curve where $x^2-8ax+a^2=0$, or $x=(8-\frac{1}{8})a$ or $\frac{1}{8}a$, nearly;

near $(a, 0)$, $a^2\xi^2+6a^3y=0$;

near $(0, -a)$, $a^2\eta^2-6a^3x=0$;

where $y=mx$ meets the curve

$$a^2(m^2+1)+2a(m-1)^3x+(m^4+1)x^2=0;$$

therefore if x be real, $(m^4+1)(m^2+1)-(m-1)^6<0$,

$$\therefore\ 6m^5-14m^4+20m^3-14m^2+6m<0,$$

or $2m\{3(m^2+1)-4m\}(m^2+1-m)<0$,

hence m must be negative, and therefore x positive, so that the whole curve lies in the angle xOy', and consists of an oval and the conjugate point.   Fig. 16.

PLATE
III.

CURVATURE OF BRANCHES AT MULTIPLE POINTS.

80. To find the diameter of curvature of the branch of
the curve whose tangent is $u_1 = 0$, the equation of the curve
being $u_1 v_1 + u_3 + u_4 + \ldots = 0$.

Let $u_1 \equiv ax + by$, $\quad v_1 \equiv a'x + b'y$, $\quad u_3 \equiv f(x, y)$.

The second approximation gives $u_1 v_1 + u_3 = 0$, hence the
diameter of curvature

$$= \mathrm{Lt}\, \frac{\sqrt{a^2 + b^2}(x^2 + y^2)}{\pm u_1} = \mathrm{Lt}\, \frac{\sqrt{a^2 + b^2}(x^2 + y^2) v_1}{\mp u_3}$$

$$= \mp \frac{(a^2 + b^2)^{\frac{3}{2}}(a'b - b'a)}{f(b, -a)},$$

since $\dfrac{x}{b} = \dfrac{y}{-a}$ ultimately.

81. Example. *To compare the diameters of curvature
of the two branches through the origin of the curve*

$$(a - x)y^2 = (4a - y)x^2.$$

The equation may be written

$$a(y - 2x)(y + 2x) - xy(y - x) = 0.$$

The diameters of curvature of the two branches are the
limits, when $y = \pm 2x$, of

$$\frac{x^2 + y^2}{y \mp 2x}\sqrt{5} \quad \text{or} \quad \frac{(x^2 + y^2)(y \pm 2x)}{xy(y - x)}\sqrt{5}a\,;$$

they are $5\sqrt{5} \cdot \frac{4}{2}a$ and $5\sqrt{5} \cdot \frac{4}{6}a$, and in the ratio $3:1$.

MULTIPLE POINTS OF HIGHER ORDERS.

82. These discussions of particular forms of the homogeneous functions are sufficient to shew how they can be
dealt with in all ordinary cases.

The different forms which u_3 could assume if the first of
the existing functions were of the third degree, will suggest
themselves readily, as when there is only one real branch,
when there are three branches, when two of the three or
all three osculate; also whenever variations arise in con-

PLATE
III.

sequence of peculiar forms of the succeeding functions similar to those mentioned in Arts. **72** and **76**.

Thus, there would be three osculating branches, if the equation reduced to the form

$$(u_1 - t_2)(u_1 - v_2)(u_1 - w_2) + u_5 + \ldots = 0.$$

83. A few of the varieties occur in the following curves.

Ex. 1. $a(\mathbf{y}^2 - \mathbf{x}^2)(\mathbf{y} - 2\mathbf{x}) - \mathbf{y}^4 = 0.$

This curve has three branches through the origin, the deflexions from the tangents to which are given by

$$a(y - x) + \tfrac{1}{2}y^2 = 0, \quad a(y + x) - \tfrac{1}{6}y^2 = 0, \quad a(y - 2x) - \tfrac{4}{3}y^2 = 0;$$

near $(0, a)$, $2x + y - a = 0$,

near (∞, ∞), $2ax^3 = y^4$.   Fig. 17.

Ex. 2. $a(\mathbf{y} - \mathbf{x})(\mathbf{x}^2 + \mathbf{y}^2) + \mathbf{x}^4 = 0.$

Through the origin there is a branch of the form of $2a(y - x) + x^2 = 0$, and there is also a conjugate point called a point-circle, $x^2 + y^2 = 0$.

Near $(a, 0)$, $y + x - a = 0$,

near (∞, ∞), $ay^3 + x^4 = 0$.   Fig. 18.

Ex. 3. $a(\mathbf{y} - \mathbf{x})^2(\mathbf{y} + \mathbf{x}) - \mathbf{y}^4 - \mathbf{x}^4 = 0.$

Since the interchange of x and y does not alter the equation, there is symmetry with respect to the line $x = y$; near the origin,

$$a(y - x)^2 = x^3 \quad \text{and} \quad 2a(y + x) = x^2;$$

near $(a, 0)$, $y + x - a = 0$.   Fig. 19.

Ex. 4. $a^2(\mathbf{y} - \mathbf{x})^3 - 2a\mathbf{x}^4 + a\mathbf{y}^4 - \mathbf{x}^5 = 0.$

Near the origin,

$$a^2(y - x)^3 - ax^4 = 0, \quad \text{or} \quad y - x = x^{\frac{4}{3}}/a^{\frac{1}{3}};$$

near $(0, -a)$, if $y = -a + \eta$, $\eta + 3x = 0$;

near $(-a, 0)$, if $x = -a + \xi$, $3ay + \xi^2 = 0$;

near (∞, ∞), $ay^4 - x^5 = 0$.   Fig. 20.

Ex. 5. $2a^2(\mathbf{y} - \mathbf{x})^2(\mathbf{y} + \mathbf{x}) - 4a\mathbf{x}^3(\mathbf{y} - \mathbf{x}) + 2\mathbf{x}^5 - \mathbf{x}^4\mathbf{y} = 0.$

For the branches whose common tangent is $y = x$,

$$4a^2(y - x)^2 - 4ax^2(y - x) + x^4 = 0$$

is the next approximate equation, and it gives two coincident parabolas. To separate the branches we must conduct the approximation a step further; in the smaller terms put $y = x + x^2/2a$, then

$$4a^2(y-x)^2\left(x + \frac{x^2}{4a}\right) - 4ax^3(y-x) + x^5 - \frac{x^6}{2a} = 0,$$

or $x\{4a^2(y-x)^2 - 4ax^2(y-x) + x^4\} = -ax^2(y-x)^2 + \dfrac{x^6}{2a}$;

whence $2a(y-x) = x^2 \pm \dfrac{x^{\frac{5}{2}}}{\sqrt{2a}}$ is the approximation, which

gives a ramphoid cusp.

For the branch touching $y + x = 0$, $\quad a(y+x) + x^2 = 0$,

where $y = 0$, $\quad 2a^2x^3 + 4ax^4 + 2x^5 = 0$, $\quad$ or $\quad x^3(x+a)^2 = 0$;

near $(-a, 0)$, $\quad -2a^2x^2y - 4ax^3y - x^4y + 2x^3(x+a)^2 = 0$;

$$\therefore \ (x+a)^2 = \tfrac{1}{2}ay.$$

The rectilinear asymptote is $y = 2x - 4a$, the guiding parabolic asymptotes are $x^2 = \pm\sqrt{2ay}$.

Fig. 21.

Examples IV.

1. $\qquad\qquad (y-2)^2 = (x-1)^2 x.$

Find the branches which pass through $(1, 2)$, and shew that the radius of curvature of each branch is $2\sqrt{2}$.

2. $\qquad\qquad (2a-x)y^2 = x(\tfrac{3}{2}a - x)^2.$

Shew that the branches at $(\tfrac{3}{2}a, 0)$ cut Ox at angles $60°$ and $120°$; the radius of curvature of each branch is $a\sqrt{3}$.

3. $\qquad\qquad x^{\frac{2}{3}} + y^{\frac{2}{3}} = c^{\frac{2}{3}}.$

Prove that the radius of curvature at the point where $x = y$ is $\tfrac{3}{2}c$.

4. $\qquad\qquad (a-x)y^2 = (a+x)x^2.$

Shew that the centres of the circles of curvature of the branches through the origin are at the points $(-a, \pm a)$; and that the greatest breadth of the loop measured parallel to Oy is $\tfrac{2}{11}a$ nearly.

5. In the curve of Art. 81, shew that the diameter of curvature at $(a, 4a)$ is very little less than $43a$.

6. Discuss the case of Art. 82, when

$$(\text{i}) \ t_2 = v_2 = w_2 \quad \text{and} \quad (\text{ii}) \ t_2 = v_2 \neq w_2.$$

PLATE
III.

7. $x^4 + y^4 - 2ax^3 + a^2(x+y)^2 = 0.$

Shew that there is a ceratoid cusp at the origin, and find the form of the curve near $(a, 0)$.   Prove that there is only one tangent, besides the axis of x, which passes through the origin, and that m, the tangent of the inclination to the axis of x, is given by the equation

$$m^5 + 2m^4 + m^3 + m + 2 = 0,$$

approximate to its value by the method of Arts. **47** and **49**.

8. $x^6 + y^6 - a^2(x^2 - y^2)^2 = 0.$

Shew that the curve consists of four loops, and that the radius of curvature of each branch through the origin is $2a$.

9. Find the forms of the branches at the origin, for the two curves

$$x^4 - ax^2y + \tfrac{1}{4}a^2y^2 - ay^3 = 0$$

and $x^4 - ax^2y - \tfrac{3}{4}a^2y^2 - ay^3 = 0.$

Prove that the breadths of the two loops measured parallel to Ox are about $\tfrac{2}{7}a$ and $\tfrac{7}{10}a$.

10. The curve, fig. 20, Art. **88** (4), is parallel to Ox, where it meets the curve $3a^2(y-x)^2 + 8ax^3 + 5x^4 = 0,$

or $3a^2y(y-2x) + x^2(x+a)(5x+3a) = 0.$

Trace the last curve, and shew roughly where the three points of intersection are situated.

CHAPTER V.

FORMS OF BRANCHES WHOSE TANGENTS AT THE ORIGIN ARE THE COORDINATE AXES.

PLATE
III.

84. I have now to call attention to the cases in which x and y are of different orders of magnitude, for points taken very near the origin along any branch of a curve whose equation is given.

Such cases arise when the equation of the curve can be shewn to be correctly replaced by a simpler equation of the form $ax^m = by^n$, when m and n are unequal. For example, if the equation of a curve were

$$x^4 + ax^2y + bxy^2 + cy^3 = 0,$$

the simpler equation $x^2 + ay = 0$ would make bxy^2 of the order x^5, and cy^3 of the order x^6, and the equation would be $x^2 + ay(1 + \epsilon) = 0$, where by diminishing x, ϵ might be made as small as we please; so that one series of small values of x and y will satisfy the equation $x^2 + ay = 0$, which, therefore, gives the form of one branch of the curve.

85. The variety of cases which arise is so great, that I shall attempt no subdivision of the two cases in which x is small compared with y, and y small compared with x, reserving for a future chapter the application of Newton's parallelogram and De Gua's analytical triangle to the discrimination of the branches of a curve which pass through the origin; it will there be seen that these artifices save the trouble of thinking in a great measure, but my object is rather to give the student distinct ideas of the work which he is doing in making approximations, than merely to obtain results.

PLATE III.

86. I shall therefore in this chapter discuss such a number of particular cases as will be sufficient to show how any case, which is not very complicated, may be handled, taking as examples curves which are given by equations which either contain only a small number of terms, or are reducible, by simple considerations, to a small number of terms.

87. A simple case to begin with is the curve whose equation is $$x^4 - axy^2 + y^4 = 0.$$

Here x and y cannot be of the same order of magnitude, since in that case axy^2 would be of the order x^3, so that the equation would become $axy^2 = 0$, which is contrary to the supposition.

We try first whether x can be small compared with y, in which case x^4 would be small compared with y^4, and the equation would become $-axy^2 + y^4 = 0$, or $ax = y^2$; therefore, since for a short distance along this curve, whose form is $\dashv\!\!\!<$, the value of x^4, which we neglected, is of the order y^8, this is an approximate form of one part of the curve.

We then try whether y can be small compared with x, in which case y^4 could be neglected compared with x^4, and the equation would be reduced to $x^3 - ay^2 = 0$; along this curve, whose form is $\dashv\!\!\!\!<$, y^4 is of the order x^6, and the result is consistent with the assumption that y^4 might be rejected. This is therefore the form of another branch at the origin.

The curve is then easily drawn, since it is symmetrical with respect to Ox, and x cannot be negative.

Fig. 22.

88. The next which I shall consider is a more difficult case, and will serve as an illustration of the circumstance that, if the rationalized equation of a curve be arranged in homogeneous functions of x and y ascending in degree, such as $u_r + u_s + \ldots = 0$, u_r does not necessarily belong to the terms which can give the first approximation to every branch of the curve passing through the origin; that is, the functions are not arranged in order of magnitude for all branches of the curve.

The equation of the curve is

$$\mathbf{x^3y^2 + xy^5 - y^7 - x^7 = 0.}$$

Here x and y cannot be of the same order of magnitude; we must try, therefore, whether $x:y$ or $y:x$ can be small.

First, suppose $y:x$ small, *i.e.* as small as we please by diminishing x; if so, y^7 is small compared with x^7 and the equation reduces, so far, to

$$x^2y^2 + y^5 - x^6 = 0.$$

Again, since y^3 is small compared with x^2, y^5 may be neglected, and $y^2 = x^4$ gives an approximate form, $\rangle\!\!\langle$, where we observe that the terms neglected, namely xy^5 and y^7, are of the orders x^{11} and x^{14}, while those retained are of the order x^7.

Next, suppose $x:y$ small, in which case x^7 vanishes compared with y^7, and the equation is reduced to

$$x^3 + xy^3 - y^5 = 0.$$

If in any branch x^3 can be neglected, $x = y^2$, and $x^3 = y^6$, hence the term neglected is small compared with y^5 retained, $\dashv\!\!\vdash$ is therefore the form of a branch.

If xy^3 could be neglected, $x^3 = y^5$, then one condition would be satisfied, viz. that $x:y$ should be small, but $xy^3 \infty y^{\frac{5}{3}+3}$ or $y^{4+\frac{2}{3}}$, which is greater than the term y^5 retained; there is therefore no such branch through the origin.

If y^5 be neglected, $x^2 = -y^3$, and y^5, which $\infty x^{\frac{10}{3}}$, is small compared with the term x^3 retained $\underline{+}$ is therefore the form of a branch.

The four branches have thus been shewn to be given by the equations

$$y = x^2, \quad y = -x^2, \quad x = y^2, \quad \text{and} \quad x^2 = -y^3.$$

PLATE
III.

The terms of the original equation, which give rise to the branch $x = y^2$, are $xy^5 - y^7$; therefore the term $x^3 y^2$, which is the first term in the arrangement by homogeneous functions, is of the order y^8 in this branch, and does not form an element in the equation giving the approximation, as was mentioned in Art. **88**.

It will hereafter be seen how, by placing the terms of this equation in De Gua's triangle, the trouble of this discussion is removed, but I have thought it better to shew by this method how to select the combinations which give the forms of the branches, although when the number of terms is large, the examination becomes too complicated for practice, and recourse must be had to the triangle.

89. When there are only three terms in the equation, as in $\mathbf{x^3 + y^3 - 3axy = 0}$, it is easy to obtain the form at the origin by trying whether, on neglecting any term, the resulting relation makes that term small compared with those retained.

Thus neglecting x^3, $y^2 = 3ax$, with which relation x^3 is of the order y^6, therefore properly neglected.

Similarly, neglecting y^3, $x^2 = 3ay$, and y^3 is of the order x^6.

But if xy be neglected $y + x = 0$; therefore xy is of the order x^2, and could only be neglected upon supposition of x and y being very great. See fig. 2, plate V.

90. If these tentative methods should be attempted in cases of equations which contain a large number of terms, the number is capable of being greatly reduced by the following considerations:

(1) The coefficient of any power of y being a function of x, we can reject, as small by comparison, all but the term involving the lowest power of x in that coefficient.

(2) Similarly for the coefficient of any power of x.

(3) If we are going to try for a branch in which y is small compared with x, from any homogeneous function of more than one term, which may form part of the equation,

PLATE
III.

we may reject all the terms except that which contains the highest power of x.

(4) If, after the above simplifications, a term x^n remain not having y in its coefficient, no term involving y need be retained, in which the sum of the indices of x and y is n or any greater quantity.

91. The student should obtain the branches near the origin in the following curves, and after this practice he will probably be able to perform the requisite operations with ease, the arguments passing through his mind almost involuntarily.

Ex. 1. $\qquad ax(y-x)^2 - y^4 = 0.$

Near the origin, x and y of the same order gives $y = x \pm x^{\frac{3}{2}}/a^{\frac{1}{2}}$; $x : y$ small, gives $ax = y^2$; $y : x$ small, gives $ax^3 = y^4$, which contradicts the assumption if x and y are small, but agrees with it if x and y be very large; hence Fig. 23. $ax^3 = y^4$ gives the direction of bending at an infinite distance.

Ex. 2. $\qquad x^4 - a^2xy - b^2y^2 = 0.$

The curve is symmetrical in opposite quadrants.

Near the origin, $a^2x + b^2y = -b^2x^3/a^2$, and $x^3 - a^2y = 0$; near (∞, ∞), $x^4 = b^2y^2$, observe that the branch $x^3 = a^2y$ lies Fig. 24. closer to the axis of x than these parabolas.

Ex. 3. $\qquad x^5 - a^2(x^3 + y^3) + a^3xy = 0.$

Near the origin, x^5 may be rejected, and the branches are of the two parabolic forms, $x^2 = ay$, and $y^2 = ax$; $(\pm a, 0)$ and $(a, \pm a)$ are points in the curve, near which $y = \mp 2\xi$ and $2\eta = (2 \pm 1)\xi$; the asymptotic guiding curve is $x^5 = a^2y^3$, lying Fig. 25. above the branch $x^2 = ay$ and crossing the curve at (a, a).

Ex. 4. $\qquad x^5 - 3bx^3y - bxy^3 + 4b^2y^3 = 0.$

Near the origin, xy^3 may be neglected compared with y^3;
$$\therefore \quad x^2 = 3by \quad \text{and} \quad 3x^3 = 4by^2$$
give two branches at the origin.

Near (∞, ∞) y^3 may be rejected, and $x^4 = by^3$ gives a guiding asymptote, cutting the curve where $x = \frac{64}{27}b$.

Where $\qquad x = 4b, \quad y = \infty$ or $\tfrac{16}{3}b$;

where $\qquad x = y, \quad x^2 - 4bx + 4b^2 = 0,$

where $\qquad x = 2b, \quad y = 2b,\ 2b,$ or $-4b,$

where $\qquad y = 2b, \quad x = 2b,\ 2b,$ or $-(3-\tfrac{1}{9})b$ nearly;

near $(2b, 2b)$, $\qquad$ if $x = 2b + \xi, \quad y = 2b + \eta,$

$\qquad y = x(1 + \alpha)$, where $\quad \alpha = (\eta - \xi)/2b + \dots,$

and $\quad \therefore (x - 2b)^2 - 3b\alpha x + b(4b - x)(3\alpha + 3\alpha^2 + \dots) = 0,$

or $\qquad (x - 2b)^2 - 6b\alpha(x - 2b) + 6b^2\alpha^2 + \dots = 0,$

$\qquad \therefore \xi^2 - 6b\alpha\xi + 6b^2\alpha^2 \equiv \xi^2 - 3\xi(\eta - \xi) + \tfrac{3}{2}(\eta - \xi)^2 = 0,$

whence $11\xi^2 - 12\xi\eta + 3\eta^2 = 0$, giving the directions of the branches at the multiple point $(2b, 2b)$ and showing that they are inclined to one another at the angle $\cot^{-1}4$ nearly. Fig. 26.

Ex. 5. $\qquad x^5 - ax^3y - axy^3 + a^2y^3 = 0.$

Near the origin, $x^2 = ay$ and $x^3 = ay^2$;

near (∞, ∞), $\qquad x^4 = ay^3,$

also, when $x = a$, $\qquad y = \infty$ or a.

Note that $x = y$ is the tangent at (a, a).

The curve is parallel to the axis of y where $2ay = 3x^2$ or

$\qquad 27(x - a)x + 4a^2 = 0$, or $x = \tfrac{1}{5}a$ and $\tfrac{4}{5}a$ nearly. Fig. 27.

Ex. 6. $\qquad (y^2 + x^2)^2 - 6axy^2 - 2ax^3 + a^2x^2 = 0,$

or $\qquad (y^2 + x^2 - 3ax)^2 = 4ax^2(2a - x).$

The curve is symmetrical with respect to Ox; x cannot be negative nor greater than $2a$; there are two osculating branches through the origin, given by $y^2 = (3 \pm \sqrt{8})ax = \tfrac{23}{4}ax$ or $\tfrac{1}{4}ax$ nearly.

Near $(2a, a\sqrt{2})$, $\qquad\qquad\qquad\qquad\qquad$ Fig. 28.

$\qquad$ if $x = 2a + \xi, \quad y = a\sqrt{2} + \eta, \quad \eta^2 + 2a\xi = 0,$

near $(a, 0)$, $\qquad -4a^2y^2 + a^2\xi^2 = 0.$

Ex. 7. $\qquad y^4 - 2axy^2 - 3a^2x^2 + x^4 = 0,$

or $\qquad (y^2 - ax)^2 = x^2(4a^2 - x^2).$

The curve is symmetrical with respect to Ox, and $x = 2a$ is a tangent where $y = \pm a\sqrt{2}$; $y^2 = 3ax$ and $-ax$ give branches through the origin. Near $(\pm a\sqrt{3}, 0)$,

$\qquad$ if $x = \pm a\sqrt{3} + \xi, \quad y^2 = 3a\xi.$ $\qquad\qquad$ Fig. 29.

PLATE
IV.

Shew that the curve is parallel to Ox at the points whose coordinates are $(1\cdot61a, 1\cdot87a)$ and $(-1\cdot08a, \cdot86a)$.

Ex. 8. $x^5 - ax^3y - 2a^2xy^2 + a^2y^3 = 0.$

Near the origin, if $y : x$ be small,
$$x^4 - ax^2y - 2a^2y^2 = 0,$$
$$\therefore \ x^2 = -ay \quad \text{or} \quad 2ay,$$

and y^3, ∞ x^6, is small compared with x^4; x and y of the same order gives $y = 2x + x^2/2a$, and the tangent $y = 2x$ meets the curve again at $(2a, 4a)$, where $a\eta + 7\xi^2 = 0$ gives the parabolic form.

Fig. 1.   Near (∞, ∞), $x^5 + a^2y^3 = 0$; the curve really crosses the asymptote at $(8a, -32a)$, too far to be shewn in the figure.

Ex. 9. $x^6 + ax^4y - cx^2y^2 + dxy^3 \pm ey^4 = 0.$

If x and y be of the same order, $-cx^2 + dxy \pm ey^2 = 0$ gives two branches through the origin when the factors are real.

If y be small compared with x, $x^4 + ax^2y - cy^2 = 0$ gives two osculating parabolic branches.

Fig. 2.   The figure is drawn with d and e small compared with c, and with the upper sign in the equation.

If the lower sign be taken, $x^6 - ey^4 = 0$ gives two semi-cubical parabolic asymptotes, since with this relation the remaining terms are of orders lower than x^6.

Figs. 3, 4.   The two figures correspond to $4ec <$ and $> d^2$.

Ex. 10. $x^6 + a^2y^4 + a^2x^3y + a^3xy^2 = 0.$

Near the origin, if $x : y$ small, $y^2 + ax = 0$,
if $y : x$ small, $x^5 + a^2x^2y + a^3y^2 = 0$,
$$\therefore \ x^3 + a^2y = 0, \quad \text{and} \quad x^2 + ay = 0 ;$$

Fig. 5.   the origin is therefore a triple point.

92. The following examples will serve for practice of the method spoken of in Art. **89**, in which the equations of the curves either contain only three terms, or are reducible immediately to three terms by the considerations given in Art. **90**.

PLATE
IV.

The curves which I have selected can be traced completely by the methods already described, and will be useful as an introduction to the chapters on asymptotes which succeed.

Ex. 1. $x^4 - axy^2 - a^3y = 0.$

Rejecting xy^2 compared with y, $x^4 = a^3y$ is a form near the origin; rejecting x^4, $yx + a^2 = 0$ is an approximation if x be very small and y very large, therefore the axis of y is an asymptote, and the curve lies to the left above, to the right below; lastly, rejecting y, $x^3 = ay^2$ holds if x and y be both infinite, giving a semi-cubical parabolic asymptote.   Fig. 6.

Ex. 2. $x^4 - axy^2 - ay^3 = 0.$

Neglecting x^4, $x + y = 0$, near the origin; neglecting y^3, $x^3 = ay^2$ makes y^3 of the order $x^{4+\frac{1}{2}}$, and gives a semi-cubical parabola at the origin; neglecting xy^2, $x^4 = ay^3$ makes xy^2 of the order $x^{3+\frac{2}{3}}$, correctly neglected at an infinite distance.   Fig. 7.

Ex. 3. $x^4 - a^2xy - ay^3 = 0.$

Near $(0, 0)$,
$$ax + y^2 = 0 \quad \text{and} \quad x^3 - a^2y = 0;$$
near (∞, ∞), $x^4 = ay^3.$ Fig. 8.

Ex. 4. $x^4 + ax^2y - ay^3 = 0.$

Near $(0, 0)$, $x^2 = y^2$ and $x^2 + ay = 0;$
near (∞, ∞), $x^4 = ay^3.$ Fig. 9.

Ex. 5. $x^4 - axy^2 - a^2y^2 + by^3 = 0.$

Near the origin, axy^2 and by^3 may be rejected compared with a^2y^2, so that $x^4 - a^2y^2 = 0$ gives two branches through the origin.

Near (∞, ∞), y^2 vanishes compared with y^3,
$$\therefore \quad x^4 - axy^2 + by^3 = 0,$$
if x^4 be neglected, $ax = by$; therefore x^4 was improperly neglected compared with the terms kept; if xy^2 be neglected, $x^4 + by^3 = 0$, and xy^2, being of the order $x^{3+\frac{1}{3}}$, was properly neglected; if y^3 were neglected, $x^3 - ay^2 = 0$, y^3 would be of the order $x^{4+\frac{1}{2}}$, or greater than the terms retained; therefore

PLATE
IV.

Fig. 10.

$x^4 + by^3 = 0$ is the only asymptote. The figure is drawn for $a = 2b$ nearly.

Ex. 6. $x^5 - a^3xy - a^2y^3 = 0.$

Near $(0,0)$, $ax + y^2 = 0$ and $x^4 - a^3y = 0$;

Fig. 11. near (∞, ∞), $x^5 - a^2y^3 = 0.$

Ex. 7. $x^5 - a^3xy - ay^4 = 0.$

Near $(0,0)$, $a^2x + y^3 = 0$ and $x^4 - a^3y = 0$;

Fig. 12. near (∞, ∞), $x^5 - ay^4 = 0.$

Ex. 8. $x^3y^2 - ax^4 + a^2y^3 = 0.$

Near $(0,0)$, $x^4 = ay^3$;

Fig. 13. near (∞, ∞), $x^3 + a^2y = 0$ and $y^2 - ax = 0.$

Ex. 9. $x^3y^2 - a^3x^2 + ay^4 = 0.$

Near $(0,0)$, $a^2x^2 = y^4$;

near (∞, ∞), $x^3 + ay^2 = 0$;

Fig. 14. near $(\infty, 0)$, $xy^2 - a^3 = 0.$

Ex. 10. $x^5 - ax^4 - a^3xy + ay^4 = 0.$

Near the origin, $x^4 + a^2xy - y^4 = 0,$

rejecting x^4, $a^2x - y^3 = 0,$

$\dots\dots\dots$ y^4, $x^3 + a^2y = 0$;

near (∞, ∞), $x^5 + ay^4 = 0$;

when $x = a$, $y = 0$ or $a,$

near $(a, 0)$, $y = x - a,$

Fig. 15. $\dots\dots$ (a, a), $4\xi^2 + 3a\eta = 0.$

Examples V.

1. Trace the curve

$$(x^2 + y^2)^2 - 6axy^2 - 2ax^3 + 2a^2x^2 = 0.$$

Find the position of a line parallel to Oy, on which the three portions intercepted by the curve are all equal. Shew that the distance from Oy is $\frac{5}{4}a$ nearly.

2. Shew that the asymptote of the curve $ax(y - x)^2 - y^4 = 0$ cuts the curve at a finite distance at a point at which the curve runs parallel to the axis of y. Find at what point the curve is parallel to the axis of x.

3. Find the points in the loop at which the curve $x^4 - axy^2 - ay^3 = 0$ is parallel to the axes.

PLATE IV.

4. Find the three points where the tangent at (a, a) in the curve of Art. **91** (3) meets the curve again.

5. Draw the curve $x^4 - a^2xy + by^3 = 0$.

Shew the effect of varying the middle term in the following five curves :

6. $x^5 - ax^2y^2 + by^4 = 0$.   **7.** $x^5 - ax^3y + by^4 = 0$.

8. $x^5 - axy^3 + by^4 = 0$.   **9.** $x^5 - a^2x^2y + by^4 = 0$.

10. $x^5 - a^2xy^2 + by^4 = 0$.

Trace the following curves :

11. $y^5 + ax^4 = b^2xy^2$.   **12.** $(x^2 + y^2)^3 = 4a^2x^2y^2$.

13. $x^4 - 4ax^2y + 4a^2y^2 - ax^3 = 0$.   **14.** $a^2xy - 2ax^2y + x^4 + y^4 = 0$.

15. $x^5 - ay^4 + 2bx^3y + b^2xy^2 = 0$.   **16.** $a^2y^3 - a^2by^2 + a^2x^2y + x^5 = 0$.

CHAPTER VI.

ASYMPTOTES. POINTS OF INTERSECTION AT AN INFINITE DISTANCE. ASYMPTOTES PARALLEL TO THE AXES.

PLATE
IV.

93. In the preceding chapters I have shewn how to find by approximation the forms of curves in the neighbourhood of the origin.

I have shewn in fact how it is that the equation of the curve may be replaced by simpler equations, representing near the origin with sufficient accuracy the different branches of the curve.

In the present chapter I propose to apply the same principles of approximation to discover the forms of the branches of curves, which extend to a distance from the origin very great compared with the unit distance employed in the equation, simple cases of which have occurred in many of the curves already traced.

ASYMPTOTES.

94. Since in tracing curves we profess to include every point whose coordinates satisfy the equations, whether the points are at a finite or infinite distance, it becomes necessary to examine every case in which it is possible that either one coordinate or both may be infinite, and to indicate the course of the curve corresponding to all such cases.

For this purpose simpler relations than that represented by the equation are discovered, to which the equation very nearly reduces, when one or both of the coordinates are very large.

PLATE
IV.

The lines which are the loci of these simpler equations are called generally asymptotes, or asymptotic curves, and, since it is easy to recognise the forms and positions of these lines, they become guides for determining the general form of the proposed curve, which runs along them on one side or the other.

95. Asymptotes which are rectilinear have already been defined, Art. **5**; they might also be defined as tangents at a point which is infinitely distant, this definition implying the same property as the former, since no straight line can lie closer to the curve than the tangent, in the neighbourhood of the point of contact.

The lines which are called curvilinear asymptotes, as being sufficient to guide us as to the final direction in which the curve bends, ought to be called by such a name as a quasi-asymptote, since the distance between the curve and asymptote does not ultimately vanish, although it vanishes compared with the distance from the origin.

Although it would be always possible by successive approximations to obtain a simpler curve than the original, which would satisfy the conditions of indefinite approach, the advantage gained would not counterbalance the trouble of working the approximation; I shall therefore use the expression asymptote for the simplest curve which determines the direction of the flexure at a great distance.

In some of the examples I shall find the proper asymptote, to shew that there is no advantage gained towards obtaining the general shape of the curve, considering that no figure professes to do more than indicate very roughly what would take place at a very great distance.

POINTS OF INTERSECTION AT AN INFINITE DISTANCE.

96. Before proceeding to the discussion of particular forms of equations, and the corresponding branches of their loci, at an infinite or very great distance from the origin, it will be useful to make some general observations relating to the intersection of curves with straight lines, especially with regard to those points of intersection which may be at an infinite distance.

I must first remind the student that, if

$$ax^n + bx^{n-1} + \ldots + k = 0$$

be an equation which has one infinite root, then $a = 0$; if it have two infinite roots, both $a = 0$ and $b = 0$, and so on.

This is easily seen if for x we write z^{-1}, which makes the equation $a + bz + \ldots + kz^n = 0$; and this equation must be satisfied by $z^2 = 0$, if there be two roots equal to zero.

97. Some elementary treatises on Algebraical Geometry speak of a straight line, drawn parallel to the axis of the parabola as meeting the curve in one point; this, although justifiable from one point of view, is not a satisfactory way of disposing of the question concerning the intersection of a parabola with a straight line, and is liable to mislead the student in his examination of curves in general, and especially with respect to the branches which are at an infinite distance.

The separation of curves into classes of different degrees is effected by arranging them analytically into curves in which the greatest sum of the indices of the current coordinates in any one term of the equations is $1, 2, \ldots n$; or, geometrically, into curves which are met by a straight line in $1, 2, \ldots n$ points.

There are obvious advantages, in choosing an interpretation of the analytical and geometrical classification, which makes the classes coextensive, and it is unfortunate when expressions are used which are inconsistent with such an interpretation.

To take the case of a parabola, alluded to above, as an example, $y^2 = 4ax$ may be considered as a particular case of the general equation of the second degree, from which some of the terms are excluded, which ought to have appeared in the form $0 \cdot x^2$, $0 \cdot xy$, etc. In this point of view the straight

PLATE
IV.

line $y = c$, parallel to the axis, intersects the curve at points whose abscissæ are given by the equation

$$0 \cdot x^2 + 4ax - c^2 = 0,$$

one root of which is infinitely great and the other finite.

Thus the geometrical and analytical classifications of curves are made to agree.

And this does not interfere with the geometrical definition of a parabola as a curve which is the locus of a point whose distances from a fixed point and a fixed straight line are equal; for a point which is at an infinite distance satisfies this condition, and is therefore a point in the curve.

On this principle, if $k = 0$, where k is a constant, be considered as a particular case of an equation of the first degree, it is the equation of a straight line at an infinite distance; if it be considered as a particular case of the equation of the second degree, it is the equation of a conic section or two straight lines at an infinite distance.

98. In considering the intersection of a curve of the nth degree by any straight line, we ought to be able to account for all the n points of intersection, and, if the equations of the curve and straight line give a resulting equation of the $(n-r)^{\text{th}}$ degree, we must conclude that r points of intersection, real or imaginary, are at an infinite distance.

Now, as no straight line can be drawn, which is so near a curve in the neighbourhood of any point, as the particular line which passes through the next consecutive point as well (Art. **57**), the same being true, however distant these consecutive points are, it follows that a line which meets the curve in two points at an infinite distance is *generally* the nearest line that can be drawn to the curve at an infinite distance, and is a rectilinear asymptote.

99. In order to find what sort of exceptions may occur to this general statement we ought to consider the variations which occur in finding the tangent to a curve at a

PLATE
IV.

point at a finite distance, and so deduce the corresponding variations in cases of rectilinear asymptotes.

100. In the first place, at a point of inflexion where the straight line is constructed which passes through the point of inflexion and a consecutive point, it, at the same time, passes through a second consecutive point on the opposite side; so that, although we cannot generally construct a straight line so as to pass through more than two consecutive points, it happens in this particular case that the constructed line passes also through a third. The corresponding case for an asymptote is that of three points at an infinite distance.

101. In the next place, if we try to find a tangent to a branch of a multiple point, say of r branches, we observe that any straight line which passes through the r-ple point, passes through r points in the curve, one for each branch, in whatever direction it be drawn; and that, when a straight line not only passes through the r-ple point but also is a tangent to one of the branches, it will contain two coincident points on that branch. It follows that there are r directions in which a straight line can be drawn through an r-ple point, for which it contains $r+1$ coincident points.

If one of the branches have a point of inflexion at the r-ple point, it is plain from the last article that the tangent to that branch will contain $r+2$ coincident points instead of $r+1$.

Suppose now this r-ple point to be at an infinite distance, all straight lines which contain $r+1$ points coincident with the r-ple point are parallel, and, being tangents, are asymptotes, to the curve; any other parallel straight line contains r points on the curve at an infinite distance.

102. If $y-mx=0$ pass through an r-ple point at an infinite distance, any line $y=mx+\alpha$ will also pass through it; hence, if $y=mx+\alpha$ be combined with the equation of the curve there will be r infinite roots of the resulting equation in x or y, whatever be the value of α. The rectilinear asymptote which corresponds to the tangent to a branch, must then be found by the condition that one more root has an infinite value; and this condition will determine the r parallel asymptotes.

103. Take as an example the curve of the third degree, whose equation is

$$x(y-x)^2 - b^2y = 0.$$

Any straight line parallel to $y=x$ has an equation $y=x+\alpha$ and meets the curve where

$$0 \cdot x^3 + 0 \cdot x^2 + (\alpha^2 - b^2)x - b^2\alpha = 0,$$

so that there are two infinite values of x for all lines parallel to $y=x$. In order to obtain the nearest possible straight line to the curve at an infinite distance, we must make $\alpha^2 = b^2$, so that either of the straight lines, $y = x \pm b$, meets the curve at three points at an infinite distance.

If $x=0$, the values of y are given by

$$0 \cdot y^3 + 0 \cdot y^2 - b^2y = 0,$$

which shews the axis of y as an asymptote.

Near the origin, $x^3 - b^2y = 0$, ⟶⟨; also the curve is symmetrical in opposite quadrants.   Fig. 16.

104. In this curve we observe that there are two branches at an infinite distance from both axes, and that these two branches both pass through the point in which all lines parallel to $y=x$ intersect, so that this point is a true multiple point at an infinite distance; and each of these parallel lines intersects the curve at two points at an infinite distance, for that reason. Also $y = x + b$ represents a straight line which passes through two consecutive points on the same branch, and the third point at an infinite distance is that in which it meets the branch whose tangent is $y = x - b$.

105. These considerations of infinitely distant points of intersection supply a complete method of determining recti-

PLATE
IV.

linear asymptotes to a curve, as will be seen by a few examples. It is well to know this method, although that of approximation has a decided advantage, both because it supplies a knowledge of the side of the asymptote on which the curve lies, and also because it gives the curvilinear as well as the rectilinear asymptotes.

106. The general method spoken of may be explained by the following process.

Consider the intersection of a curve of the nth degree with a straight line whose equation is $y = \alpha x + \beta$.

If we eliminate y we obtain an equation of the nth degree in x, giving the n values of x at the points of intersection; this equation is of the form

$$Px^n + Qx^{n-1} + Rx^{n-2} + \ldots = 0,$$

where P is a function of α, and Q, R, etc. are functions of α and of the first, second, etc. degrees in β. Since for an asymptote two values of x must be infinite, we have the equations $P = 0$ and $Q = 0$, which generally determine α and β.

Thus, if the terms of the nth degree in the equation of the curve be

$$ay^n + bxy^{n-1} + \ldots + lx^n,$$

$$P \equiv a\alpha^n + b\alpha^{n-1} + \ldots + l,$$

and $P = 0$ determines n values of α, real or imaginary.

If α_1 be one of these values, we have learned that the straight line $y = \alpha_1 x + \beta$ meets the curve at one point at an infinite distance; if now we substitute this value of α in the equation $Q = 0$, β can be determined, and since Q is of the first degree in β, there is only one such value of β for each value of α.

Thus, generally, there are n asymptotes completely determined by these equations.

107. The exceptions to this general statement are of great variety; it will be sufficient to take one case, viz.

that in which $P=0$ has two equal roots, each equal to α_1, in which case, when $\alpha=\alpha_1$,

$$n a \alpha_1{}^{n-1}+(n-1) b \alpha_1{}^{n-2}+\ldots=0,$$

that is, the coefficient of β in Q vanishes for this value of α.

When Q vanishes for $\alpha=\alpha_1$, independently of the value of β, all straight lines parallel to $y=\alpha_1 x$ meet the curve at two points at an infinite distance, which means that there is a double point there, and the equation $R=0$, of the second degree in β, determines the two values of β for which $y=\alpha_1 x+\beta$ meets the curve in three points at an infinite distance, thus giving the two asymptotes.

When Q is finite for $\alpha=\alpha_1$, there is no asymptote parallel to $y=\alpha_1 x$, since there is then only one point of intersection at an infinite distance.

108. This exceptional case may be further illustrated by the curve $\mathbf{y(y-x)^2(y-2x)+3a(y-x)x^2-2a^2x^2=0.}$

The equation may also be written in the form

$$(y-x)^4-(y-x-2a)(y-x-a)x^2=0.$$

Each of the lines $y-x=2a$ and $y-x=a$ meets the curve at four points at an infinite distance, three of which are consecutive points on the infinite branch to which each is a tangent, and the fourth on the branch to which the other is a tangent. This is the case of a multiple point of two branches at an infinite distance, each having a point of inflexion at the common point.

It is easily seen that no point of the curve lies between these two asymptotes.

Again $y-2x=\beta$ meets the curve where

$$0 \cdot x^4+(2x+\beta)(x+\beta)^2\beta+3a(x+\beta)x^2-2a^2x^2=0,$$

so that one point of intersection is at an infinite distance for all values of β. A second point is at an infinite distance, if $2\beta+3a=0$; therefore $y-2x+\frac{3}{2}a=0$ is an asymptote. This asymptote also meets the curve at two points at a finite distance where $9y^2=17x^2$,

or $\qquad \frac{19}{4}x^2-\frac{27}{2}ax+\frac{81}{16}a^2=0,$

whence $\frac{9}{4}a=\{3\pm\frac{1}{2}\sqrt{(17)}\}x$, and $x=\frac{9}{20}a$ or $\frac{9}{4}a$ nearly.

PLATE
IV.

A fourth asymptote $2y + 3a = 0$ meets the curve at two points infinitely distant, and two at a finite distance.

The shape at the origin is given by $y^4 = 2a^2x^2$, .

Fig. 17.

At $(-\tfrac{2}{3}a,\ 0)$, the tangent is $y = \tfrac{9}{13}(x + \tfrac{2}{3}a)$.

109. As an example of the use of the intersections of a curve and a line to obtain information about the shape of the curve, note that $y - x = \alpha$ meets the curve at points given by $(\alpha - 2a)(\alpha - a)x^2 - \alpha^4 = 0$, two points at an infinite distance being the intersections with the two asymptotes. The points at a finite distance are equidistant from the axis of y, which, therefore, bisects all chords parallel to $y = x$.

If $y - x = \alpha$ passes through a point where the curve is parallel to Oy, $4\alpha^3 = (2\alpha - 3a)x^2$, which, with the equation above, gives $2\alpha^2 - 9a\alpha + 8a^2 = 0$. The two values of α are $\tfrac{13}{4}a$ and $\tfrac{5}{4}a$ nearly, and the latter being between a and $2a$ is impossible; hence the chord joining the two points where the curve is parallel to Oy is bisected by Oy.

110. The following general examples will serve as illustrations:

Ex. 1. $\qquad \mathbf{x(y-x)^2 - a^3 = 0,\quad (a > 0).}$

The straight line $y = x$ gives for the points of intersection,
$$0 \cdot y^3 + 0 \cdot y^2 + 0 \cdot y - a^3 = 0,$$
and, since x cannot be negative, the curve lies on both sides of one end of the asymptote, and the three infinite roots correspond to a cusp at an infinite distance. Similarly for the asymptote $x = 0$, the curve lies on the same side at both ends, and the point at infinity on $x = 0$ corresponds to a

Fig. 18. point of inflexion.

Ex. 2. $\qquad \mathbf{x^5 + y^5 - 5ax^3y = 0.}$

Any straight line parallel to $x + y = 0$ meets the curve at one infinitely distant point.

The straight line $y + x = \alpha$ meets it at points given by
$$x^5 - (x - \alpha)^5 + 5ax^3(x - \alpha) = 0,$$
or $\qquad 0 \cdot x^5 + 5(\alpha + a)x^4 - (10\alpha^2 + 5a\alpha)x^3 + \ldots = 0.$

PLATE IV.

Hence, there are two points of intersection at an infinite distance if $\alpha = -a$, and $y + x + a = 0$ is therefore the asymptote; the three other points of intersection are given by $$5x^3 + 10ax^2 + 5a^2x + a^3 = 0.$$

By the method given in Arts. **47, 48** it is easily shewn that this equation gives only one real value of x, which is negative, and not far from $-\tfrac{4}{3}a$ or $-\tfrac{7}{5}a$. It may be obtained by drawing the two curves

$$(x+a)^2 = ay \quad \text{and} \quad 5yx + a^2 = 0.$$

The branches near the origin are

$$x^2 - 5ay = 0 \; \searrow\!\!\nearrow, \quad y^4 - 5ax^3 = 0 \; \curvearrowleft;$$

also $x = y$ meets the curve where $x = y = \tfrac{5}{2}a$, which guides as to the size of the loop.

Fig. 19.

Ex. 3. $$y^2(x^2 - y^2) - 2ay^3 + 2a^3x = 0.$$

$x \mp y = 0$ gives one infinite root, and $x \mp y = \alpha$ meets the curve where

$$0 \cdot y^4 + y^2\alpha(\alpha \pm 2y) - 2ay^3 + 2a^3(\alpha \pm y) = 0.$$

Two roots are infinite, if $\pm\alpha = a$, and the finite roots are given by $$a^2y^2 \pm 2a^3y + 2a^4 = 0,$$

or $$(y \pm a)^2 = (1 \mp 2)a^2.$$

The roots are impossible for the upper sign, hence the curve does not cross the asymptote $x - y = a$ at a finite distance, but it does cross the asymptote $x + y + a = 0$ at the points $\{-(2 \pm \sqrt{3})a, (1 \pm \sqrt{3})a\}$ or $(-\tfrac{1}{4}a, -\tfrac{3}{4}a)$ and $(-\tfrac{15}{4}a, \tfrac{11}{4}a)$ nearly.

Fig. 21.

$y = 0$ gives three infinite values of x, and, neglecting y^4 and y^3 compared with x, $y^2 = -2a^3/x$ nearly, therefore the curve lies on both sides of the negative end of xOx'.

Near the origin, $y^3 = a^2x$; near $(0, -2a)$, $4\eta + x = 0$.

Ex. 4. $$(x-a)y^3 = (y-b)x^3,$$

or $$xy(y^2 - x^2) - ay^3 + bx^3 = 0.$$

$x = a$ gives for y,

$$0 \cdot y^4 + 0 \cdot y^3 + 0 \cdot y^2 - a^3y + ba^3 = 0,$$

PLATE
IV.

and is therefore an asymptote; so is $y = b$; $y - x = \alpha$ meets the curve where

$$x(x+\alpha)\{(x+\alpha)^2 - x^2\} - a(x+\alpha)^3 + bx^3 = 0,$$

and if the coefficient of x^3 be 0, as well as that of x^4, $2\alpha - a + b = 0$;

$$\therefore \ y - x = \tfrac{1}{2}(a - b) \text{ is an asymptote.}$$

Similarly $\quad y + x = -\tfrac{1}{2}(a + b)$ is an asymptote.

Near $(0, 0)$, $\qquad\qquad y = \sqrt[3]{\dfrac{b}{a}}\,x\,;$

near (a, b), $\qquad\qquad y - b = \dfrac{b^3}{a^3}(x - a).$

Fig. 20.
It will be found that, with the proportions of a and b given in the figure, the second asymptote cuts the curve where $x = -\tfrac{1}{3}\{7 \pm \sqrt{(13)}\}b$, while the first cuts it in no real point; also that Oy is parallel to the curve where $x = \tfrac{3}{2}b$.

To assist in finding the manner in which the curve runs, it may be observed that a straight line drawn through the origin can only meet the curve in one point besides the origin.

From the way in which the curve has been drawn in the quadrant yOx', it appears as if a tangent could be drawn from the origin, in which case there would be two points of intersection. How the curve really runs may be shewn as follows:

Let the radius $y + mx = 0$ meet the curve and the asymptote $y + x + \tfrac{1}{2}(a + b) = 0$, in points P and Q respectively, and let PM, QN be perpendicular to Oy.

Then $\qquad QN - PM = \dfrac{(2m+1)ma - (m+2)b}{2m(m+1)}.$

Hence, P is further from or nearer to the origin than Q, according as

$$am(2m+1) < \quad \text{or} \quad > b(2+m)$$

and the curve and asymptote intersect, if $ra = b$, where

$$m^2 + \tfrac{1}{2}(1 - r)m - r = 0.$$

PLATE
IV.

The roots of this equation are real when r is positive, and since in the figure, $r = \frac{1}{3}$ nearly, $m = \frac{1}{6}(-1 \pm \sqrt{13}) = \frac{13}{30}$ and $-\frac{23}{30}$ nearly. When m is nearly 1, the difference of the distances of P and Q from the origin approaches $\frac{3}{4}(a-b)\sqrt{2}$; this ultimate constant distance does not prevent the indefinite approach of the curve to the asymptote, since the perpendicular distance is ultimately $\frac{3}{4}(a-b)\sqrt{2} \times \sin\theta$, where θ is indefinitely small.

DETERMINATION OF ASYMPTOTES BY APPROXIMATION.

111. I shall now shew in this and following chapters how the asymptotes of a curve may be found by successive approximations, and also how the side of the asymptote on which the curve comes into sight from an infinite distance may be discovered.

112. In order to arrive at all the infinite branches of a curve, we must examine the following cases which include all possible ways in which a curve can pass off to infinity.

(1) x may be infinite, while y is finite or 0.

(2) y may be infinite, while x is finite or 0.

Both x and y may be infinite, dividing into three cases.

(3) x and y may be of the same order of magnitude, or $x : y$ finite.

(4) x may be large compared with y, or $y : x$ vanish ultimately, when x and y are increased indefinitely.

(5) y may be large compared with x, or $x : y$ vanish ultimately, when x and y are increased indefinitely.

Classes (1) and (2) include the cases in which curves run off to infinity parallel to the axes of coordinates.

Class (3) includes rectilinear asymptotes which are inclined at finite angles to the axes, and as special cases parabolic asymptotes.

Classes (4) and (5) include general curvilinear asymptotes. These will be discussed separately.

PLATE
IV.

CASE OF x ALONE INFINITE.

113. To try whether x can be infinite while y remains finite, we must suppose the equation arranged in descending powers of x in the form

$$f(y)x^r + \phi(y)x^s + \ldots = 0, \ldots\ldots\ldots\ldots\ldots(1)$$

or $\qquad\qquad f(y) + \phi(y)\dfrac{1}{x^{r-s}} + \ldots = 0,$

hence making x infinite, we have $f(y) = 0$.

In order, therefore, that this case should occur, it is necessary that the term containing the highest power of x in the equation should involve y. If b be a root of $f(y) = 0$, $y = b$ will be an asymptote, since, even if there be not two roots equal to b, the condition of having two points at an infinite distance would be satisfied, because, if the curve be of the nth degree, r cannot be greater than $n-1$, nor s greater than $n-2$, and in the equation resulting from the substitution of b for y the first finite term can involve no higher power than x^{n-2}. If $f(y) = 0$ have t roots, real or imaginary, r cannot be greater than $n-t$, nor s greater than $n-t-1$; therefore, when b is put for y, in the resulting equation the first finite term cannot involve a higher power of x than x^{n-t-1}, and hence there must be $t+1$ infinite roots.

The $t+1$ infinite roots are accounted for as follows : the equation $f(y) = 0$ gives t parallel lines, which therefore all meet at an infinite distance in the same point; any straight line parallel to these lines meets the curve in t points at an infinite distance, but is not an asymptote, since it does not contain on itself two such points; each of the parallel lines corresponding to solutions of $f(y) = 0$ contains two such points besides the $t-1$ in which it intersects the other lines.

This is the case of a multiple point of t branches at an infinite distance, spoken of in Art. **101**.

114. It is important, in tracing a curve, to know on which side of an asymptote the curve makes its appearance from an infinite distance. This may be obvious from our

PLATE
IV.

knowledge of other parts of the curve; but it is necessary
to have some general method of determining this feature of
an asymptote directly from the equation of the curve. If
$y = b$ be an asymptote, it must be possible to put the
equation of the curve in the form

$$y - b = \frac{A}{x^r} + \frac{B}{x^s} + \frac{C}{x^t} + \cdots, \quad \ldots\ldots\ldots\ldots\ldots\ldots(2)$$

where r, s, t, are positive, either integers or fractions, and
$r < s < t$. When x is taken sufficiently large, the sign of
the series will be determined from that of the first term.
This is generally sufficient to determine the side of the
asymptote on which the curve lies; but it may be necessary
to consider other terms. To shew this it is sufficient to
consider such a form as

$$y - b = \frac{a^2}{x} + \frac{B}{x^{\frac{3}{2}}}.$$

If we took into account the first term only, the curve
would be above the asymptote at the positive and below at
the negative end, but the second term has two values when
x is $+$, both less than a^2/x, and is impossible when x is $-$,
so that the curve has two branches above the positive end
of the asymptote, and none at the negative end.

115. It is obvious from what has been said in the last
article that there must be a very great variety of forms,
and I shall not attempt to give an account of all those, but
trust to an examination of several curves, by which the processes to be adopted will be illustrated. The most simple
case can however be stated, and peculiarities indicated.

Take the form (1) in Art. **113**.

If $y = b$ be a single root of $f(y) = 0$, so that

$$f(y) = (y - b)f_1(y), \quad \text{where } f_1(b) \text{ is not zero,}$$

we have $\qquad y - b + \dfrac{\phi(y)}{f_1(y)} \dfrac{1}{x^{r-s}} + \ldots = 0\,;$

$\therefore$ if $\phi(b)$ be not zero, $\quad y = b - \dfrac{\phi(b)}{f_1(b)} \dfrac{1}{x^{r-s}} \ldots.$

PLATE
IV.

Hence, when $r-s$ is even, the curve is on the same side of the asymptote $y=b$ at both ends, above or below according as $\dfrac{\phi(b)}{f_1(b)}$ is negative or positive.

When $r-s$ is odd, the curve lies above the asymptote at one end and below at the other.

116. Peculiarities occur in particular cases, such as when $f(y)=0$ has repeated roots, or when $\phi(y)$ vanishes when $y=b$, or when any of the succeeding coefficients vanish at the same time as $\phi(y)$. In such cases it may happen that the term involving the highest power of x is not one of the principal terms for all the infinite branches running parallel to Ox.

Thus, for the curve

$$(y-b)^4x^4+ay^3(y-b)x^3+a^7x+a^8=0,$$

the second and third terms will give a correct approximation to the value of y, viz. $b-a^6/b^3x^2$, because with this value $(y-b)^4x^4$ is of the order x^{-4}, and the terms retained are of the order x.

The first term, however, is one of the principal terms for another branch. Thus, taking the first and second terms together, $(y-b)^3+ab^3/x=0$, which relation makes the terms retained of the order $x^{\frac{8}{3}}$, and therefore larger than those rejected.

117. The following examples of varieties which may occur will suffice to·explain how to determine the position of a curve with respect to its asymptotes which are parallel to either axis. The asymptotes which are not parallel to the axes may, for the present, be taken as additional illustrations of the method by infinite roots given above.

Ex. 1. $$(x-a)y^2-a^2x=0.$$

$x=a$ and $y^2=a^2$ are asymptotes.

Near (a, ∞), $\qquad x-a=\dfrac{a^2x}{y^2}=\dfrac{a^3}{y^2},$

near (∞, a), $y - a = \dfrac{ay^2}{x(y+a)} = \dfrac{a^2}{2x}$,

near $(\infty, -a)$, $y + a = \dfrac{ay^2}{x(y-a)} = -\dfrac{a^2}{2x}$.

These approximations determine the sides on which the curve lies, when it comes into sight from infinity in the direction of the asymptotes.

To trace the curve, we observe that it is symmetrical with respect to the axis of x, and that, near the origin, $y^2 + ax = 0$.   Fig. 22.

Ex. 2. $(x-a)(x-b)y^2 - a^2x^2 = 0, \quad a > b.$

$x = a$ and $x = b$, $y^2 = a^2$ are four asymptotes;

near (a, ∞), $x - a = \dfrac{a^2x^2}{(x-b)y^2} = \dfrac{a^4}{(a-b)y^2}$,

near (b, ∞), $x - b = \dfrac{a^2x^2}{(x-a)y^2} = -\dfrac{a^2b^2}{(a-b)y^2}$,

near (∞, a), $\{x^2 - (a+b)x\}y^2 - a^2x^2 + \ldots = 0$,

or $y^2 - a^2 = (a+b)\dfrac{y^2}{x}$,   therefore $y - a = (a+b)\dfrac{a}{2x}$,

and $y + a = -(a+b)\dfrac{a}{2x}$.

There is symmetry with respect to Ox, and near the origin, $by^2 = ax^2$.

The asymptotes $y^2 = a^2$ meet the curve where $(a+b)x = ab$, and no part of the curve lies between the other asymptotes.   Fig. 23.

Note 1.   When $a = b$, the curve degenerates into two hyperbolas $(x-a)(y \pm a) = \mp a^2$, whose form is obvious from the figure when the asymptotes move up to one another.

Note 2.   When $b = 0$, the curve degenerates into the axis of y, combined with the locus in the last example.

Ex. 3. $y^2x(y-x) - ay^3 - byx^2 + a(a+b)x^2 = 0,$

or $y^3(x-a) - x^2(y-a)(y+a+b) = 0.$

The asymptotes parallel to the axes are

$$x = a, \quad y = a, \quad \text{and} \quad y = -(a+b);$$

PLATE
IV.

near (a, ∞), $x - a = \dfrac{a^2}{y}$,

near (∞, a), $y - a = \dfrac{a^3}{(2a+b)x}$,

near $\{\infty, -(a+b)\}$, $y + a + b = \dfrac{(a+b)^3}{(2a+b)x}$.

If $y - x = \alpha$, the points of intersection are given by

$$0 \cdot x^4 + (\alpha - a - b)x^3 + \ldots = 0,$$

and $y - x = a + b$ is therefore an asymptote.

Near the origin, $y^3 = (a+b)x^2$,

near (a, a), $a\xi = (2a+b)\eta$,

near $\{a, -(a+b)\}$, $(a+b)^3\xi = a^2(2a+b)\eta$.

Fig. 24.   The figure is drawn for $b = a$ nearly.

Note 1.   The curve is parallel to Oy, where

$$y = -b - \surd(3a^2 + 3ab + b^2);$$

the other root gives impossible values of x; in the figure $y = -\tfrac{1}{3}a$ nearly.

Note 2.   The curve is parallel to Ox where $x = 2a$, which gives two positive values and one negative value of y.

Ex. 4. $(\mathbf{x} - \mathbf{a})\mathbf{y}^3 = (\mathbf{y} - \mathbf{b})^2\mathbf{x}^2$.

The asymptotes parallel to the axes are

$$x = a   \text{and}   (y - b)^2 = 0.$$

Near (a, ∞), $x - a = a^2/y$,

near (∞, b), $(y - b)^2 = b^3/x$.

Rearranging the equation by homogeneous functions

$$xy^2(y - x) - ay^3 + 2bx^2y - b^2x^2 = 0,$$

we find that $y - x = \beta$ meets the curve at points given by the equation,

$$0 \cdot x^4 + (\beta - a + 2b)x^3 + \ldots = 0.$$

If $\beta = a - 2b$, there will be two points at infinity, or $y - x = a - 2b$ will be an asymptote. It meets the curve in the points given by

$$(3b^2 - a^2)x^2 - 2(a+b)(2b-a)^2x + a(2b-a)^3 = 0,$$

the roots of which are real, when $2b > a$.

PLATE
IV.

Near $(0, 0)$, $ay^3 + b^2x^2 = 0$,   near (a, b), $b^3\xi - a^2\eta^2 = 0$.

The curves are drawn for $a < b\sqrt{3}$, which gives two imaginary, and for $a > 2b$ which gives two real points of intersection with the asymptote parallel to $y = x$.

Figs. 25, 26.

Note. The curve is parallel to Ox, where $x = 2a$, and to Oy where $y = 3b$, unless these two take place simultaneously, which will occur when the point $(2a, 3b)$ is a point on the curve, in which case $16a = 27b$ and $(2a, 3b)$ is a multiple point.

With regard to this multiple point, we may observe that, if $(\alpha + \xi, \beta + \eta)$ be a point near (α, β), the tangent at such a point is parallel to Ox if $\eta = A\xi^2$, and to Oy if $\xi = B\eta^2$, but there is a multiple point if $A\xi^2 + 2B\xi\eta + C\eta^2 = 0$.

In the first case the coefficient of ξ in the expansion vanishes, in the second that of η, and in the third the coefficients of both ξ and η vanish.

In the case considered, the substitution of $2a + \xi$, $3b + \eta$ in the equation gives

$$27^2\eta^2 = 3 . 16^2\xi^2, \quad \text{or} \quad \eta = \pm\sqrt{(\tfrac{256}{243})}\xi = \pm\tfrac{40}{39}\xi \text{ nearly.}$$

Fig. 27.

It is worth examining how the form of the curve for this case separates the two forms drawn for $a < \sqrt{3}b$ and $> 2b$.

Ex. 5. $(x^2 - a^2)(x - 2a)y^2 - a^2x^3 + 4a^4y = 0$.

The three asymptotes parallel to Oy are $x = \pm a$ and $2a$, cutting the curve where $y = \pm\tfrac{1}{4}a$ and $2a$; also two parallel to Ox are $y = \pm a$, the first of which intersects the curve where $x = \tfrac{3}{2}a$ and $-2a$.

Near (a, ∞),	$x = a + 2a^2/y$,
near $(-a, \infty)$,	$x = -a - 2a^2/3y$,
near $(2a, \infty)$,	$x = 2a - 4a^2/3y$,
near (∞, a),	$y = a + a^2/x$,
near $(\infty, -a)$,	$y = -a - a^2/x$,
near $(0, 0)$,	$x^3 = 4a^2y$,
near $(0, -2a)$,	$x + \eta = 0$,
near $(2a, 2a)$,	$2a\eta + 5\xi^2 = 0$.

Also $(\tfrac{3}{2}a, \tfrac{27}{5}a)$ is a point in the curve.

Fig. 28.

PLATE
IV.
_____

Ex. 6. $(\mathbf{xy} - \mathbf{ab})^2 = \mathbf{b}^2\mathbf{d}(\mathbf{c} - \mathbf{y}).$

Both axes are asymptotes;

near $(0, \infty)$, $\qquad x = \pm b\sqrt{(-d/y)},$

near $(\infty, 0)$, $\qquad y = b[a \pm \sqrt{(cd)}]/x.$

When $\qquad\qquad x = 0, \quad y = c - a^2/d.$

The first figure is drawn for $a^2 > cd$, the second for
$a^2 < cd.$

Figs. 29, 30.

Note. The curve is parallel to Oy, where

$$2x(xy - ab) = -b^2d;$$

whence $\qquad (2cx - ab)^2 = b^2(a^2 - cd),$

the roots of which are only possible when $a^2 > cd.$

The distance between the tangents parallel to Oy in the
first figure is $\sqrt{(a^2 - cd)}b/c.$

$y = c$ gives equal values of x, where the curve runs
parallel to Ox, in both figures.

Ex. 7. $\qquad \mathbf{x}^3\mathbf{y}^2 - 2\mathbf{a}^2\mathbf{x}^2\mathbf{y} + \mathbf{a}^4\mathbf{x} - \mathbf{b}^5 = 0, \quad \mathbf{b} > 0.$

Since $x(xy - a^2)^2 = b^5$, x is positive.

Both axes are asymptotes; for Oy, $x^3 = b^5/y^2$; for Ox,
$y = a^2/x \pm \sqrt{(b^5/x^3)}$; hence the curve comes into sight from an
infinite distance along Ox like the branches of a ramphoid
cusp.

Fig. 31.

The curve is parallel to Ox, where $3xy = a^2$, or $4a^4x = 9b^5.$

Ex. 8. $\qquad \mathbf{x}^2\mathbf{y}^2 - 2\mathbf{a}^2\mathbf{xy} - \mathbf{b}^2\mathbf{y}^2 + 2\mathbf{a}^2\mathbf{b}^2 - \mathbf{b}^4 = 0.$

The curve is symmetrical in opposite quadrants.

Ox is an asymptote, and near $(\infty, 0)$, $(xy - a^2)^2 = (a^2 - b^2)^2,$

$\qquad \therefore \; y = b^2/x, \quad \text{and} \quad (2a^2 - b^2)/x.$

Asymptotes parallel to Oy are $x = \pm b$, which intersect
the curve where $2a^2y = \pm(2a^2 - b^2)b$, and near $(\pm b, \infty)$,
$x \pm b = a^2/y.$

Figs. 32, 33.

The figures are drawn for the cases in which $2a^2 >$ and
$< b^2$; in the critical case in which $2a^2 = b^2$ the curve is
compounded of the axis of x and another curve whose
equation is $(x^2 - b^2)y = b^2x.$

Examples VI.

1. $$y(x-a)^2 = x(y-4a)^2.$$
Find on which sides of the asymptotes Ox and Oy the curve lies.
Shew that the radii of curvature of the branches through $(a, 4a)$ are $5\sqrt{5a}$.

2. $$(x^2-ay)^2 = y^2(b^2-x^2).$$
Shew how the curve lies with respect to the asymptote parallel to Oy, when $b > a$; when $a > b$, shew that the branches at the origin are of the form $x^2 = (a \pm b)y$. In both cases shew that the curve is parallel to Oy, where $x = \pm b$.

3. $$\cdot(x-a)(x+a)^2y^2 - a^2x^3 + 4a^4y = 0.$$
Find the sides of the asymptotes on which the curve lies, at an infinite distance.

4. $$a^2(y-x)^2 = x^2(y^2+x^2).$$
Trace the curve, and shew that any straight line, drawn perpendicular to the tangent at the origin, intersects the curve in points from which the radii to the origin are, in pairs, equally inclined to the axes.

5. $$(x-a)y^4 + x^2y^3 + a^5 = 0.$$
Find the three asymptotes, and shew that the curve intersects one of the asymptotes in Oy, and that the tangents at the two points where the curve crosses Oy are equally inclined to Ox.

6. $$x^4y^3 = a^2(a-x)^3(2x-a)^2.$$
Prove that at one point where the curve cuts Ox there is a ceratoid cusp, and that the tangent at the other cuts the curve in two more points, the lines to which from the origin are equally inclined to Ox.

7. $$x^2(x^2-y^2)^2 = a^4(x^2+y^2).$$
Find the form of the curve at the ends of the three asymptotes, and prove that the line $y = a\sqrt{3}$ cuts the curve in six real points.

8. $$x^2y^3 - a^3xy + a^5 = 0.$$
Prove that three branches come into sight at the positive, one at the negative end of Ox, and two at the negative end of Oy. Shew that the curve is parallel to Ox, where $x = 8a$, and to Oy, where $x = 2\frac{7}{4}a$.

9. $$(x-a)(x-2a)y^2 = x(y - \tfrac{2}{3}a)^3.$$
Find the sides of the asymptotes Ox and Oy on which the curve lies; and shew that the third asymptote intersects the curve at points $\{\frac{1}{9}(16 \pm \sqrt{13})a, \frac{1}{9}(7 \pm \sqrt{13})a\}$.
Shew that $(a, \frac{2}{3}a)$ and $(2a, \frac{2}{3}a)$ are points of inflexion, and that there are three points, at which the curve runs parallel to Ox, in $x + a\sqrt{2} = 0$, and one in $x - a\sqrt{2} = 0$.

10. $$4xy^3 = 3\sqrt{3}a^2(x^2+y^2-a^2).$$
Trace the curve, and shew that there is a multiple point
$$(\tfrac{1}{2}a\sqrt{2}, \ \tfrac{1}{2}a\sqrt{6}).$$

CHAPTER VII.

ASYMPTOTES NOT PARALLEL TO THE AXES.
ASYMPTOTES TO HOMOGENEOUS CURVES.

PLATE
V.

118. In this chapter I shall shew how to approximate to the forms of the infinite branches which are not ultimately parallel to either axis.

In the first place, I shall consider the cases in which x and y, being both infinite, can be of the same order of magnitude. This is the general case of rectilinear asymptotes, although by including rectilinear asymptotes which are at an infinite distance, certain parabolic asymptotes appear in the course of the examination.

In the second part of the chapter I shall add some more illustrations, to those which have already been incidentally given, of the cases in which x and y are of different orders of magnitude.

119. In order to make the general statement more easy to understand, it will be well to take a few particular cases, and to shew how the method of approximation is to be employed to determine the asymptotes, and the side on which the curve lies, when it first comes into sight from an infinite distance, in the case in which x and y are both infinitely great, and of the same order of magnitude.

Ex. 1. $\qquad x^2(y+b) = y^2(x+a).$

Arranging the equation in homogeneous functions descending in degree, $xy(y-x) - bx^2 + ay^2 = 0.$

For the first approximation, neglecting quantities of the second order, compared with those of the third, $y = x.$

PLATE
V.

Since
$$y - x - \frac{bx}{y} + \frac{ay}{x} = 0,$$

the second approximation, obtained by writing $y = x$ in the smaller terms, is $y - x = b - a$, the equation of the asymptote.

For the third approximation, we must, according to Art. **51**, write in the smaller terms $y = x + b - a$.

Whence $y = x + b \left(1 + \frac{b-a}{x}\right)^{-1} - a \left(1 + \frac{b-a}{x}\right)$;

therefore, neglecting terms of higher order than $\frac{1}{x}$,

$$y = x + b - a - \frac{b^2 - a^2}{x}.$$

Hence, if $b > a$ the curve lies below the asymptote at the positive and above it at the negative end.

Fig. 1.

Ex. 2. $\mathbf{x^3 + y^3 - 3axy = 0.}$

The first approximation gives $y + x = 0$, and, since

$$y + x = \frac{3axy}{x^2 - xy + y^2},$$

the second approximation gives, by writing $-x$ for y in the smaller term, $y + x + a = 0$, which is the equation of the asymptote.

For the next approximation, writing in the smaller term $y = -x - a$, since $x^2 - xy + y^2 = -3xy + a^2$,

$$y + x = -a(1 - a^2/3xy)^{-1} = -a + a^3/3x^2,$$

hence the curve lies above the asymptote at both ends.

Fig. 2.

Another method of determining the side on which the curve lies is by assuming as the next approximation $y + x + a = \alpha$, where α is small compared with a.

Substituting in the original equation,

$$x^3 - (x + a - \alpha)^3 + 3ax(x + a - \alpha) = 0 ;$$

therefore, neglecting α^2, $3\alpha(x^2 + ax + a^2) = a^3$, which gives the same result as before.

PLATE
V.

Ex. 3. $(x-a)y^3 = (y-2a)^2x^2.$

A first approximation is $y = x$, and since

$$xy^3 - y^2x^2 - ay^3 + 4ax^2y - 4a^2x^2 = 0,$$

$$y - x - \frac{ay}{x} + \frac{4ax}{y} - \frac{4a^2x}{y^2} = 0 ;$$

$\therefore \ y - x - a + 4a = 0$ is the asymptote, crossing the curve where $x = \frac{48}{11}a$ and $\frac{6}{11}a$ nearly.

For the next approximation to the form of the curve

$$y - x - a(1 - 3a/x) + 4a(1 + 3a/x) - 4a^2/x = 0 ;$$

$$\therefore \ y = x - 3a - 11a^2/x.$$

See a more general case, page 84, (**4**), Plate IV., fig. 25.

120. In all these cases it must be observed that the first approximation gives, of all straight lines which can be drawn through the origin, that particular line which lies nearest to the infinite branch considered. The second approximation is represented by moving the line first found parallel to itself, until it becomes nearer to the curve than any other straight line which can be drawn.

The corresponding process with regard to points on a curve at a finite distance would be the following:

Take P a point on the curve, TP the tangent at P, meeting Ox in T, and let PO revolve about P until it assumes the position PT, nearer to the curve than any line which can be drawn through P.

If P move off to an infinite distance, we have at once the case of PO twisting round P until it coincides with PT, replaced by PO moving parallel to itself until it coincides with the asymptote; at first passing through only one point at infinity and afterwards through two consecutive points, the condition for an asymptote being thus satisfied.

121. The general statement of the process for treating asymptotes not parallel to the axes may be now made thus:

Let the rationalised equation of the curve be arranged

PLATE
V.

in homogeneous functions of x and y in descending order of dimensions, viz.

$$F_n(x, y) + F_{n-1}(x, y) + F_{n-2}(x, y) + \ldots = 0,$$
or $$u_n + u_{n-1} + u_{n-2} + \ldots = 0.$$

When x and y are both capable of indefinite increase, remaining of the same order of magnitude, along the infinite branches these functions are in descending order of magnitude.

The first approximation is $u_n \equiv F_n(x, y) = 0$, which represents, generally, n straight lines through the origin which are parallel to the asymptotes.

Consider one solution of the equation, $ax = by$, and suppose first that the factor $ax - by$ only appears once, so that $F_n(x, y) \equiv (ax - by)f_{n-1}(x, y)$, or $u_n \equiv (ax - by)v_{n-1}$, where v_{n-1} is not zero when ax is written for by.

The second approximation gives $ax - by + c = 0$, where $c = \dfrac{F_{n-1}(b, a)}{f_{n-1}(b, a)}$, Art. **3** (3) and Art. **51**; this is the asymptote parallel to $ax = by$, being the straight line which more nearly coincides with the curve at an infinite distance than any other straight line drawn in that direction.

122. Where there is no function of the $(n-1)^{\text{th}}$ degree, $ax = by$ is an asymptote.

In this case the next approximation is easily made, supposing u_{n-r} to be the first function which follows u_n.

Since $$ax - by + \frac{x^{r-1}F_{n-r}(x, y)}{f_{n-1}(x, y)} \frac{1}{x^{r-1}} + \ldots = 0,$$

the next approximation gives

$$ax - by + \frac{A}{x^{r-1}} = 0, \quad \text{where } A = \frac{b^{r-1}F_{n-r}(b, a)}{f_{n-1}(b, a)},$$

and this determines the side on which the curve lies.

123. Thus, for the hyperbola $a^2x^2 - b^2y^2 = 1$, the asymptote $ax - by = 0$ passes through the centre; and for the next approximation $ax - by = Ax^{-1}$, where A is the value of $x/(ax + by)$, when $by = ax$, that is $A = 1/(2a)$.

124. Recurring to the case considered in Art. **121**, in which u_{n-1} exists, the approximation for the sides of the asymptote $ax - by + c = 0$, on which the curve lies at an infinite distance, is conducted as follows:

Instead of $x : y = b : a$, as in the first approximation, we must write in the smaller terms $x : y = b : a + cx^{-1}$; hence, if we neglect terms of the order x^{-2} and lower orders,

$$\frac{u_{n-1}}{v_{n-1}} = \frac{F_{n-1}(b,\, a + cx^{-1})}{f_{n-1}(b,\, a + cx^{-1})} = c + \frac{dc}{x}, \text{ say,}$$

and

$$\frac{xu_{n-2}}{v_{n-1}} = \frac{bF_{n-2}(b,\, a)}{f_{n-1}(b,\, a)} = e, \text{ say.}$$

Hence the curve is more nearly represented by

$$ax + by + c + \frac{dc + e}{x} = 0, \quad \dots\dots\dots\dots\dots\dots(i)$$

e.g. Art. **119**, Ex. 1.

If $dc + e = 0$, $\dfrac{u_{n-1}}{v_{n-1}}$ must be expanded as far as $\dfrac{1}{x^2}$, $\dfrac{u_{n-2}}{v_{n-1}}$ as far as $\dfrac{1}{x}$, and $\dfrac{x^2 u_{n-3}}{v_{n-1}}$ becomes $\dfrac{b^2 F_{n-3}(b,\, a)}{f_{n-1}(b,\, a)} = k$, say. So that the approximation is

$$ax - by + \left(c + \frac{dc}{x} + \frac{gc^2}{x^2}\right) + \left(\frac{e}{x} + \frac{hc}{x^2}\right) + \frac{k}{x^2} = 0,$$

or

$$ax - by + c + \left(\frac{gc^2 + hc + k}{x^2}\right) = 0. \quad \dots\dots\dots\dots(ii)$$

The equations (i) and (ii) determine the sides on which the curve lies in the two cases.

125. Consider now the case in which the factor $ax - by$ appears twice, so that $u_n = (ax - by)^2 v_{n-2}$.

If there be a function of the $(n-1)^{\text{th}}$ degree, the second approximation will give

$$(ax - by)^2 - c'x = 0, \quad \dots\dots\dots\dots\dots\dots(i)$$

where

$$-c' = \frac{F_{n-1}(b,\, a)}{b f_{n-2}(b,\, a)},$$

or more generally, $(ax - by)^2 - c''(\lambda x + \mu y) = 0$,

where

$$-c'' = \frac{F_{n-1}(b,\, a)}{(\lambda b + \mu a) f_{n-2}(b,\, a)}.$$

In this case the infinite branch has a parabolic form, in which $ax = by$ gives the direction of the axis; or, if we write $bx + ay$ for $\lambda x + \mu y$, it is the axis itself of the parabola and the origin is the vertex.

126. The parabola (i) is not generally a proper asymptote, to obtain which we must make a further approximation, as follows:

From $(ax - by)^2 = c'x$ we obtain $y = \dfrac{x}{b}\left(a + \sqrt{\dfrac{c'}{x}}\right)$, which must be substituted in $\dfrac{u_{n-1}}{v_{n-2}}$.

This gives
$$\frac{u_{n-1}}{xv_{n-2}} = \frac{F_{n-1}\left(b,\, a + \sqrt{\dfrac{c'}{x}}\right)}{bf_{n-2}\left(b,\, a + \sqrt{\dfrac{c'}{x}}\right)} = -c'\left(1 + d\sqrt{\dfrac{c'}{x}}\right).$$

Hence the approximation is
$$(ax - by)^2 = c'x\left(1 + d\sqrt{\dfrac{c'}{x}}\right),$$
or
$$by = ax + (c'x)^{\frac{1}{2}} + \tfrac{1}{2}c'd,$$

the next term vanishing when x is infinite.

Thus
$$(by - ax - \tfrac{1}{2}c'd')^2 = c'x \quad \ldots\ldots\ldots\ldots\ldots\ldots(ii)$$

is a proper parabolic asymptote, since the difference of the values of y for the curve and this parabola vanishes when x is infinite.

127. The parabola (ii) found at the end of the last article is the simplest parabola which has the property of all proper asymptotes, but the following example will shew how the same parabola placed in a different position may be a proper asymptote, lying much closer to the curve at an infinite distance.

Ex. 1. $\mathbf{x(y - x)^2 = ay^2},$

or $x^{\frac{1}{2}}(y - x) = a^{\frac{1}{2}}y.$

Here $y = x(1 - a^{\frac{1}{2}}x^{-\frac{1}{2}})^{-1} = x + a^{\frac{1}{2}}x^{\frac{1}{2}} + a + a^{\frac{3}{2}}x^{-\frac{1}{2}} + \ldots.$

PLATE
V.

By taking the first two, three, and four terms as successive approximations, we obtain three parabolas, viz.:

$$(y-x)^2 = ax, \dots\dots\dots\dots\dots\dots\text{(i)}$$
$$(y-x-a)^2 = ax, \dots\dots\dots\dots\dots\dots\text{(ii)}$$
$$(y-x-a)^2 = ax + 2a^2. \dots\dots\dots\dots\dots\text{(iii)}$$

The differences between the ordinates of these three parabolas and those of the curve at an infinite distance are a, $a^{\frac{3}{2}}x^{-\frac{1}{2}}$ and $a^2 x^{-1}$, hence (i) is what I have called a quasi-asymptote, serving very well as a guide to the direction of flexure of the infinite branches of the curve; (ii) and (iii) are proper asymptotes, the latter being ultimately more nearly coincident with the curve.

Fig. 3.

Further, $x = a$ is an asymptote, and the form near the origin is $x^3 = ay^2$ ⊣〈 . The two dotted lines marked 1 and 2 in the figure represent the two parabolas (i) and (ii), and shew that, for the general form of the curve, there is no necessity to obtain a proper asymptote.

Note. Considering the parabola $(y-x-\alpha)^2 = a(x+\beta)$, $x+\beta = 0$ touches the parabola at the extremity of the latus rectum SL, where S is the focus,

$$\therefore \ (y-x+\alpha)^2 = 4SL(x+\beta)\sqrt{2},$$

therefore the latus rectum $2SL = \frac{1}{4}a\sqrt{2}$.

Hence, the latera recta of the three parabolas are all equal, and the axes are in the same direction.

Ex. 2. $\mathbf{y(y-x)^2(y+2x) = 9cx^3}$.

For the asymptote corresponding to $(y-x)^2$, writing x for y in $\dfrac{9cx^3}{y(y+2x)}$, we obtain

$$(y-x)^2 = 3cx. \dots\dots\dots\dots\dots\text{(i)}$$

For the next approximation, write $x + \sqrt{3cx}$ for y in the second term.

Then $(y-x)^2 = \dfrac{9cx^3}{(x+\sqrt{3cx})(3x+\sqrt{3cx})}$

$$= \dfrac{3cx}{1 + \dfrac{4}{3}\sqrt{\dfrac{3c}{x}} + \dfrac{c}{x}}.$$

PLATE
V.

Hence $\qquad y-x=\sqrt{3cx}\left(1-\dfrac{2}{3}\sqrt{\dfrac{3c}{x}}+\dfrac{A}{x}\cdots\right),$

or $y-x+2c=\sqrt{3cx}+$ terms which vanish when x is infinite. Thus we have the approximation

$$(y-x+2c)^2=3cx. \quad\ldots\ldots\ldots\ldots\ldots\ldots\ldots\text{(ii)}$$

The first parabola (i) is sufficient for the direction of the branches; the second (ii) is a proper asymptote.

The asymptote parallel to $y+2x=0$ is $y+2x=-\tfrac{1}{2}c$; $2y=9c$ is another asymptote, which meets the curve where

$y^2=3x^2$. The form near the origin is $y^4=9cx^3 \;\text{\footnotesize⊢}.$

Fig. 4.

128. If, in Art. **125**, u_n have a factor $(ax-by)^2$, and u_{n-1} a simple factor $ax-by$, the equation may be written

$$(ax-by)^2v_{n-2}+(ax-by)w_{n-2}+u_{n-2}+\ldots=0,$$

and if u' be the value of u when $x=b$, and $y=a$, the next approximation will give

$$(ax-by)^2v'_{n-2}+(ax-by)w'_{n-2}+u'_{n-2}=0,$$

or $\qquad (ax-by+\alpha)(ax-by+\beta)=0,$

which is the equation of two parallel rectilinear asymptotes, real, coincident, or imaginary.

129. To find the side of the asymptote $ax-by+\alpha=0$ on which the curve lies, write, in the functions w_{n-2}/v_{n-2} and u_{n-2}/v_{n-2}, b for x and $a+\alpha x^{-1}$ for y, whence

$$\frac{w_{n-2}}{v_{n-2}}=\alpha+\beta+\frac{c}{x}, \quad\text{and}\quad \frac{u_{n-2}}{v_{n-2}}=\alpha\beta+\frac{d}{x},$$

and the approximate form of the equation of the curve is

$$(ax-by+\alpha)(ax-by+\beta)+\frac{(ax-by)c}{x}+\frac{d}{x}=0,$$

therefore $\qquad ax-by+\alpha+\dfrac{\alpha c}{\alpha-\beta}\cdot\dfrac{1}{x}+\dfrac{d}{x}=0,$

with variations such as when the coefficient of $1/x$ vanishes, in which case the approximation must be carried to higher powers of $1/x$; or when $\beta=\alpha$, in which case $(u'_{n-2})^2=4u'_{n-2}v'_{n-2}$, and $ax-by+\alpha=(\alpha c-d)^{\frac{1}{2}}x^{-\frac{1}{2}}$.

PLATE
V.

130. The following curves afford examples of these peculiarities :

Ex. 1. $\qquad y(y-x)^2(y+2x)=3c^2x^2.$

The second approximation to $y=x$ gives $(y-x)^2=c^2$, two parallel asymptotes, which meet the curve where $y=-3x$, each asymptote having only one real point of intersection.

The other asymptotes are $y=0$, $y+2x=0$.

The curve is symmetrical in opposite quadrants; and

Fig. 5. near the origin $y^4=3c^2x^2$, ⨉.

Ex. 2. $\qquad (x+2y)(x-y)^2-6a^2(x+y)=0.$

Here $(x-y)^2=4a^2$ gives two asymptotes, also $x+2y=0$ is an asymptote; the equation may therefore be written

$$(x+2y)(x-y-2a)(x-y+2a)-2a^2(x-y)=0.$$

To trace the curve, observe that it is symmetrical in opposite quadrants.

Near the origin, $\qquad x+y=\tfrac{2}{3}y^3/a^2$;

near $(0,\,a\sqrt{3})$, $\qquad\qquad 4\eta=5x$;

near $(a\sqrt{6},\,0)$, $\qquad\qquad y=2\xi.$

Fig. 6. In the figure, the asymptote is not meant to be a tangent at the point of inflexion.

Ex. 3. $\qquad (x+2y)^2(x-y)^2-a^3(x+y)=0.$

The asymptotes are $(x-y)^2=0$, and $(x+2y)^2=0$.

For the position of the curve relative to the asymptotes $(x-y)^2=\tfrac{2}{9}a^3/x$, and $(x+2y)^2=\tfrac{2}{9}a^3/x$.

Fig. 7. $\qquad\qquad x+y=0$ is the tangent at the origin.

Ex. 4. $\qquad 2x(x-y)^2-3a(x^2-y^2)+4a^2y=0.$

For the asymptotes parallel to $x-y=0$,

$$(x-y)^2-3a(x-y)+2a^2=0, \quad\therefore\ x-y=a,\ \text{or}\ 2a.$$

For the asymptote parallel to Oy, $2x+3a=0$, and the equation may therefore be written

$$(2x+3a)(x-y-a)(x-y-2a)+5a^2(x-y)-6a^3=0.$$

PLATE
V.

The cross asymptotes do not meet the curve except at an infinite distance; that parallel to Oy cuts the curve where $10y = -27a$.

Also $(0, -\frac{4}{3}a)$ and $(\frac{3}{2}a, 0)$ are points in the curve, and near the origin $3x^2 = 4ay$.

These considerations are sufficient to give the form of the curve.

Fig. 8.

131. These methods of obtaining the cross asymptotes are, I think, the best to use in almost any case, when the practical application is well understood; but it is obvious that a more direct method of approximation must sometimes have the advantage.

Thus, when y can be expressed explicitly in terms of x, it can be expanded in descending powers of x, as was done in Art. **127** (Ex. 1). Take, for instance, the following curve:

$$x(x+1)y = (x^2+x+1)(x-2),$$

or
$$x(x+1)(y-x+2) = x-2;$$

$$\therefore\ y-x+2 = x^{-1}(x-2)/(x+1) = x^{-1},$$

when x and y are both infinite; the asymptotes parallel to Oy are $x = 0$ and -1; near $(0, \infty)$, $x = -2y^{-1}$; near $(-1, \infty)$, $x+1 = 3y^{-1}$; near $(2, 0)$, $6y = 7(x-2)$.

Fig. 9.

132. In tracing curves, it should be noticed by the student that, if an asymptote be looked upon as a tangent to a curve at a point infinitely distant, when this point is not a singular point of any kind, the curve lies on opposite sides at the two ends of the asymptote.

Thus, the axis of x is an asymptote of the common hyperbola, whose equation is $xy = c^2$, meeting the curve at two points at an infinite distance; and the side of the asymptote on which the curve lies is determined by $y = c^2/x$, shewing that, since y is of the same sign as x, the curve is on opposite sides of the asymptote at the two ends.

If there be three points at an infinite distance, *i.e.* when the asymptote is a tangent at a point of inflexion at an infinite distance, the curve lies on the same side at both ends; as in

PLATE
V.

Art. **119**, Ex. 2; thus, if $(x-a)y^2 = c^3$ be the equation of the curve, $x - a = 0$ is an asymptote meeting the curve at three points at an infinite distance, and since $x - a = c^3/y^2$, the curve lies on the same side at both ends.

Fig. 10.

But, when the asymptote is a tangent to a branch of a double point at an infinite distance, two of the three points belong to the branch which is touched by the asymptote, and one to the other branch, and in this case the curve lies on opposite sides of each of the two asymptotes.

Thus $(x-a)(x-b)y = c^3$ is a curve which has two asymptotes $x = a$ and b.

$x = a$ meets the curve in three points at an infinite distance, one of these points is the point in which it meets the branch which touches $x = b$, and the other two are the consecutive points, the passage through which makes it a tangent to another branch.

Fig. 11.

$x - a = c^3/(a-b)y$ being the next approximation, shews that the curve lies on opposite sides at the two ends.

If the origin be transferred to a point half-way between the asymptotes parallel to Oy, the equation becomes $\{x^2 - \frac{1}{2}(b-a)^2\}y = c^3$, so that, when $b = a$, the branch on the negative side of xOx' passes off to an infinite distance.

These considerations are useful, because, prior to proof, we ought to draw the curve in such a way that it shall leave the asymptote on opposite sides, and we are thus led to examine the points at a finite distance at which the curve crosses the asymptotes.

133. Take, as an example, the curve

$$x^5 - ax^3y - bx^2y^2 + y^5 = 0.$$

Near (∞, ∞), the first approximation is $x + y = 0$, the second gives $x + y = \frac{1}{5}(b - a)$.

Near $(0, 0)$, x, y of the same order of magnitude gives

$$ax + by = -(b^5 - a^5)x^2/b^4a, \quad \dots\dots\dots\dots(i)$$

x small compared with y gives $y^3 = bx^2$, $\dots\dots\dots(ii)$

y small compared with x gives $x^2 = ay$. $\dots\dots\dots(iii)$

Now, without further examination, we might be disposed to connect the forms already obtained, so that the curve would lie on the same side of the asymptote. But the consideration given above would lead us to draw the curve so as to cross the asymptote and proceed to the opposite side. If we tried to draw the curve without further calculation we should have to judge from its direction which of the branches would be more likely to cross. Thus if $b < a$ the branch (iii) would be more likely to cross than (i), since it has so close a contact with Ox. If $b > a$, the same reason would make us select the branch (ii).

We might then test by proceeding to the next approximation to the asymptote, or by absolutely finding the points of intersection with the asymptote; the first process is always possible and easy, the second involves the solution of an equation of a degree generally less by two than that of the curve; in this case the equation is a cubic.

If we write $x + y = \alpha$ in the equation, we get
$$x^5 - (x-\alpha)^5 + ax^3(x-\alpha) - bx^2(x-\alpha)^2 = 0,$$
or
$$(5\alpha - b + a)x^4 - \alpha(10\alpha + a - 2b)x^3 \ldots = 0.$$
If $5\alpha = b - a$ we have the asymptote, and for the next approximation
$$y = -x + \tfrac{1}{5}(b-a) - \tfrac{1}{25}(b-a)a/x,$$
which proves that the branches (ii) and (iii) cross the asymptote according as b is greater or less than a.

The direction of flexure of the branch (i) would be alone sufficient to shew which branches form the loop in $x'Oy$.

The cubic, which gives all the points of intersection, at a finite distance, of the curve and asymptote, is
$$ax^3 + \alpha(b - 2a)x^2 - 5\alpha^3 x + \alpha^4 = 0.$$

The figures are drawn for $b = 2a$, and $a = 2b$. The three Figs. 12, 13. roots are real in the first case, and two are impossible in the second.

In the case $a = b$, the curve is composed of the straight line $x + y = 0$, and the curve whose equation is
$$x^4 - x^3 y + x^2 y^2 - xy^3 + y^4 - ax^2 y = 0,$$

PLATE
V.

the forms at the origin being $y^3 = ax^2$, and $x^2 = ay$, and near (a, a), $3\xi^2 + a\eta = 0$.

Observe that no straight line through the origin can meet the curve in more than one point, so that y cannot be negative.

Fig. 14.

ASYMPTOTES TO HOMOGENEOUS CURVES.

134. A class of curves, sometimes called homogeneous curves, the equations of which are of the form $u_n = $ constant, where u_n is a homogeneous function of x and y, of the nth degree, illustrates the manner in which the continuity of a curve is preserved in passing through the infinitely distant points indicated by the asymptotes.

The equation of the asymptotes in this case is $u_n = 0$.

It is easy to trace these curves, because they intersect none of the asymptotes at any point at a finite distance, and cut no straight line through the origin in more than one point if n be odd, or two points if n be even; so that, knowing where the curve cuts the axes, we can tell, without calculation, on which side of the asymptotes to draw it.

Ex. 1. $(y - x)(y - 4x)(y + 2x) = a^3.$

Fig. 15.

Here the three asymptotes are real, and $(0, a)$, $(\frac{1}{2}a, 0)$, are the points on the axes of x and y.

Note. The asymptotes are tangents at points of inflexion, since three points at an infinite distance lie on each.

If we test, by proceeding to the next approximation, for $y = x$, we have $y - x = -a^3/9x^2$, shewing that the curve is below the asymptote at both ends.

Ex. 2. $(y - x)(y - 4x)(y + 2x) = 2a^2x.$

This and following curves are given to illustrate the superior simplicity derived from having the right-hand member constant.

The three asymptotes all pass through the origin, and, since they cut the curve at only two points at an infinite distance, they are ordinary tangents, and the curve therefore

PLATE
V.

lies on opposite sides of each; this is also shewn by the
nearer approximations $y - x = -2a^2/9x$, etc.

At the origin, $y^3 = 2a^2x$, and the form is ⊬.   Fig. 16.

Ex. 3. $(y - x)(y - 4x)(y + 2x) = 8ax^2.$

The asymptotes do not pass through the origin, they are
$$y - x = -\tfrac{8}{9}a, \quad\dotfill\text{(i)}$$
$$y - 4x = \tfrac{4}{9}a, \quad\dotfill\text{(ii)}$$
$$y + 2x = \tfrac{4}{9}a ; \quad\dotfill\text{(iii)}$$
for the radii drawn from the origin to the points where
these asymptotes intersect the curve,

(i) $(y - 4x)(y + 2x) = -9x^2$, or $(y - x)^2 = 0$;

(ii) $(y - x)(y + 2x) = 18x^2$, $\therefore$ $y + 5x = 0$;

(iii) $(y - x)(y - 4x) = 18x^2$, $\therefore$ $y - 7x = 0$;

the first asymptote meets the curve at three infinitely distant
points.

The form at the origin is the cusp $y^3 = 8ax^2$.   Fig. 17.

Ex. 4. $(y - x)^2(y + x)(y + 2x) = 16a^4.$

The curve comes into sight from an infinite distance on
both sides of each end of the asymptote $y = x$; it cuts Ox
where $x = \pm a\sqrt[4]{}/8$, and Oy where $y = \pm 2a$; also it is symmetrical in opposite quadrants.   Fig. 18.

Ex. 5. $(y - x)^2(y + x)(y + 2x) = 6ax^3.$

With this variation there is for two of the infinite branches
a parabola $(y - x)^2 = ax$, which shews how these branches
bend, but which is not a proper parabolic asymptote.

The other asymptotes are $y + x = \tfrac{3}{2}a$, $y + 2x = -\tfrac{2}{3}a$.

$y + x = \tfrac{3}{2}a$ meets the curve where $(y - x)^2(y + 2x) = 4x^3$,

$\therefore$ $(y^2 - 4x^2)y + x^2y - 2x^3 = (y - 2x)(y + x)^2 = 0$,

or $y - 2x = 0$ gives the only point at a finite distance.

$y + 2x = -\tfrac{2}{3}a$ meets the curve where $(y - x)^2(y + x) = -9x^3$,

whence $(y + 2x)(y^2 - 3xy + 5x^2) = 0$,

which gives no real points at a finite distance.

Near the origin, $y^4 = 6ax^3$; near $(3a, 0)$, $y = 2(\xi - 3a)$.   Fig. 19.

PLATE
V.

135. I shall conclude this chapter by giving materials for tracing curves which have infinite branches of the various kinds which have been discussed, by which the student may practise himself in completing curves from the known forms of particular parts, only using my figures as a check.

Ex. 1. $x^5 - 2a^3xy + y^5 = 0.$

Note the symmetry with respect to $x = y$, and that $x = y$ meets the curve where $x = y = a$.

Near the origin, $x^4 = 2a^3y$ and $y^4 = 2a^3x$;

Fig. 20. and $x + y = 0$ is an asymptote.

Ex. 2. $x^5 - 5ax^2y^2 + y^5 = 0.$

Observe the symmetry, and that $x = y$ meets the curve where $x = y = \frac{5}{2}a$.

Near the origin, $x^3 = 5ay^2$ and $y^3 = 5ax^2$,

Fig. 21. near (∞, ∞), $x + y = \lim 5ax^2y^2/(x^4 - x^3y + \ldots + y^4) = a.$

Ex. 3. $x^5 - a^2x^2y - b^2xy^2 + y^5 = 0.$

The curve is symmetrical in opposite quadrants.

Near the origin, if $x : y$ can be small, $y^3 = b^2x$; if $y : x$ can be small, $x^3 = a^2y$; and if x and y can be of the same order of magnitude, $a^2x + b^2y = 0.$

Also $y + x = 0$ is an asymptote.

Fig. 22. The figure is drawn for $a > b$, but looks too much as if a/b were infinite.

Ex. 4. $y^2(3x - 4y)^3 - a^4x = 0.$

This is symmetrical in opposite quadrants.

Near the origin, $64y^5 + a^4x = 0$;

near the ends of the asymptote $x'Ox$,

$$y^2 = a^4/27x^2;$$

near those of the cross asymptote,

Fig. 23. $(3x - 4y)^3 = 4a^4/3y.$

Ex. 5. $\{x(y - x) - a^2\}^2y^3 = a^7,$ $(a > 0).$

Observe that y cannot be negative.

PLATE
V.

Near $(0, a)$, $\eta = a + \tfrac{2}{3}x$,

near (a, a), $\eta + 2\xi = 0$,

near $(0, \infty)$, $x = a^2 y^{-1} + a^{\frac{7}{2}} y^{-\frac{5}{2}}$,

near $(\infty, 0)$, $y = x^{\frac{7}{3}} x^{-\frac{4}{3}}$,

near (∞, ∞), $y - x = a^2 x^{-1} + a^{\frac{7}{2}} x^{-\frac{5}{2}}$.   Fig. 24.

Ex. 6. $4a^2(y-x)^2(y+x) - 8ax^3(y-x) + x^5 + y^5 = 0$.

The asymptote is $x + y + \tfrac{16}{5}a = 0$;

near the origin, where x and y are of the same order,

$$y - x = 0, \dots\dots\dots\dots\dots\dots\dots\text{(i)}$$

and
$$y + x = 0. \dots\dots\dots\dots\dots\dots\dots\text{(ii)}$$

For the next approximation to (i),

$$4a^2(y-x)^2 - 4ax^2(y-x) + x^4 = \{2a(y-x) - x^2\}^2 = 0.$$

For a further approximation,

$$\frac{y}{x} = 1 + \frac{x}{2a};$$

therefore
$$\frac{x}{y+x} = \left(2 + \frac{x}{2a}\right)^{-1} = \tfrac{1}{2}\left(1 - \frac{x}{4a}\right),$$

and
$$\frac{x^5 + y^5}{(x+y)x^4} = \frac{2 + \dfrac{5x}{2a}}{2 + \dfrac{x}{2a}} = 1 + \frac{x}{a}.$$

Substituting, we obtain

$$4a^2(y-x)^2 - 4ax^2\left(1 - \frac{x}{4a}\right)(y-x) + x^4\left(1 + \frac{x}{a}\right) = 0,$$

or
$$\{2a(y-x) - x^2\}^2 + \frac{x^5}{2a} + \frac{x^5}{a} = 0,$$

whence
$$y = x + \frac{x^2}{2a} + \sqrt{\left(\frac{-3x^5}{8a^3}\right)},$$

shewing that there is a ramphoid cusp touching (i).

For the branch (ii) through the origin,

$$4a^2(y+x) + 4ax^2 = 0, \quad \text{or} \quad y = -x - x^2/a.$$

To find the side of the asymptote on which the curve lies,
let $y = -x - \tfrac{16}{5}a + \alpha$, and expand α in descending powers
of x as far as x^3;

$$\therefore \ 5\alpha x^4 - 10(\tfrac{16}{5}a)^2 x^3 + 8 \cdot \tfrac{16}{5}a^2 x^3 = 0, \quad \text{and} \quad \alpha = \tfrac{384}{5}a^2 x^{-1}.$$

PLATE
V.

Fig. 25.

If $y = 0$, $\qquad 4a^2x^3 + 8ax^4 + x^5 = 0$;

$\qquad\qquad \therefore\ x^2 + 8ax + 16a^2 = 12a^2$;

$\therefore\ x = -2a(2 \pm \surd 3) = -2a \tan \tfrac{5}{12}\pi \quad \text{or} \quad -2a \tan \tfrac{1}{12}\pi.$

Ex. 7. $\qquad (\mathbf{x}^2 - \mathbf{y}^2)^2 - 4\mathbf{y}^2 + \mathbf{y} = 0.$

Observe the symmetry of the curve with respect to Oy, which it cuts at the origin and where $y^3 - 4y + 1 = 0$. The roots of this equation are two positive and one negative, say α, β, and $-\gamma$, so that the equation of the curve may be written, $x^2(2y^2 - x^2) = y(y - \alpha)(y - \beta)(y + \gamma)$; whence near the three points $(0, \alpha)$, $(0, \beta)$, and $(0, -\gamma)$,

$$2\alpha x^2 = (\alpha - \beta)(\alpha + \gamma)\eta,$$
$$2\beta x^2 = -(\alpha - \beta)(\beta + \gamma)\eta,$$
and $\qquad\qquad 2\gamma x^2 = -(\alpha + \gamma)(\beta + \gamma)\eta$;

near the origin, $x^4 + y = 0$; near $(\tfrac{1}{4}, \tfrac{1}{4})$, $\xi^2 = 4\eta$.

By expanding in descending powers of y,

$$x^2 = y^2 \pm 2y(1 - \tfrac{1}{8}y^{-1} + \dots),$$
whence $\qquad\qquad x = y \pm 1 - (\tfrac{1}{2} \pm \tfrac{1}{8})y^{-1},$
and $\qquad\qquad -x = y \pm 1 - (\tfrac{1}{2} \pm \tfrac{1}{8})y^{-1},$

from which we obtain four asymptotes, and the side on which the curve lies at each end; these asymptotes inter-
Fig. 26.
sect the curve where $y = \tfrac{1}{3}$ and $-\tfrac{1}{5}$.

Ex. 8. $\quad \mathbf{y}(\mathbf{y} - \mathbf{x})^2(\mathbf{y} - 2\mathbf{x}) + 3a(\mathbf{y} - \mathbf{x})\mathbf{x}^2 - 2a^2\mathbf{x}^2 = 0.$

The asymptote parallel to Ox is $2y + 3a = 0$; the three cross asymptotes are $y - x = a$ or $2a$, and $y - 2x = -\tfrac{3}{2}a$; and the equation may be written

$$(y - x)^4 - x^2(y - x - a)(y - x - 2a) = 0,$$

which form shews that the parallel asymptotes do not inter-sect the curve except at infinity, and that no part of the curve lies between them.

Near the origin, $\qquad y^4 = 2a^2x^2,$
giving two parabolic forms;

near $(-\tfrac{2}{3}a, 0)$, where the curve crosses the axis $x'Ox$,
Fig. 27.
$$y(-2x + 3a) - 3a(x + \tfrac{2}{3}a) = 0 ; \quad \therefore\ 13y = 9\xi.$$

Ex. 9. $\quad y^2x(y-x)-ay^3-byx^2+c^2x^2=0$,

or $\quad\quad (x-a)y^3-x^2(y-\alpha)(y+\beta)=0$.

Near the asymptotes parallel to the axes,

$$x=a+a^2y^{-1}, \quad\quad y=\alpha+\alpha^3x^{-1}/(\alpha+\beta),$$
$$y=-\beta+\beta^3x^{-1}/(\alpha+\beta).$$

The cross asymptote $y-x=a+b$ intersects the curve where $ay^2-bxy=c^2x^2/(a+b)$, the roots of which are of opposite signs.

For the next approximation

$$y-x=a+b+(a^2-b^2-c^2)x^{-1}.$$

The curve is drawn for $a>b$ and $c^2>a^2-b^2$. $\quad$ Fig. 28.

Note. When $c^2=a^2-b^2$, the curve is above the cross asymptote at both ends, and when $c^2<a^2-b^2$ it crosses the asymptote at a point below $x'Ox$.

Ex. 10. $\quad x^7-x^3y^4+a^4y^3-ax^2y^4=0$.

Near $(0,\infty)$, $\quad x^2=a^3y^{-1}$ $\quad$ and $\quad x+a=a^2y^{-1}$.

The other asymptotes can be found, as well as the side on which the curve lies, from $x^5-(x+a)y^4=0$; so that

$$y=\pm x(1+ax^{-1})^{-\frac{1}{4}}=\pm(x-\tfrac{1}{4}a+\tfrac{5}{32}a^2x^{-1}).$$

Near the origin, $\quad\quad x^7+a^4y^3=0$;

near $(-a, a)$, $\quad\quad\quad 2\xi+\eta=0$;

and near (a, a), $\quad\quad\quad 2\xi-5\eta=0$. $\quad\quad$ Fig. 29.

Ex. 11. $\quad x^2y-y^2x=a(x-b)^2-b(y-a)^2$.

If $ab=c^2$, we may write the equation in the forms

$$(x-b)y^2+(2c^2-x^2)y+a\{(x-b)^2-c^2\}=0,$$

or $\quad (y-a)x^2+(2c^2-y^2)x+b\{(y-a)^2-c^2\}=0$.

If $x=0$, $\quad y=a\pm c$; if $y=0$, $\quad x=b\pm c$.

If $x=b$, $\quad y=\infty$ $\quad$ or $\quad a^2/(2a-b)$;

if $y=a$, $\quad x=\infty$ $\quad$ or $\quad b^2/(2b-a)$;

near (c, c), $\quad\quad (3c-2a)\xi=(3c-2b)\eta$;

and near $(-c, -c)$, $\quad (3c+2a)\xi=(3c+2b)\eta$.

The cross asymptote is $x-y=a-b$, which meets the curve where $ax+by=3ab$. $\quad\quad$ Fig. 30.

PLATE
V.

Examples VII.

1. Trace the curve $x^5 - ax^4 + y^5 = 0$, and prove that the coordinates of the point at which it is parallel to Ox are $\frac{4}{5}a$ and $\frac{3}{5}a$ nearly.

2. Find the tangents to the curve $x(y-x)^2 = c^3$ which pass through $(c, 0)$, and shew that the point of contact of one is $(\frac{1}{4}c, \frac{9}{4}c)$, and that the other is inclined to Ox at an angle $\tan^{-1}\frac{3}{2}$.

3. Trace the curve $y(y-x)^2(y+2x) = c^3x$.

Prove that the lines joining the origin and the points at which the curve is parallel to Oy are inclined to Ox at angles whose tangents are $\sqrt{2}\sin 15°$ and $-\sqrt{2}\cos 15°$.

4. Shew that the curve $y^4 + 2axy^2 - x^4 = 0$ intersects its asymptotes at points whose distances from Oy are $\frac{1}{4}a\sqrt{2}$.

5. At the points where the curve, Plate V., fig. 23, is parallel to Ox, $x = \pm\frac{1}{5}a\sqrt{2}$; and $y = \frac{3}{10}x$ passes through the points where it is parallel to Oy.

6. Trace the curve $(x-y)^2(x+y)(2x+y) = a^3y$, and shew that the radii from the origin to the points where the curve is parallel to Ox are inclined to Ox at angles $\tan^{-1}\frac{25}{4}$ and $\tan^{-1}\frac{5}{4}$ nearly.

7. Shew that there is a cusp at the origin in the curve
$$(x-y)^2(x+y)(x^2+y^2) = a^3x^2,$$
and another at an infinite distance.

8. $x^5 - ax^3y - \frac{9}{5}ax^2y^2 + y^5 = 0$ crosses the asymptote at the three points at which $x = \frac{1}{31}a$ and $\pm\frac{1}{7}a$ nearly.

9. Describe the symmetry of the curve
$$x(y^2 - \frac{1}{2}a^2) - y(x^2 - \frac{1}{2}a^2) = a^3.$$
Shew that the radius of curvature at $(a, -a)$ is $\frac{5}{4}a\sqrt{2}$; and that the curve cuts the asymptotes Ox and Oy at an angle $\cot^{-1}7$.

10. $(y^2 - x^2)^2 - a^2y^2 + b^2x^2 = 0.$

Discuss the cases of $a >$ and $< b$, and in the latter examine the variations when $b >$, $=$ or $< a\sqrt{2}$.

11. Trace the curve $x^4 - y^4 - 2ax^2y + a^2y^2 + a^4 = 0$.

Shew that the curvatures at the points of intersection with Oy, and at (a, a) are in the ratio of $1 : \sqrt{5}$.

Prove that when a line parallel to Ox is trisected by the curve, its distance from Ox is $\frac{29}{25}a$ nearly

12. Prove that $(x - y - \frac{5}{12}a)^2 = \frac{1}{6}ay$ is a proper parabolic asymptote to the curve $(x-y)^2(x+y)(2x+y) = ay^3$.

13. Shew that the parabolic asymptote of the closest contact to the curve, Art. **127**, Ex. 2, is $(y - x + 2c)^2 = 3cx + 17c^2$.

CHAPTER VIII.

CURVILINEAR ASYMPTOTES.

PLATE
VI.

136. THE only cases of infinite branches which remain to be discussed are those in which, when x and y are both infinite, they are not of the same order of magnitude, so that $x : y$ or $y : x$ vanishes ultimately.

The equation of a curve being given, it may, generally, if it contain many terms, be simplified considerably by considerations similar to those given in Art. **95** for the investigation of branches through the origin.

Suppose that we intend to examine whether $x : y$ can ultimately vanish in any infinite branch of the curve.

(1) All homogeneous functions of x and y may be replaced by the term which involves the highest power of y.

(2) The coefficient of any power of x being a function of y, the term involving the highest power of y is the only term which need be retained.

(3) A similar observation holds with respect to the coefficient of any power of y.

(4) If two terms $ax^s y^{r+1}$, $bx^t y^r$ remain, since their ratio is $ay : bx^{t-s}$, $t-s$ must be >1, therefore the indices of x must ascend by steps of 2 or more, if the equation be rational.

These considerations reduce the equation to a comparatively small number of terms, and it must then be tried whether, on neglecting one or more terms, a relation such as $y = x^r$, $r > 1$, is obtained, and whether with this relation the terms rejected are smaller than those retained

PLATE
VI.

137. In tracing curves, the case of x being great with respect to y, or *vice versâ*, in any infinite branch is always to be examined carefully, for with a cursory glance, which is generally sufficient, such a branch often escapes notice, and is only eventually detected by the impossibility of uniting the parts which have been discovered.

138. The examples which I have given in this chapter should be especially followed out as far as the asymptotes are concerned, which I have for this reason placed at the commencement in each case.

In the previous chapters, in order to draw the curves, I have been obliged to consider curvilinear asymptotes, which are not generally proper asymptotes, and in the particular case of parabolic asymptotes I have anticipated an important part of the subject of this chapter by giving the complete process to be followed in finding parabolas which are proper asymptotes.

With regard to the more general curvilinear asymptotes such as semicubical parabolas, it is obvious that so many terms would have to be taken in order to make them proper asymptotes that they would be harder to draw than the curve itself; they will, therefore, in the examples of this chapter, remain only quasi-asymptotes, guiding roughly but sufficiently to the direction of flexure at a great distance, too great in fact to give any idea of the form of the curve on a piece of paper of a moderate size.

Ex. 1. $\qquad\qquad \mathbf{x}^6 + 2\mathbf{a}^2\mathbf{x}^3\mathbf{y} - \mathbf{b}^3\mathbf{y}^3 = 0.$

There are no asymptotes parallel to the axes; the only infinite branches occur where $y : x$ is large, the form being $x^2 = by$, where $x^3 y \propto x^5$, and may be neglected compared with the term x^6 retained in the first approximation.

The parabola, $x^2 = by$, is not a proper asymptote, but is sufficient as a guide to the general direction of the infinite branches. The proper asymptotes may be thus obtained:

$$by = x^2\Big(1 + \frac{2a^2y}{x^3}\Big)^{\frac{1}{3}} = x^2\Big(1 + \frac{2a^2y}{3x^3} - \frac{4a^4y^2}{9x^6} + \dots\Big),$$

PLATE
VI.

for the second approximation,

$$by = x^2\left(1 + \frac{2a^2}{3bx}\right);$$

for the third,

$$by = x^2\left\{1 + \left(\frac{2a^2}{3bx} + \frac{4a^4}{9b^2x^2}\right) - \frac{4a^4}{9b^2x^2}\right\}$$

$$= x^2 + \frac{2a^2x}{3b},$$

or
$$\left(x + \frac{a^2}{3b}\right)^2 = b\left(y + \frac{a^4}{9b^3}\right),$$

and, since the values of y in this parabola and the curve differ by a quantity which vanishes when x is infinite, it is a proper asymptote.

Near the origin, $x^3 + 2a^2y = 0$, and $2a^2x^3 - b^3y^2 = 0$.

The curve is parallel to Oy, where $2a^2x^3 = 3b^3y^2$, whence the point of contact of the only tangent parallel to Oy is where $9b^3y + 8a^4 = 0$, for although Oy meets the curve in three coincident points at the origin it is not a tangent there.

The curve is parallel to Ox, where $x^3 + a^2y = 0$, giving the origin, at which Ox is a tangent, and the point $(a^2/b, \; -a^4/b^3)$.

In the figure the proper asymptote is drawn as well as the guiding asymptote, which is the first approximation to it.   Fig. 1.

Ex. 2. $x^2(y - x)^3 - ay^4 = 0.$

There are no asymptotes parallel to the axes. When x and y are of the same order of magnitude, $(y - x)^3 = 0$, and $y - x = a^{\frac{1}{3}}x^{\frac{2}{3}}$ for a second approximation; the proper asymptote, obtained by proceeding with the approximation, until we come to negative indices of x is

$$y = x + a^{\frac{1}{3}}x^{\frac{2}{3}} + \tfrac{4}{3}a^{\frac{2}{3}}x^{\frac{1}{3}} + 2a. \quad \dots\dots\dots\dots\dots(i)$$

When y is large compared with x,

$$x^2 = ay. \quad \dots\dots\dots\dots\dots\dots\dots(ii)$$

To obtain the proper parabolic asymptote in this case, write the equation in the form

$$ay = x^2\left(1 - \frac{3x}{y} + \frac{3x^2}{y^2} - \frac{x^3}{y^3}\right),$$

PLATE
VI.

whence for the second approximation,

$$ay = x^2\left(1 - \frac{3a}{x}\right),$$

and for the third,

$$ay = x^2\left\{1 - \frac{3a}{x}\left(1 + \frac{3a}{x}\right) + \frac{3a^2}{x^2}\right\},$$

or $$ay = x^2 - 3ax - 6a^2,$$

which may be written

$$\left(x - \frac{3a}{2}\right)^2 = \left(y + \frac{33a}{4}\right). \quad \dots\dots\dots\dots\dots(\text{iii})$$

We may observe that x is large compared with y, near the origin only, where $x^5 + ay^4 = 0$.

The curve meets the guiding asymptote, $x^2 = ay$, in no real point except the origin, and that it runs along the proper parabolic asymptote (ii) is accounted for by the parabolas (ii) and (iii) intersecting at $(-2a, 4a)$, so that the latter is inside the former after this point.

Fig. 2.

The effect of taking the proper asymptote instead of the approximate one is to throw the branch in the angle xOy further from the origin, but it is to be observed that the general form indicated by the guiding parabola is sufficiently accurate.

The asymptote (i) is drawn in the figure taking into account only the first two terms in the value of y.

Neither branch could be represented on a moderately sized piece of paper, since the point where the curve runs parallel to Oy has for its coordinates $\frac{19a}{2}$ and $38a$ nearly.

Ex. 3. $\qquad a(x^5 + y^5) - x^3 y^3 = 0.$

If x^5 can be rejected, $ay^2 = x^3$, which, near (∞, ∞), makes x small compared with y; similarly y^5 can be rejected near (∞, ∞), giving $ax^2 = y^3$. Again $x^3 y^3$ can be rejected near $(0, 0)$, and the form is given by the next approximation

Fig. 3. $y + x = -\tfrac{1}{5} x^2 / a.$

PLATE
VI.

Ex. 4. $\quad axy^3 - (x-a)^4y + a^5 = 0.$

Near $(0, \infty)$, $x = a^3/y^2,$

near $(\infty, 0)$, $y = a^5/x^4,$

near (∞, ∞), $x^3 = ay^2,$

near $(0, a)$, $\eta = 5x,$

near $(a, -a)$, $3\eta = \xi.$ Fig. 4.

Note. The curve is parallel to Oy at two points, in the intersection of the curves $y(x-a)^4 = \frac{3}{2}a^5$ and $xy^3 = \frac{1}{2}a^4$, and it is parallel to Ox at one point, in the intersection of

$$4(x-a)^3 = ay^2 \quad \text{and} \quad (3x+a)y^3 + 4a^4 = 0.$$

Ex. 5. $\quad axy^3 + (x-a)^3y^2 + a^5 = 0.$

Near $(0, \infty)$, $x = a^2/y,$

near $(\infty, 0)$, $y^2 = -a^5/x^3,$

near (∞, ∞), $ay + x^2 = 0,$

near $(0, a)$, $\eta = 2x,$

near $(0, -a)$, $\eta = -x,$

near $(a, -a)$, $3\eta = \xi.$

The curve is parallel to Ox at the intersection of

$$ay + 3(x-a)^2 = 0 \quad \text{and} \quad (2x+a)y^3 + 3a^4 = 0,$$

which gives three negative values of y, and two positive, one negative value of x.   Fig. 5.

Ex. 6. $\quad a^3(y+x) - 2a^2x(y+x) + x^4 = 0,$

or $\quad a^2(a-2x)y + x(x-a)(x^2+ax-a^2) = 0.$

Near $(\frac{1}{2}a, \infty)$, $x - \frac{1}{2}a = a^2/32y\ ;$

near (∞, ∞), $-2a^2y + x^3 = 0\ ;$

near $(0, 0)$, $y + x + x^4/a^3 = 0.$

Where $y = 0$, $x = a$, and $\frac{1}{2}(\pm\sqrt{5}-1)a$, $=\alpha a$ and βa suppose.

Near $(a, 0)$, $y = \xi\ ;$

near $(\alpha a, 0)$, $(1-2\alpha)y + \alpha(\alpha-1)(\alpha-\beta)\xi = 0,$

and $\quad \alpha^2 - \alpha = 1 - 2\alpha, \quad \therefore y + \sqrt{5}\xi = 0\ ;$

near $(\beta a, 0)$, $y - \sqrt{5}\xi = 0.$ Fig. 6.

PLATE
VI.

Ex. 7. $y^4 - 2(3x - 4a)ay^2 + a^2x^2 = 0,$

or $(y^2 - 3ax + 4a^2)^2 = 8a^2(x - 2a)(x - a).$

Near (∞, ∞), $y^2 = (3 \pm 2\sqrt{2})ax$, for a first approximation; the proper asymptotes are $y^2 = (3 \pm 2\sqrt{2})a(x \mp a\sqrt{2})$.

The origin is a conjugate point, and x cannot give real values of y when it is between a and $2a$.

Fig. 7. Further, $x = 2a$ is a tangent where $y = \pm a\sqrt{2}$.

Ex. 8. $x^4 - 3ax^2y + 2a^2y^2 - ay^3 = 0.$

Near (∞, ∞), $x^4 - ay^3 = 0$;

near the origin, ay^3 may be rejected, therefore $x^2 = ay$, or $2ay$;

near $(0, 2a)$, $x^2 = -\frac{2}{3}a\eta$;

near $(\sqrt{6}a, 2a)$, $11\eta = 6\sqrt{6}\xi.$

Observe that y cannot be negative, and that, near the origin, the two parabolas lie nearer to $x'Ox$ than the guiding
Fig. 8. asymptote.

Ex. 9. $x^7 - x^4y^3 + a^3y^4 - axy^5 = 0.$

Near $(0, \infty)$, $x = a^2/y$;

near (∞, ∞), if x and y are of the same order, we have

$$x - y - \tfrac{1}{3}a = 0,$$

Fig. 9. and for the next approximation $x = y + \tfrac{1}{3}a - \dfrac{4a^2}{3y}.$

Again, if $x : y$ be small, x^7 and y^4 may be rejected, therefore $x^3 + ay^2 = 0$, and for the next approximation to this asymptote, taking the term x^7 into account,

$$x^3 = -ay^2 + x^6y^{-3} = -ay^2 + a^2y,$$

shewing that the curve lies nearer to Oy in the upper branch of the asymptote and farther from Oy in the lower; and, since it is easily seen that the curve and asymptote intersect only at the points $(-a, \pm a)$, there is a branch of the curve which lies between the rectilinear and curvilinear asymptotes at the lower end without intersecting them. To find the way in which the other part of the curve in the quadrant $x'Oy$ runs, it must be observed that $x^7 + a^3y^4 = 0$ gives the shape at the origin, and that the line $x + a = 0$ cuts the curve where $y^2 = a^2$ and $a(y^2 + a^2) + y^3 = 0$. The only real solution of the latter equation is, by the method of Art. **47**, a little less than $-\frac{3}{2}a$, and if we put $y = (-\frac{3}{2} + \alpha)a$, neglecting α^2, we obtain $\alpha = \frac{1}{30}$.

Let β be any one of the three roots, then, writing $x = -a + \xi$ and $y = \beta + \eta$, we obtain, near $(-a, \beta)$,

$$(7a^5 + 4a^2\beta^3 - \beta^5)\xi = (3a^2\beta^2 - 4a\beta^3 - 5\beta^4)a\eta,$$

and the forms corresponding to $\beta = a$, $-a$, and $(-\frac{3}{2} + \frac{1}{30})a$ are given by $\eta = -\frac{5}{3}\xi$, $\eta = 2\xi$, and $\eta = -\frac{7}{24}\xi$, nearly.

Between the last two values of β the curve runs parallel to yOy' very near the point $(-\frac{7}{6}a, -\frac{4}{3}a)$.

Ex. 10. $a(x^5 + y^5) - a^2x^3y + x^2y^4 = 0$.

Near (∞, ∞), $x : y$ large gives $ax^3 + y^4 = 0$; $y : x$ large gives $ay + x^2 = 0$.

Near the origin, if $x : y$ be small, $ay^4 - a^2x^3 + x^2y^3 = 0$; therefore $y^4 - ax^3 = 0$, which makes x^2y^3 of the order $x^{4+\frac{1}{4}}$.

If $y : x$ be small, rejecting y^5 and x^2y^4, $x^2 = ay$.

Where $x = y$, $x = (\pm\sqrt{2} - 1)a = -\frac{2}{5}a$ or $-1\frac{2}{5}a$ nearly.   Fig. 10.

Ex. 11. $x^7 - a^3x^2y(x - y) + a^5(x - y)^2 = 0$.

Near (∞, ∞), $x^5 + a^3y^2 = 0$;

near the origin, by the first approximation, $y = x$; by the second, $a^5(y - x)^2 + a^3x^3(y - x) + x^7 = 0$, $\therefore$ neglecting x^7, $y - x = -x^3/a^2$, hence $(y - x)^2 \infty x^6$, which is greater than the rejected term; and neglecting $(y - x)^2$, $y - x = -x^4/a^3$, where $(y - x)^2 \infty x^8$, properly rejected.

Near $(-a, 0)$,

$$a^2 . 5a^4\xi + a^6y + 2a^6y = 0, \quad \text{or} \quad 3y + 5\xi = 0.$$ Fig. 11.

Ex. 12. $ay^2(y - a) - x^2(y^2 - a^2) + 2axy^2 - x^4 = 0$,

or $ay^3 - (x - a)^2y^2 - x^2(x^2 - a^2) = 0$.

Near (∞, ∞), y large compared with x gives $ay = x^2$; near the origin, $y^2 = x^2$; and near $(0, a)$, $a^3\eta + 2a^3x = 0$, or by the next approximation, $\eta + 2x = -4x^3/a^2$.

Near $(a, 0)$, $y^3 = 2a^2\xi$; and near $(-a, 0)$, $2y^2 = a\xi$.

PLATE
VI.

Fig. 12.

The tangent at $(0, a)$, drawn in the figure, meets the curve again at the point $(\frac{4}{5}a, -\frac{3}{5}a)$ only.

Note. The proper asymptote is $a(y-a)=(x-a)^2$, which meets the curve in only one point at a finite distance.

Ex. 13. $c^6 y^2 - (a+b)c^3 x^3 y + abx^6 - c^3 x^3 y^2 = 0.$

The equation may be written

$$(c^3 y - ax^3)(c^3 y - bx^3) - c^3 x^3 y^2 = 0,$$

or $c^3(c^3 - x^3)y^2 - \{(a+b)c^3 y - abx^3\}x^3 = 0.$

Near (c, ∞), $x = c\{1 - (a+b)/3y\}$,

near (∞, ∞), $abx^3 - c^3 y^2 = 0,$

Fig. 13. near $(0, 0)$, $c^3 y = ax^3$,   or bx^3.

Note. The two asymptotes are cut by the curve at points equidistant from Ox.

Ex. 14. $yx^2(y-x) - ay^3 - byx^2 + c^2 x^2 = 0,$

or $yx^3 - (y^2 - by + c^2)x^2 + ay^3 = 0.$

Near $(\infty, 0)$, $y = c^2/x$.

Near (∞, ∞), if x and y are of the same order, $y - x = a + b$; this asymptote meets the curve at a finite distance, where

$$a(a+b)(x+a+b)(2x+a+b) - c^2 x^2 = 0, \ldots\ldots\ldots(i)$$

one of whose roots is positive, the other negative if $c^2 > 2a(a+b)$, but both are negative if $c^2 < 2a(a+b)$.

When y and x are both infinite and of different orders, $x^3 - yx^2 + ay^2 = 0$; $\therefore$ $x^2 = ay$ is a guiding asymptote, the proper asymptote being $ay = x^2 - ax - a(a+b)$.

Near the origin, $ay^3 = c^2 x^2$.

Fig. 14. The figure includes the case $c^2 = 2a(a+b)$, in which case the equation (i) becomes $(y-x)(y+2x) = 0$; therefore the curve meets the asymptote in only one point at a finite distance; the branches marked b and d belong to this value of c^2, also, when $c^2 > 2a(a+b)$, a and d are the branches, and when $c^2 < 2a(a+b)$, b and c are the branches.

Ex. 15. $(y-x-a)y^3 - byx^2 + mabx^2 = 0.$

Near (∞, ma), $y = ma - m^3 a^3/bx$; the asymptote $y = ma$ meets the curve where $x = (m-1)a$, the same point at which the tangent at $(0, a)$ meets it.

Near (∞, ∞), if x and y be of the same order of magnitude,
$$y = x + a + b - [(m+2)ab + 2b^2]/x;$$
this cross asymptote meets the curve where
$$y^3 - yx^2 + max^2 = 0,$$
or $\qquad (a+b)(x+a+b)(2x+a+b) + max^2 = 0,$
the roots of which are real and both negative, if $4ma < a+b$, in which case the curve cuts the asymptote in the compartment $x'Oy$ below the line $x+y=0$.

If, near (∞, ∞), $x:y$ be large, $y^2 + bx = 0$.

Near $(0, 0)$, $\qquad mbx^2 = y^3;$

near $(0, a)$, $\qquad y - x - a = -\dfrac{(m-1)bx^2}{a^2},$

so that the curve bends upwards or downwards, according as $m <$ or > 1, and when $m = 1$, there is a point of inflexion.

The curve is parallel to Ox where $x = 2(y-a)$; in figure 16, the points a, b, c are points in $2y - x - 2a = 0$, where the curve is parallel to Ox.

To illustrate the different forms which the curve can assume, it is drawn for three cases,

$$b = a, \qquad \tfrac{1}{2} < m < 1, \qquad\qquad \text{Fig. 15.}$$
$$b = a, \qquad 1 < m < 2, \qquad\qquad \text{Fig. 16.}$$
and $\qquad 2b = 3\sqrt{3}a, \quad m = 2; \qquad\qquad$ Fig. 17.

the last being an intermediate case in which there is a multiple point, viz. where $x = (\sqrt{3}-1)^2 a$, $y = (3 - \sqrt{3})a$.

Examples VIII.

1. $\qquad y^2(x+1) = x^2 + 1.$

Prove that the curve is parallel to Ox where $x = \sqrt{2} - 1$; also that the tangent at the point $(0, 1)$ intersects the curve at $(7, -\tfrac{5}{2})$.

2. $\qquad axy^3 - (x-a)^3 y^2 + a^5 = 0.$

Prove that the proper parabolic asymptote is
$$(x - \tfrac{3}{2}a)^2 = a(y - \tfrac{3}{4}a),$$
and that the curve lies below on the positive, and above on the negative side of Oy. (Note that the equation can be written in the form
$$x^2 - 3ax + 3a^2 - ay = \frac{a^3}{x} + \frac{a^5}{xy^2}.)$$

3. $$(y-b)(y^2+b^2)x^3+bxy^4-b^3y^3=0.$$

Prove that the proper parabolic asymptote is
$$x^2+b(y+b)=0\ ;$$
and shew that the curve cuts one of the rectilinear asymptotes at an angle $\cot^{-1}3$.

4. $$c^3y^2=(x-2c)^2x^3.$$

Shew that $c^3y^2=(x-\frac{4}{5}c)^5$ gives the direction of the curve near $(\infty,\ \infty)$. Trace the curve near the points where it crosses Ox.

5. $$y^3-y^2-64x^6-36x^5-2x^4=0.$$

Shew that the proper parabolic asymptote is
$$y-\frac{51}{16^2}=4\left(x+\frac{3}{32}\right)^2.$$

Prove that the loop intercepts a length $\frac{7}{16}$ on Ox, and that the curvatures at the points of section are in the ratio $1:4096$.

6. $$x^2y+a(y-x)^2=0.$$

Shew that the curve cuts the rectilinear and proper parabolic asymptote at the same distance $\frac{1}{2}a$ from $y'Oy$, and that the tangents to the curve at the points of section are inclined to Ox at angles $\tan^{-1}\frac{8}{3}$ and $\tan^{-1}\frac{1}{3}$. Prove that the curve runs parallel to Oy at $(4a,\ -4a)$.

7. $$a(x^5+y^5)-xy^5=0.$$

Prove that, if the tangent be drawn from $(a,0)$ to the curve, the point of contact is at a distance $5a$ from the axis of y, and that its inclination to Ox is not very different from $\tan^{-1}\frac{2}{5}$. Shew that the curve runs parallel to Ox where $x=\frac{4}{5}a$, and $y=\frac{-11}{10}a$ nearly.

8. If in Ex. 14, page 114, $b=3a$, $c^2=4a^2$, prove that the guiding parabola touches the curve and intersects the proper parabolic asymptote at the point $(-4a,16a)$.

9. $$x^4-3a^2xy+ay^3+ax^3=0.$$

Prove that $ay^3+(x+\frac{1}{4}a)^4=0$ is a guiding asymptote, the curve lying below the asymptote on the positive side of Oy and above on the negative side.

Shew that $x=a$ is a tangent to the curve, cutting it again at an angle $\tan^{-1}\frac{9}{13}$; also that the curve cuts $x'Ox$ at an angle $\tan^{-1}\frac{1}{3}$.

10. The curve in Art. 73, Ex. 1, intersects its guiding asymptote $2ax^3+y^4=0$ where it meets the curve $2y^2-3xy-2x^2=yx^2/a$. Shew that this latter curve has a proper parabolic asymptote $(x+\frac{3}{2}a)^2=2ay(y-\frac{7}{8}a)$ which it intersects in $(-\frac{4}{3}a,\frac{8}{9}a)$, and a rectilinear asymptote $y+2a=0$.

11. Prove that $(y-x+\frac{5}{12}a)^2=ax$ is a proper parabolic asymptote to the curve, Ex. 5, page 101, but that $(y-x+\frac{5}{12}a)^2=ax+\frac{101}{144}a^2$ has a closer contact.

CHAPTER IX.

THE ANALYTICAL TRIANGLE. PROPERTIES OF THE ANALYTICAL TRIANGLE.

PLATE VI.

139. I HAVE now shewn how, in all cases of curves represented by equations containing a *moderate* number of terms, simpler curves can be found, which very nearly coincide with the curves near particular points, when they are at a finite distance, and nearly enough for practical purposes when they are at an infinite distance.

In this chapter I shall give some account of the *Analytical Triangle*, and its use as a machine for saving the trouble of the comparison of the relative magnitude of the different terms of the equation of a curve, at an infinite distance, and in the neighbourhood of the origin, when the curve passes through it.

140. The triangle is a modification of Newton's parallelogram, which was an arrangement of squares, like those on a chess-board, each square being appropriated to one of the terms of the general equation of any degree, as in the figure.

Fig. 18.

141. It is easily seen, by observing the squares which contain the terms of four and lower dimensions, that all the terms of a complete equation of any degree are contained in squares which occupy half of Newton's parallelogram; this circumstance led De Gua to replace the parallelogram by a triangle containing one more square on each side than the degree of the equation considered, which is represented in the figure for an equation of the fourth degree.

Fig. 19.

PLATE
VI.

142. An equation is said to be placed upon the triangle, by making a cross, or some definite mark, in the centre of each square which corresponds to a term of the equation.

Thus, the equation

$$ay^4 + bx^2y^3 + cx^3y^2 + dx^4y + ex^2y^2 + fx^2 + gxy = 0$$

Fig. 20.
is placed on the triangle as in the figure, the letters $\alpha\beta\eta\gamma\zeta\delta\epsilon$ corresponding to the terms in order.

143. The property which makes the triangle so valuable as an analyzer, is that, if crosses be joined, so as to form a convex polygon $\alpha\beta\gamma\delta\epsilon$, exterior to which no cross lies, when the terms of the equation, which correspond to any side, are equated to zero, the locus of the equation so formed is one or more simple parabolic curves, or straight lines, each of which, as will be proved immediately, is a first approximation to the form of the curve, *either* at an infinite distance, if all the rejected crosses lie on the same side of the line as the right angle, *or,* near the origin, if they lie on the opposite side, when the equation has no constant term.

Thus, corresponding to $\alpha\beta$ the equation is $ay^4 + bx^2y^3 = 0$, or $ay + bx^2 = 0$, and with this relation between x and y, every other term vanishes compared with the terms in α and β, when x and y are indefinitely great.

Again, corresponding to $\beta\eta\gamma$, we have the equation $bx^2y^3 + cx^3y^2 + dx^4y = 0$, or $by^2 + cxy + dx^2 = 0$, which represents two straight lines, and, with this relation, when x and y are large, every other term vanishes compared with any one of the three terms retained.

Again, taking the side $\gamma\delta$, the equation is $dx^4y + fx^2 = 0$, or $dx^2y + f = 0$, with which relation, x being infinite, and y indefinitely small, every other term will vanish compared with the terms retained, thus xy and x^2y^3 will be of the order x^{-1} and x^{-4} respectively.

Corresponding to $\delta\epsilon$, $fx + gy = 0$, and, with this relation, every other term vanishes when x and y are indefinitely small.

PLATE
VI.

Lastly, $\epsilon\alpha$ gives $ay^3 + gx = 0$, which relation makes every other term vanish for points taken near the origin, relative to the terms retained.

144. I think the following method of considering this triangle is much more convenient, both for placing the terms in any particular case, and for exhibiting the properties of the polygon, also, when necessary, in fixing more accurately the position of whatever marks are employed which may correspond to fractional indices of x and y.

Instead of making squares, which act as cells in which the terms are placed, take a right-angled isosceles triangle, whose sides are in the direction Ox and Oy, measure equal distances along both sides, numbered, or supposed to be so, from 1 to n, and, through each such division, draw lines parallel to the sides, and terminated by the hypotenuse. Each point of intersection of such lines corresponds to a term of the complete general equation of the nth degree.

The simplest way of drawing the figure is to divide the hypotenuse into as many equal parts as the degree of the equation, and to draw parallel lines from the points of division.

The equation given in the last article would be placed upon the triangle as in the figure.

Fig. 21.

If a fractional term occurred in the equation, such as $x^{\frac{3}{2}}y^{\frac{7}{4}}$, we should register its position by the intersection of two lines parallel to Oy and Ox, bisecting 12 in Ox and passing through the first point of trisection of 23 in Oy.

I shall adopt this form of the Analytical Triangle, using a small circle instead of a cross as being the most convenient mark to place in the intersection of two lines.

PROPERTIES OF THE ANALYTICAL TRIANGLE.

145. When all the terms of an equation of a curve are placed by circles upon the triangle, the following properties hold, with respect to any straight line which contains two or more of the circles.

PLATE
VI.

i. If every term of the equation be rejected, except the terms which correspond to the circles which lie in a given line L, the resulting equation gives one or more constant values of the ratio $y^s : x^r$, the values of r and s depending only on the direction of the line, and being therefore the same for all parallel lines.

ii. If the straight line L meet both sides of the triangle, or these produced beyond the hypotenuse, the terms of the original equation will vanish compared with those whose circles are in L, in the two cases, (1) when x and y are infinitely great and the circles corresponding to these terms lie on the same side as the right angle O, (2) when x and y are infinitely small, there being no constant term in the equation, and these circles and O lie on opposite sides of L.

iii. When the line L intersects one of the sides, say Ox, produced backwards through O, and all terms are rejected, except those which correspond to circles lying on L, the resulting equation gives constant values to $x^r y^s$, and when y is infinitely great, and therefore x indefinitely small, all terms, whose circles lie on the same side of L as O, vanish compared with those which form the equation which determines $x^r y^s$; when x is infinitely great, y indefinitely small, the terms which vanish relatively are those whose circles lie on the sides of L opposite to that on which O lies. Similarly, if L intersect Oy produced backwards through O.

iv. When the line is parallel to one of the sides, say to Ox, the resulting equation gives one or more straight lines which are parallel to Oy; the terms whose circles are on L will be greater than any other term of the equation, if the corresponding circle is on the same side of L as O when y is infinitely great, or on opposite sides if y be indefinitely small.

v. When the line coincides with a side of the triangle, the solution of the resulting equation gives the points of intersection with the corresponding axis.

PLATE
VI.

146. The truth of these propositions is easily seen by taking particular cases, but they may be proved generally as follows:

Suppose the equation of a curve to be what is called placed upon the triangle, and let $x^a y^\beta$ be one of any number of terms, whose representatives on the triangle all lie on the same straight line L; α, β must, therefore, satisfy the equation $\beta + m\alpha = c$, where m is constant for all parallel lines, and c for any one of these lines; and so

$$x^a y^\beta = x^a y^{-ma+c} = (xy^{-m})^a y^c.$$

Hence, if all the terms in the equation be rejected except those whose circles lie on the line L, since y^c is the same for every term, the result will be an equation $f(xy^{-m}) = 0$; which, if $m = s/r$, proves i. If m and c be positive, which is the case of ii, and $x^{a'} y^{\beta'}$ be a rejected term whose circle is not in the line L, let a line L' parallel to L be drawn through the circle corresponding to $x^{a'} y^{\beta'}$, c' being written for c, the roots of the equation determining xy^{-m} are not the same in the case of the two lines L and L', but being independent of x and y, the orders of the two terms are given by y^c and $y^{c'}$. The rejected term vanishes compared with those retained when $y^{c'} : y^c$ vanishes; this happens when x and y are infinitely large and $c' < c$, also, when x and y are infinitely small and $c' > c$. It should be observed that when m is positive x and y are both infinitely large or both infinitely small together. Thus ii is proved.

If the line L meet one of the sides, suppose Ox, produced through O backwards, we must write $-m$ for m, and the term $x^a y^\beta$ becomes $(xy^m)^a y^c$, and as before a rejected term $x^{a'} y^{\beta'}$ vanishes compared with $x^a y^\beta$ when $y^{c'} : y^c$ is indefinitely small. Hence, when y is infinitely great, c' must be less than c; when y is indefinitely small, or x, which varies as y^{-m}, infinitely great, c' is greater than c. This proves iii, and iv and v are evident.

147. From the proof given above we may remark, that if any line give the first approximation to an asymptote,

PLATE
VI.

the terms to be taken into account for the second approximation are found by moving the line parallel to itself until it passes through another circle or set of circles, all of which correspond to the terms required to be taken into account.

148. I shall now shew the use of the triangle by applying it to assist in tracing the following curves:

Ex. 1. $\qquad$ $x^6 + 2a^2x^3y - b^3y^3 = 0$.

Place the equation on the triangle, and draw the polygon, two sides of which correspond to branches through the origin and one to the infinite branch, viz.

Fig. 22.

Fig. 23. $\quad x^3 + 2a^2y = 0 \succ\!\!\!\prec, \quad 2a^2x^3 - b^3y^2 = 0 \dashv\!\!\!\prec, \quad$ and $x^2 - by = 0$.

Ex. 2. The next example is one which has already been considered in Art. **88**, viz. $x^3y^2 + xy^5 - y^7 - x^7 = 0$.

Fig. 24. Placing the equation on the triangle we obtain the quadrilateral $\alpha\beta\gamma\delta$.

$$\alpha\beta \text{ gives } y^2 - x^4 = 0,$$
$$\beta\gamma \ \ldots\ldots\ x^2 + y^3 = 0,$$
$$\gamma\delta \ \ldots\ldots\ x - y^2 = 0,$$
$$\delta\alpha \ \ldots\ldots\ y^7 + x^7 = 0.$$

The first approximation to the asymptote given by $\delta\alpha$ is $y + x = 0$; the next approximation is found by taking into account the circle γ (Art. **147**), the first which $\delta\alpha$ meets when it moves parallel to itself towards O; the resulting equation gives the rectilinear asymptote, viz. $y + x + \frac{1}{7} = 0$.

The next approximation gives $y + x + \frac{1}{7} = \frac{5}{49}x^{-1}$, taking into account the circle β.

To trace the curve, observe that $x = y$ meets the curve where $x = y = 1$, or $-\frac{1}{2}$.

Near $(1, 1)$, if $x = 1 + \xi$, $y = 1 + \eta$, the coefficient of $\eta = 0$; therefore, proceeding to η^2, $3\xi + 10\eta^2 = 0$.

Near $(-\frac{1}{2}, -\frac{1}{2})$, if $x = -\frac{1}{2} + \xi$, $y = -\frac{1}{2} + \eta$, $\xi = 3\eta$.

Again, $x = -y$ meets the curve where $x = -y = 1$, and near $(1, -1)$, $5\xi + 4\eta = 0$.

PLATE
VI.

Fig. 25.

To find the size of the smallest of the three loops, note that the line $y = -mx$ meets the curve where

$$m^2 - m^5x + (m^7 - 1)x^2 = 0,$$

and the values of x are real, equal, or impossible, according as $m^{10} - 4m^2(m^7 - 1)$, or as $m^8 - 4m^7 + 4$ is $+$, 0, or $-$. The two values of x are equal if m be a little less than 4; let $m = 4 - \alpha$, then $(m - 4)m^7 + 4 \equiv 4 - \alpha(4 - \alpha)^7$, whence $\alpha = 4^{-6}$, nearly.

For this value $x^2 - xm^{-2} + m^{-5} = 0$ very nearly; and $x^2 - m^{-2}x + \frac{1}{4}m^{-4} = 0$ since $m = 4$, giving two equal values of x, viz. $\frac{1}{32}$, for which $y = \frac{1}{8}$.

For values of m between 0 and 4, the line $y = mx$ does not cut the curve except at the origin, the loop is thus seen to be extremely small; when $m = 5$ it can be shewn that the values of y are $-\frac{1}{18}$ and $-\frac{1}{7}$ nearly.

A magnified figure of the shape near the origin is given on account of the difficulty of shewing the form of the small loop.

Fig. 26.

The continuity of the curve may be seen by commencing at the asymptote in $x'Oy$, passing through the origin along $y = x^2$, tracing the loop in xOy, passing through the origin along $y^2 = x$, tracing the small loop in xOy', through the origin along $x^2 + y^3 = 0$, then along the loop in $x'Oy'$, through the origin along $-y = x^2$, and so to the other end of the asymptote.

Ex. 3. $\mathbf{x(x^2 - ay)^2 - y^5 = 0.}$

Placing on the triangle, we obtain the two forms at the origin $(ay - x^2)^2 = 0$, and $a^2x = y^3$.

Fig. 27.

The next approximation to $ay = x^2$ is $ay = x^2 + x^{\frac{9}{2}}a^{-\frac{5}{2}}$.

The asymptote corresponding to $x^5 = y^5$ is $y = x - \frac{2}{5}a$, the next approximation being $y = x - \frac{2}{5}a + \frac{1}{25}a^2x^{-1}$.

To find where the curve cuts the asymptote, let $y = mx$ at the point of intersection. Hence, from the equations of the curve and asymptote, $x(m^{\frac{5}{2}} - 1) = -ma$, and $(m - 1)x = -\frac{2}{5}a$; whence, if $m = \mu^2$, $2\mu^5 - 5\mu^4 + 5\mu^2 - 2 = 0$. But the curve meets the asymptote in at least two points at infinity, so

Fig. 28.

PLATE
VII.

that $(\mu-1)^2$ must be a factor of the left side of this equation, which reduces the equation to

$$2\mu^3 - \mu^2 - 4\mu - 2 = 0,$$

the only real root of which is 1·862 nearly. Therefore

$$m = 3\cdot467 \quad \text{and} \quad x = -\cdot162a.$$

The curve is parallel to Ox at a point near $(\tfrac{1}{3}a, \tfrac{5}{9}a)$.

Ex. 4. $\quad (y^2 - x^2)^2 + 2axy^2 - 5ax^3 = 0.$

Fig. 1.

Place the equation on the triangle, as in the figure.

$\beta\gamma$ gives for the points of intersection with Ox,

$$x^3(x - 5a) = 0,$$

and for the next approximation, by moving $\beta\gamma$ parallel to itself until it passes through δ, we obtain

$$x^3(x - 5a) + 2axy^2 - 2x^2y^2 = 0,$$

whence $\qquad 8y^2 = 25a(x - 5a).$

$\gamma\delta$ gives $2y^2 = 5x^2$ near the origin.

$\delta\alpha$ gives $y^2 + 2ax = 0$ also near the origin.

$\alpha\beta$ gives $(y^2 - x^2)^2 = 0$ at an infinite distance, the next approximation being $(y^2 - x^2)^2 = 3ax^3$.

To obtain the proper asymptotes, we write the equation in the form $(y^2 - x^2 + ax)^2 = 3ax^3 + a^2x^2$, whence

$$y^2 = x^2 - ax \pm \sqrt{(3ax^3)} \quad \text{or} \quad y = x\{1 \pm \sqrt{(3ax^{-1})} - ax^{-1}\}^{\frac{1}{2}}.$$

$$\therefore \ y = x \pm \tfrac{1}{2}\sqrt{(3ax)} - \tfrac{7}{8}a, \quad \text{or} \quad (y - x + \tfrac{7}{8}a)^2 = \tfrac{3}{4}ax.$$

The other parabolic asymptote is given by the symmetry.

Fig. 2.

For the size of the loops we can shew that the curve runs parallel to Oy at the points $(-\tfrac{1}{3}a, \pm\tfrac{2}{3}a)$, and parallel to Ox, where $y^2 = 5x^2$ from which $x = -\tfrac{5}{16}a$.

Ex 5. $\quad x^6 - 2bx^3y^2 - 2abx^4 + b^2y^4 - 2ab^2xy^2 + a^2b^2x^2 = 0.$

Fig. 3.

Place the equation on the triangle as in the figure.

The side $\alpha\beta$ contains three circles, giving

$$x^6 - 2bx^3y^2 + b^2y^4 = 0, \quad \text{or} \quad (x^3 - by^2)^2 = 0,$$

as a first approximation at an infinite distance; moving the line parallel to itself it passes through two circles which

PLATE
VII.

belong to the next approximation, viz. $-2abx^4 - 2ab^2xy^2$, whence $by^2 = x^3 \pm 2\sqrt{(ab)}x^2$.

The side $\alpha\gamma$ contains three circles, giving as the form near the origin $(y^2 - ax)^2 = 0$, and moving the line parallel to itself, two terms $-2bx^3y^2 - 2abx^4$ are introduced, giving, as the next approximation, $ax = y^2 \pm 2y^4/\sqrt{(a^3b)}$.

The third side $\beta\gamma$ gives the points of intersection with Ox, $x^6 - 2abx^4 + a^2b^2x^2 = 0$, and again, moving the line parallel to Ox, the next approximation is, making $b = n^4a$,

$$x^2(x^2 - n^4a^2)^2 - 2n^4axy^2(x^2 + n^4a^2) = 0 ;$$

writing n^2a for x in the term involving y^2, we obtain   Fig. 4.

$$(x^2 - n^4a^2)^2 = 4n^6a^2y^2,$$

or $\qquad\qquad x^2 = n^4a^2 \pm 2n^3ay,$

whence $\qquad\qquad x = n^2a \pm ny,$

as x cannot be negative. These are the tangents at the double point $(n^2a, 0)$.

Without using the triangle, observe that the equation may be written $n^4ay^2 = x(x \pm n^2a)^2$, and we shall have the forms, near $(n^2a, 0)$, $ny = \pm \xi$, and, near (∞, ∞), $n^4ay^2 = x^3$.

The curve is either parallel to Ox, or has a multiple point where $(x - n^2a)^2 + 2x(x - n^2a) = 0$, by which $x = \tfrac{1}{3}n^2a$, or n^2a, the latter solution belonging to the double point.

Ex. 6. $\qquad \mathbf{x^3y^4 + ax^2y^3 + by^2 + cx^4y + dx = 0.}$

Placing the equation upon the triangle, the bounding   Fig. 5.
polygon is a quadrilateral, three of whose sides correspond to asymptotic branches of the curve, and one to the shape at the origin. If we denote the circles which correspond to the terms of the equation, taken in order, by 1, 2, 3, 4, 5, we are directed to the first approximations to the three asymptotes, as follows:

$\qquad$ 1-3 gives the form near $(0, \infty)$, $\quad x^3 = -by^{-2}$, $\quad$ ......(i)

$\qquad$ 1-4 gives near (∞, ∞), $\quad y^3 + cx = 0$,..................(ii)

$\qquad$ 4-5 gives near $(\infty, 0)$, $\quad cy = -dx^{-3}$,.................(iii)

the remaining side 3-5 gives near $(0, 0)$, $by^2 + dx = 0$. (iv)

PLATE
VII.

The circle corresponding to 2 lies within the quadrilateral, and does not affect the general characteristics of the curve, but points out the next most important term to be taken into account for a further approximation in cases (i), (ii), (iv). In the case of (ii), the next approximation is $cx = -y^3 + acy^{-1}$, so that the first approximation gives a proper asymptote. The terms following 4 and 5, in descending order of magnitude, are 3, 2, and 1, varying as x^{-6}, x^{-7}, and x^{-9}. Their circles are passed through in order, as 4-5 moves parallel to itself.

The asymptote (ii) cuts the curve where

$$ax^2y^3 + by^2 + dx = 0,$$

or

$$ay^9 + c^2by^2 - cdy^3 = 0.$$

The solutions of $ay^7 - cdy + c^2b = 0$

are the ordinates of the points of intersection of

$$y^7 = m^6x, \quad \text{and} \quad am^6x - cdy + c^2b = 0.$$

Whence it appears that there must be one or three real roots.   The following cases are illustrated in the figures:

a	b	c	d	
$+$	$+$	$+$	$+$	$\begin{cases}\text{two } + \text{ and one } - \text{ root,} \\ \text{or one } - \text{ root};\end{cases}$
$-$	$+$	$+$	$+$	one $+$ root;
$+$	$-$	$-$	$-$	$\begin{cases}\text{two } - \text{ and one } + \text{ root,} \\ \text{or one } + \text{ root};\end{cases}$
$-$	$-$	$-$	$-$	one $-$ root.

Figs. 6, 7.   The figures are drawn for the two cases of b, c, d being all $+$ or all $-$, and the double branches marked $+$ and $-$ correspond to $a+$ and $a-$.

Ex. 7. $a^3y^5 + x^2y^6 - x^5y^3 + ax^6y - a^6x^2 = 0.$

Fig. 8.   Placing in the triangle, the four sides $\alpha\beta$, $\beta\gamma$, $\gamma\delta$, $\delta\epsilon$, give

$$a^3 + x^2y = 0, \quad Oy \text{ being an asymptote,}$$
$$y^3 - x^3 = 0,$$
$$y^2 - ax = 0,$$
$$x^4y - a^5 = 0, \quad Ox \text{ being an asymptote.}$$

The side $\epsilon\alpha$ gives $y^5 - a^3x^2 = 0$ for the shape at the origin.

PLATE
VII.

Moving $\beta\gamma$ parallel to itself, it passes first through δ, and the second approximation gives $y - x + \frac{1}{3}a = 0$; the next may be obtained from $y^3 - x^3 + ax^4y^{-2} = 0$.

Thus
$$y = x(1 - axy^{-2})^{\frac{1}{3}}$$
$$= x(1 - \frac{1}{3}axy^{-2} - \frac{1}{9}a^2x^2y^{-4})$$
$$= x\{1 - \frac{1}{3}ax^{-1}(1 + \frac{2}{3}ax^{-1}) - \frac{1}{9}a^2x^{-2}\}$$
$$= x - \frac{1}{3}a - \frac{1}{3}a^2x^{-1}.$$

Moving $\gamma\delta$ parallel to itself, it passes next through β, and the next approximation to the parabolic asymptote is

$$y^2 - ax = \frac{y^5}{x^3} = \frac{a^3}{y},$$

shewing that the parabola is a proper asymptote; this parabola cuts the curve where $y^6 + a^5y - a^6 = 0$, the only real roots of which are the positive and negative ordinates of the two points of intersection of $a^5x = y^6$ and $x + y = a$.

Fig. 9.

Ex. 8. $(y - a)^3x^4 - 2a^4(y - a)x^2 + a^4(x - a)y^2 = 0.$

Placing on the triangle, one side of the polygon gives   Fig. 10.
$y^3x^4 - a^5y^2 = 0$, or $yx^4 = a^5$, the axis of y being an asymptote; another side gives $(y - a)^3x^4 = 0$; if this side be moved parallel to itself, the next terms are $-2a^4(y - a)x^2$. This approximation would make $(y - a)x$ finite, so that $(y - a)x^2$ is of the order x when x is infinite. To obtain the values of $y - a$ we must therefore include the next term a^4xy^2, the resulting equation being $(y - a)^3x^3 - 2a^4(y - a)x + a^6 = 0$, from which $(y - a)x$ has three values, a^2 and $\frac{1}{2}(\pm\sqrt{5} - 1)a^2$.

The shape at the origin is given by the lower side of the polygon, viz. $2x^2 - y^2 = 0$.

The curve cuts the axis of x, where $x^2 = 2a^2$, and the asymptote $y = a$, where $x = a$; and near (a, a), $2\eta = \xi$.

Near $(\pm a\sqrt{2}, 0)$, if $x = \pm a\sqrt{2} + \xi$, $\pm\sqrt{2}y = \xi$.

To assist in tracing the curve we observe that $x = y$ also   Fig. 11.
cuts the curve where

$$x = y = \frac{1}{2}(\pm\sqrt{5} + 1)a.$$

Note. The triangle may be more easily employed for the purpose of approximating to the asymptote parallel to Ox,

PLATE
VII.

Fig. 12.

by writing y for $y-a$, and placing the resulting equation
$$y^3x^4 - 2a^4yx^2 + a^4(x-a)(y+a)^2 = 0 \text{ on the triangle.}$$

The corresponding side of the polygon gives
$$y^3x^4 - 2a^4yx^2 + a^6x = 0,$$
or $\qquad yx = a^2 \quad$ and $\quad \frac{1}{2}(\pm\sqrt{5}-1)a^2.$

Ex. 9. $\qquad\qquad \mathbf{x(x^2 - ay)^2 = y^4(y - c)}.$

Fig. 13.
    Placing on the triangle, we see that, at an infinite distance,
$x^5 - y^5 = 0$; and, moving the side parallel to itself, we introduce two more terms, giving for the asymptote
$$y - x = \tfrac{1}{5}(c - 2a).$$

In the next approximation the term $\dfrac{(a-c)^2 + c^2}{25x}$ is added.

    One form near the origin is $a^2x + cy^2 = 0$; another is
$(x^2 - ay)^2 = 0$; more nearly $(x^2 - ay)^2 = -\dfrac{cx^7}{a^4}$.

When $y = c$, $\qquad x = 0,$ or $\pm\sqrt{(ac)}.$
Near $(0, c)$, $\qquad a^2x = c^2\eta + 2c\eta^2;$

near $(\pm\sqrt{ac}, c)$, $\qquad 4\xi^2 = \pm\sqrt{\dfrac{c^5}{a^3}}\eta.$

    In attempting to trace the curve with the above data, a
difficulty arises in choosing whether we shall join the
branch through $(0, c)$ to the branch $a^2x + cy^2 = 0$, or to that
through $(-\sqrt{ac}, c)$.

    It will illustrate the artifices which may be used in such
cases, if we examine the number of points where the curve
is parallel to the axis of x, and afterwards the points where
the tangent $a^2x = c^2(y - c)$ meets the curve.

    The curve is parallel to Ox, where
$$(x^2 - ay)^2 + 4x^2(x^2 - ay) = 0,$$
or where $\qquad x^2 = ay, \quad$ and $\quad 5x^2 = ay;$
the first case has been considered; in the second
$$16a^2x = 25y^2(y - c), \quad \text{or} \quad y^3(y - c)^2 = 4^4 5^{-5}a^5 = \tfrac{2}{25}a^5 \text{ nearly.}$$

    The values of y are the common ordinates of the curves
$$y(y - c) = \tfrac{1}{5}ax, \quad \text{and} \quad yx^2 = 2a^3.$$

PLATE
VII.
Figs. 14, 15.

These two curves are drawn for the cases of $c = 2a$ and $c = a$, and they shew that there are three values of y in the first case, and only one in the second. Thus, when $c = 2a$, the loop is found by joining the ends of the ramphoid cusp, and, when $c = a$, by joining one branch of the cusp with the parabolic branch through the origin.

The other plan, of examining the point where the tangent $a^2x = c^2(y - c)$ meets the curve, leads to some elegant results.

At the points of intersection of the curve and tangent,

$$c(x^2 - ay) = \pm ay^2, \quad \text{or} \quad \frac{x^2}{a} = \pm \frac{y^2}{c} + y.$$

The loci of these equations are a hyperbola, and an ellipse whose transverse axis is c, and the ratio of whose axes is $a^{\frac{1}{2}} : c^{\frac{1}{2}}$. The positions are given in the figures for $c = 2a$ Figs. 16, 17. and $c = a$, in the latter case the loci being a circle and rectangular hyperbola; the points of intersection are R, A, P, Q, for the first, R being at an infinite distance in the second.

The figure of the curve is drawn for the same relations Figs. 18, 19. between c and a. The letters A, P, Q, R correspond to the same letters in figures 16 and 17.

The points of intersection with the tangent $a^2x = c^2(y - c)$ can be found directly, for $c^2(x^2 - ay)^2 = a^2y^4$;

$$\therefore \ cx^2 = ay(\pm y + c) \quad \text{and} \quad c^5(y - c)^2 = a^5y(\pm y + c).$$

With the upper sign $(c^5 - a^5)y^2 - (2c^5 + a^5)cy + c^7 = 0$;

$$\therefore \ 2(c^5 - a^5)y = (2c^5 + a^5)c \pm c\sqrt{(8a^5c^5 + a^{10})}.$$

If $c = 2a$,

$$y = \tfrac{9}{7}c \quad \text{or} \quad \tfrac{7}{9}c, \quad \text{and} \quad x = \tfrac{8}{9}c \quad \text{or} \quad -\tfrac{8}{9}c \ \text{roughly};$$

if $c = a$, $\qquad y = \infty \quad \text{or} \quad \tfrac{1}{3}c, \quad \text{and} \quad x = -\tfrac{2}{3}c$,

and, near $(-\tfrac{2}{3}c, \tfrac{1}{3}c)$, $\qquad 19\eta + 17\xi = 0$.

With the lower sign $y = c$ or $(c^5 + a^5)y = c^6$, and the corresponding values of x are

$$x = 0 \quad \text{or} \quad (c^5 + a^5)x = -a^3c^3.$$

Thus the coordinates of the point of intersection can be written $x = -ra^3$, $y = rc^3$, where $(c^5 + a^5)r = c^3$.

To find the form of the curve near this point, let $x = -ra^3(1+\alpha)$ and $y = rc^3(1+\gamma)$; then $-ra^3\alpha = \xi$ and $rc^3\gamma = \eta$. Substituting in the equation of the curve and rejecting powers of α and γ higher than the first, we obtain

$$-ra^3(1+\alpha)\{r^2a^6(1+2\alpha) - ar^2(c^5+a^5)(1+\gamma)\}^2$$
$$= r^5c^{15}(1+5\gamma) - r^4c^{13}(1+4\gamma)$$
$$= r^5c^{10}\{c^5(1+5\gamma) - (c^5+a^5)(1+4\gamma)\};$$

hence

$$-a^5(1+\alpha)\{-c^5 + 2a^5\alpha - (c^5+a^5)\gamma\}^2$$
$$= c^{10}\{-a^5 + (c^5-4a^5)\gamma\}$$

and

$$(c^5-4a^5)a^5\alpha + \{(c^5-a^5)^2 + a^{10}\}\gamma = 0,$$

or

$$c^3a^2(c^5-4a^5)\xi = \{(c^5-a^5)^2 + a^{10}\}\eta.$$

When $c = a$,

$$x = -\tfrac{1}{2}c, \quad y = \tfrac{1}{2}c, \quad \text{and} \quad \eta + 3\xi = 0;$$

when $c = 2a$,

$$x = -\tfrac{4}{33}c, \quad y = \tfrac{32}{33}c, \quad \text{and} \quad 30\eta = 7\xi.$$

Note. In the case $c = a$, the condition that a straight line through the origin, $x + my = 0$, may be a tangent to the curve is $4m(m^5+1) = (2m^3+1)^2$, or $4m^3 - 4m + 1 = 0$; and the method of Art. **47** leads to the approximate solutions $\tfrac{1}{4}$, $\tfrac{5}{6}$, and $-\tfrac{13}{12}$, the corresponding values of y being obtained from $(2m^3+1)y = 2mc$; the points of contact are on the loop for $m = \tfrac{5}{6}$, on the branch near Oy for $m = \tfrac{1}{4}$, and on the branch near the asymptote when $m = -\tfrac{13}{12}$.

Ex. 10. $6x^7 - 2x^5y^2 - a^3x^2y^2 + 4a^3x^3y + 2a^5x^2 - 3a^5xy + a^5y^2 = 0.$

Fig. 20. Place on the triangle, and call the circles corresponding to the terms of the equation in order 1, 2, 3, 4, 5, 6, 7.

(1) The side 1-2 of the polygon, moved parallel to itself, passes through 3-4, and gives

$$2x^5(3x^2 - y^2) - a^3x^2y(y - 4x) = 0;$$
$$\therefore y = \pm x\sqrt{3} + (1 \mp \tfrac{1}{4}\sqrt{3})\frac{a^3}{x^2}.$$

This equation determines two asymptotes, the curve lying on the y side at the upper end of both, and intersecting them where $\pm\sqrt{3}(4 \mp \sqrt{3})x^2 = (\pm 3\sqrt{3} - 5)a^2$.

PLATE
VII.

Writing $\frac{7}{4}$ for $\sqrt{3}$, we have $(\pm 7-3)x^2=(\pm\frac{21}{4}-5)a^2$, whence $x=\pm\frac{1}{4}a$, and $x=\pm(1+\frac{1}{80})a$.

(2) The side 2-3-7 gives $2x^5+a^3x^2-a^5=0$ the only real root of which is $\frac{2}{3}a$ nearly, being the common abscissa of $x^3=a^2y$ and $(2y+a)x^2=a^3$, or of $y=x^5$, and $a^3x^2=a^5-2y$.

This asymptote, parallel to Oy, intersects the curve where $x(5a^2-3x^2)=(3a^2-4x^2)y$, and writing $\frac{2}{3}a$ for x, $y=2a$.

(3) The side 5-6-7 gives near the origin $2x^2-3xy+y^2=0$ or $y=x$ and $2x$.

(4) The side 1-5 gives, with 4-6, its next position when moved parallel to itself,

$$2x^2(3x^5+a^5)+a^3xy(4x^2-3a^2)=0,$$

and since $3^{-\frac{1}{6}}=\frac{4}{5}$ very nearly, it is easily shewn that near $(-3^{-\frac{1}{6}}a,\ 0)$, $y=-23\xi$.

Fig. 21.

149. It will have been seen by the illustrations which have been given, that with equations of high degrees, the use of the Analytical Triangle is almost indispensable. But at the end of this work, in which I propose to shew how the inverse process, of finding the equation of a curve when the curve is given, can be performed, it will, I think, be seen, that the value of the triangle is indefinitely increased; at all events, the new use which I have made of the triangle in this inverse process will, perhaps, excuse me for having laid so much stress upon its properties in the present chapter.

Examples IX.

In the following examples of the use of the triangle, it should be noticed what an advantage the method of Art. **147** gives in forming successive approximations.

1. $a^2y^3-2ax^3y+x^5=0.$

Shew by the triangle that the curve lies below the guiding asymptote $a^2y^3+x^5=0$ at both ends; and find by it the form of the curve at the origin. Prove that there is a thin loop, to which $y=x$ is a tangent.

2. $a^2y^3-2ax^3y+x^5=a^5.$

Prove that there is a point of inflexion on Oy, which bisects the chord drawn through it parallel to Ox.

PLATE
VII.

3. $$x^6y^2 - 2c^3x^4y + c^6x^2 - 2c^6xy + c^6y^2 = 0.$$

Prove that Ox is an asymptote, the two branches of the curve being on the same side of Ox.

Shew that the curve is parallel to Ox where $y = \frac{11}{6}x$ and $y = \frac{1}{2}x$ approximately.

4. $$x^5y - ax^2y^3 + na^2y^4 + a^4xy - n^2a^4x^2 = 0.$$

Shew that there is only one point at which the curve runs parallel to Oy, by tracing the curves

$$3x^4y - axy^3 - 4n^2a^4x + 3a^4y = 0,$$

and $$2x^2y^3 - n^2a^3x^2 - 3nay^4 = 0, \quad n < 4.$$

Shew how the curve lies with respect to the guiding asymptotes.

5. $$n^2x^6 - 2n^2cx^4y + n^2c^2x^2y^2 - 2ncxy^4 + y^6 = 0.$$

Shew that there are two loops, and two ramphoid cusps.

6. $$x^6 + y^6 - ay^5 + a(ay - cx)x^3 = 0.$$

Find the points at which the two tangents to the curve at the origin intersect the curve, and when $c = a$, shew that the diameter of curvature at one of these points is $\frac{1}{5}a$.

At the points where the curve is parallel to Oy

$$6y^5 - 5ay^4 + a^2x^3 = 0 ;$$

trace this curve and shew that it accounts for the points in question when $c = a$ and $2a$.

7. $$x^6 + y^6 - ay^5 + a^2yx^3 = 0.$$

Shew that the tangent from the origin to the curve is inclined to Ox at an angle $\tan^{-1}\frac{13}{8}$ nearly. Examine the points at which the curve runs parallel to Oy.

CHAPTER X.

SINGULAR POINTS. DIVISION INTO COMPARTMENTS. SPECIAL CURVE OF THE FOURTH DEGREE.

PLATE VII.

150. In the preceding chapters I have been endeavouring to make clear to the student processes which will enable him to determine, as exactly as he pleases, the form of a curve in the neighbourhood of any point, whether at a finite or infinite distance, which he may have occasion to consider.

I have also shewn how a certain polygon on the Analytical Triangle supplies a test whether all the branches have been considered, which may exist at an infinite distance, or pass through the origin.

151. In order to trace a curve we must generally find such a finite number of points whose coordinates satisfy the equation, that, having the tangents to the curve at those points, and the direction of the deflection of the curve from the tangents at the most important points, there shall be only one way of joining the corresponding small elements, which will not be inconsistent with the degree of the equation and the laws of continuity, and other properties obvious from the equation, such as symmetry, etc.

152. I have said *generally*, because it may be possible to obtain from the equation some geometrical construction which will amount practically to giving an infinite number of points; as, for example, $(x-a)^2+(y-b)^2=c^2$ represents that the curve is the locus of a point whose distance from (a, b) is always c; and $y^2=4ax$, is the same as

$$y^2+(x-a)^2=(x+a)^2,$$

PLATE
VII.

which expresses that the curve is the locus of a point whose distance from $(a, 0)$ is equal to its distance from the line $x + a = 0$.

153. In the case of equations which can be solved with respect to either of the coordinates, so as to express it explicitly in terms of the other, there is no limit to the number of points which may be found, but the form of the result will, in most cases, suggest the peculiar points which will most easily lead to the form of the curve, so as to limit the number of points necessary to be examined.

But in the case of equations which cannot be so dealt with, it will be found that, when we have constructed all the forms of the curve in the neighbourhood of points which readily present themselves to be examined, there will be many ways in which these elements can be connected by curved lines, none of which, on the face of it, contradict the properties of the equation, as in Ex. 9, p. 128.

Moreover, supposing that the elements so determined could be joined in only one way, some outlying portion of the curve, such as an oval, by the existence of which no law of continuity would be broken, may have been omitted entirely, if it so happened that none of the elements already found were part of it.

154. I shall now endeavour to supply some means of meeting these difficulties, not professing that they will all admit of practical application in every case, but suggesting them as methods to be tried, before the curve is given up in despair.

155. The most important points next to the infinite branches which give character to a curve are multiple points of all sorts, cusps, and conjugate points; it is therefore necessary to call special attention to the method of determining their position when they exist, although it has already been incidentally mentioned in a note, page 85.

PLATE
VII.

156. The property, from which the conditions for the existence of such points are determined, is that every straight line which passes through these points, *whatever be its direction,* must meet the curve in at least two coincident points. This is easily seen to be the case for multiple points and cusps, by shifting the straight line a small distance parallel to itself; the points which are coincident in the first position separate, and become distinct, as the line moves to the other position.

A conjugate point may be considered as the limit of a decreasing small oval or closed curve, by which supposition the property holds also in this case.

But before giving the analysis for these points I must direct attention to peculiar points which occur in some curves, for which the property spoken of holds as well as for multiple points and cusps, although nothing in the form of the curve accounts directly for it.

157. If we take a curve for which a branch through the origin is $y^4 = ax^3$, —⎸—, a straight line $y = mx$, drawn in any direction defined by m, meets the curve in three points at least at the origin.

The existence of these points which do not appear in the form of the curve, but only as an algebraical result, may be accounted for by considering the curve as degenerated from a more complete curve; this degeneration has been discussed by E. Walker and Walton in the *Quarterly Journal*.

158. As an example of this degeneration, we may consider the curve whose equation is $y^4 = ax^3$, as the limit of one whose equation is

$$y(y-\alpha)(y-\beta)(y-\gamma) = ax(x-\delta)(x-\epsilon),$$

where the constants denoted by Greek letters are made indefinitely small.

In order to trace this curve, where α, β, ... are real, twelve points are seen through which the curve passes for all combinations of values of the constants.

PLATE VII.

These points where the curve is parallel to Ox would be given generally by two real values of x, to each of which may correspond four, two, or no values of y; in particular cases these points, or some of them, might be replaced by multiple points.

The curve is parallel to Oy at points given by a cubic equation, whose solution may give one or three real values, to each of which may correspond one or three values of x.

The guiding asymptote is $y^4 = ax^3$. The forms of the curve which satisfy these conditions necessarily involve many points of inflexion, and care must be taken that no tangent at any point of inflexion cuts the curve again in two points, which would require five points of intersection.

Fig. 22.
The figures given represent various forms which might be assumed by the curve, all of which may, by gradual changes of the constants, be made to pass from one to another; while at every change of general form, the parts of the curve which bend towards each other, produce multiple points.

As the constants diminish and ultimately vanish, the four values of y, when $x = 0$, and the three values of x, when $y = 0$, are accounted for; also the three points in which the curve is met by any line drawn through the origin are explained, the fourth remaining point being at an infinite distance in the case of Ox.

159. If two values of x corresponding to $y = 0$ are impossible, as when the equation of the curve is of the form

$$y(y - \alpha)(y - \beta)(y - \gamma) = ax\{(x - \delta)^2 + \epsilon^2\},$$

it is easily seen that the equation for determining the values of x where the curve is parallel to Ox, has real, equal, or impossible roots, as δ^2 is $>$, $=$, or $< 3\epsilon^2$; and as y may have four corresponding real values, two, or none, the curve
Fig. 23. may assume any of the forms in the figures, the upper belonging to $\delta^2 > 3\epsilon^2$; the lower on the left side to $\delta^2 = 3\epsilon^2$, in which case there are four points of inflexion, the tangents

PLATE
VII.

at which are parallel to Ox; and the lower on the right side to $\delta^2 < 3\epsilon^2$.

160. As another example of the fact that a curve of the form $y^4 = ax^3$ is cut by a line drawn through the origin in three points, take the curve in the last set of examples

$$\mathbf{y}^6 + \mathbf{x}^6 - a\mathbf{y}^5 + a(a\mathbf{y} - c\mathbf{x})\mathbf{x}^3 = 0.$$

There is no infinite branch, and the forms near the origin are given by $ay - cx = 0$, and $y^4 = ax^3$.

The next approximation to $ay = cx$ is $ay - cx = \dfrac{c^5 x^2}{a^5}$, and $ay - cx = 0$ meets the curve where $(a^6 + c^6)x = a^2 c^5$. The figures are drawn for $c = 2a$ and a.

Figs. 24, 25.

Three of the six points of intersection of the curve and any straight line through the origin are accounted for by the three points in which the line meets $y^4 = ax^3$.

SINGULAR POINTS.

161. The singular points, which are now to be considered, are those points, through any of which, if a straight line be drawn *in any direction*, it will have at least two of the points of intersection with the curve coincident with that point.

Hence, if (α, β) be a singular point of the curve, whose rationalized equation is $f(x, y) = 0$, and the origin be transferred to (α, β) by writing for x and y, $\alpha + \xi$ and $\beta + \eta$, $f(\alpha + \xi, \beta + \eta)$ can contain no term of the order ξ or η. If therefore $\phi(\alpha, \beta)$ and $\psi(\alpha, \beta)$ are the coefficients of ξ and η respectively in the expansion of $f(\alpha + \xi, \beta + \eta)$, α, β must satisfy simultaneously the three equations

$$f(\alpha, \beta) = 0 \ldots \text{(i)}, \quad \phi(\alpha, \beta) = 0 \ldots \text{(ii)}, \quad \psi(\alpha, \beta) = 0 \ldots \text{(iii)}.$$

When the solutions are found, the origin of coordinates being transferred to the corresponding points, the form of curve is known by the methods of the preceding chapters.

The solutions of (i) and (ii), which do not at the same time satisfy (iii), give points where the curve is parallel to Ox,

PLATE
VII.

138   SINGULAR POINTS

the approximate equations being of the form $\eta = A\xi^m$. Similarly, the solutions of (i) and (iii), which do not satisfy (ii), give points where the curve is parallel to Oy.

162. If $\alpha^r\beta^s$ be any term of (i), $r\alpha^{r-1}\beta^s$ and $s\alpha^r\beta^{s-1}$ will be the corresponding terms of (ii) and (iii), and hence multiplying (ii) and (iii) by α and β, and adding, the corresponding term in $\alpha\phi(\alpha, \beta) + \beta\psi(\alpha, \beta)$ will be $(r+s)\alpha^r\beta^s$.

Therefore, arranging the equation (i) in the form of homogeneous functions of α, β, viz.

$$f(\alpha, \beta) \equiv u_n + u_{n-1} + \ldots + u_0 = 0,$$

we have

$$nu_n + (n-1)u_{n-1} + (n-2)u_{n-2} + \ldots + u_1$$
$$= \alpha\phi(\alpha, \beta) + \beta\psi(\alpha, \beta) = 0 \text{ by (ii) and (iii).}$$

Therefore

$$u_{n-1} + 2n_{n-2} + \ldots + (n-1)u_1 + nu_0 = 0$$

is an equation which may be used instead of, or with the three equations given above.

163. The following examples will shew how the above equations are to be applied:

Ex. 1. $(y^2 - a^2)^3 + x^4(2x + 3a)^2 = 0.$

If (x, y) be a multiple point, writing $y + \eta$ for y,

$$(y^2 - a^2 + 2y\eta + \eta^2)^3 + x^4(2x + 3a)^2 = 0;$$

therefore, equating the coefficient of η to zero,

$$6y(y^2 - a^2)^2 = 0. \quad\ldots\ldots\ldots\ldots\ldots\ldots\ldots\text{(i)}$$

Again, writing $x + \xi$ for x and equating the coefficient of ξ to zero,

$$4x^3(2x + 3a)^2 + 4x^4(2x + 3a) = 0. \quad\ldots\ldots\ldots\ldots\text{(ii)}$$

The solutions of these equations are

$$y = 0, \ \pm a, \quad \text{and} \quad x = 0, \ -\tfrac{3}{2}a, \ -a;$$

of these solutions $(0, \pm a)$, $(-\tfrac{3}{2}a, \pm a)$, and $(-a, 0)$ satisfy the given equation.

The directions of the branches at these points are given,
near $(0, \pm a)$,

$$\text{by} \quad (\pm 2a\eta)^3 + 9a^2x^4 = 0, \quad \text{or} \quad \pm 8a\eta^3 + 9x^4 = 0;$$

near $(-\frac{3}{2}a, \pm a)$,

$$\text{by} \quad (\pm 2a\eta)^3 + (\tfrac{3}{2}a)^4 . 4\xi^2 = 0, \quad \text{or} \quad \pm 32\eta^3 + 81a\xi^2 = 0;$$

near $(-a, 0)$,

$$\text{by} \quad 3a^4y^2 - a^6 + (a - \xi)^4(a + 2\xi)^2 = 0,$$
$$\text{or} \quad 3a^4y^2 - a^6 + \{a(a^2 - 4\xi^2) + a\xi^2\}^2 = 0,$$
$$\textit{i.e.} \quad \text{by} \quad 3a^4y^2 - 6a^4\xi^2 = 0, \quad \text{or} \quad y^2 = 2\xi^2.$$

Hence the three latter points are two ceratoid cusps,
and a double point respectively.

The other points of the curve which satisfy the equation
(i) are points at which the curve is parallel to Oy.

Thus if $y = 0$, $\qquad x^2(2x + 3a) = \pm a^3$.

Taking the upper sign

$$(x + a)^2(2x - a) = 0.$$

Taking the lower sign

$$2x^3 + 3ax^2 + a^3 = 0,$$

whose solution is the common abscissa of the curves

$$ay = x^2, \quad \text{and} \quad (2x + 3a)y + a^2 = 0,$$

giving only one value of x, viz. $-\frac{5}{3}a$, nearly.

$x = -a$, which satisfies (ii), gives $y^4 - 3a^2y^2 + 3a^4 = 0$, and
therefore this value of x gives no point at which the curve is
parallel to Ox.

Fig. 26.

Ex. 2. $\quad (y^2 - x^2)(x - 1)(x - \frac{3}{2}) = 2(y^2 + x^2 - 2x)^2$.

If $x + \xi$, $y + \eta$ be written for x and y, at a singular point
the coefficients of ξ and η vanish;

$$\therefore \quad y^2(2x - \tfrac{5}{2}) - 4x^3 + \tfrac{15}{2}x^2 - 3x = 8(x - 1)(y^2 + x^2 - 2x), \quad ...(i)$$
$$\text{and} \qquad y(x - 1)(x - \tfrac{3}{2}) = 4y(y^2 + x^2 - 2x). \quad ....(ii)$$

The solutions of (ii) and the equation of the curve,
which give the points where the curve is parallel to Oy as
well as the singular points, are

(a) $y = 0$, $x = 0$, or $3x^2 - \frac{21}{2}x + \frac{19}{2} = 0$, the roots of which
are impossible. Therefore, since $x = 0$, $y = 0$ satisfy (i), the
origin is a singular point:

(b) $x=1$, $y^2=1$, which satisfy (i) and therefore give two more singular points:

(c) $x=\frac{3}{2}$, $y^2=\frac{3}{4}$, which do not satisfy (i), but give points where the curve is parallel to Oy:

(d) $4(y^2-x^2)=2(y^2+x^2-2x)$; or $y^2=3x^2-2x$;

whence $(x-1)(x-\frac{3}{2})=4(4x^2-4x)$,

or $x-\frac{3}{2}=16x$, or $x=-\frac{1}{10}$, $y^2=\frac{23}{100}$,

which gives two other points where the curve is parallel to Oy.

The points where the curve is parallel to Oy could be most easily found by solving the equation

$$(y^2+x^2-2x)^2-\tfrac{1}{2}(y^2+x^2-2x)(x-1)(x-\tfrac{3}{2})$$
$$=-x(x-1)^2(x-\tfrac{3}{2}),$$

which gives $\{y^2+x^2-2x-\tfrac{1}{4}(x-1)(x-\tfrac{3}{2})\}^2$

$$=\tfrac{1}{16}(x-1)^2(x-\tfrac{3}{2})(x-\tfrac{3}{2}-16x);$$

whence $x=\frac{3}{2}$ and $x=-\frac{1}{10}$ each give equal values of y^2.

Also, where $x=0$, $\frac{3}{2}y^2=2y^4$; $\therefore$ $y^2=\frac{3}{4}$ and 0.

Near (0, 0,) $\frac{3}{2}(y^2-x^2)=8x^2$;

or $y^2=\tfrac{19}{3}x^2$, $y=\pm\frac{5}{2}x$ nearly.

Near (1, 1), $-(\eta-\xi)\xi=8\eta^2$;

Fig. 27. i.e. $\xi^2-\eta\xi+\tfrac{1}{4}\eta^2=\tfrac{33}{4}\eta^2$, or $\xi=\frac{1}{2}(1\pm\sqrt{33})\,\eta$.

Ex. 3. $xy^2+2a^2y-ax^2-3a^2x-3a^3=0$.

Writing $x+\xi$, $y+\eta$, for x and y, and equating the coefficients of ξ and η to zero we have

$$y^2-2ax-3a^2=0, \quad\text{...................}(i)$$

and $$2xy+2a^2=0. \quad\text{.....................}(ii)$$

These and the equations of the curve give $x=-a$, $y=a$. The shape near $(-a, a)$ is given by

$$-a\eta^2+2a\xi\eta-a\xi^2+\xi\eta^2=0;$$

or $$a(\eta-\xi)^2=\xi^3.$$

Near (0, ∞), $x=-2a^2/y$;

near (∞, ∞), $y^2=ax$,

near (0, $\frac{3}{2}a$), $(\frac{9}{4}a^2-3a^2)x+2a^2\eta=0$,

Fig. 28. or $8\eta=3x$.

Ex. 4.

$$(y^2 - x^2)^2 + 6axy^2 - 7ax^3 - 4a^2y^2 + 18a^2x^2 - 20a^3x + 8a^4 = 0.$$

The equations for determining singular points are

$$-4x(y^2 - x^2) + 6ay^2 - 21ax^2 + 36a^2x - 20a^3 = 0, \quad \text{......(i)}$$

and $$4y(y^2 - x^2) + 12axy - 8a^2y = 0, \quad \text{..............(ii)}$$

or $$y = 0, \quad \text{and} \quad y^2 - x^2 + 3ax - 2a^2 = 0 \,;$$

where $$y = 0, \quad x^4 - 7ax^3 + 18a^2x^2 - 20a^3x + 8a^4 = 0,$$

which reduces to $(x - a)(x - 2a)^3 = 0$.

The equation might have been written

$$y^4 - 2y^2(x - a)(x - 2a) + (x - a)(x - 2a)^3 = 0,$$

or $$\{y^2 - (x - a)(x - 2a)\}^2 = (x - a)(x - 2a)^2a.$$

Near $(a, 0)$, $\qquad y^4 - a^3\xi = 0,$

near $(2a, 0)$, $\qquad y^2 = 2\xi^2, \quad \text{and} \quad 2y^2 - a\xi = 0,$

near (∞, ∞), $\qquad (y \mp x)^2 = \tfrac{1}{4}ax.$

The proper parabolic asymptotes, as well as the side on which the curve lies, may be found by expanding y as far as terms in $x^{-\frac{1}{2}}$, as follows:

$$(y^2 - x^2 + 3ax - 2a^2)^2 = a(x^3 - 5ax^2 + 8a^2x - 4a^3).$$

Therefore $$y^2 = x^2 - 3ax + 2a^2 + (ax^3)^{\frac{1}{2}}\Big(1 - \frac{5a}{x} + \frac{8a^2}{x^2} - \ldots\Big)^{\frac{1}{2}}$$

$$= x^2 - 3ax + 2a^2 + (ax^3)^{\frac{1}{2}}\Big(1 - \frac{5a}{2x} + \frac{7a^2}{8x^2}\ldots\Big).$$

Hence $$\pm y = x\Big\{1 + \Big(\frac{a}{x}\Big)^{\frac{1}{2}} - \frac{3a}{x} - \frac{5}{2}\Big(\frac{a}{x}\Big)^{\frac{3}{2}}\ldots\Big\}^{\frac{1}{2}}$$

$$= x\Big\{1 + \frac{1}{2}\Big(\frac{a}{x}\Big)^{\frac{1}{2}} - \frac{13a}{8x} - \frac{7}{16}\Big(\frac{a}{x}\Big)^{\frac{3}{2}}\ldots\Big\}.$$

$\therefore \ (\pm y - x + \tfrac{13}{8}a)^2 = \tfrac{1}{4}ax$ is a proper asymptote, the curve lying on the concave side of both branches.

Fig. 29.

Ex. 5. $\quad 27y^4 - 9y^2(x^2 + 14ax + a^2) + 32a(a + x)^3 = 0.$

The conditions for a singular point are

$$2y\{54y^2 - 9(x^2 + 14ax + a^2)\} = 0, \quad \text{..............(i)}$$

$$-9y^2(2x + 14a) + 96a(a + x)^2 = 0. \quad \text{............(ii)}$$

PLATE
VII.

All three equations are satisfied by $x = -a$, $y = 0$, and, from (i) and (ii),

$$(x^2 + 14ax + a^2)(x + 7a) = 32a(x + a)^2,$$

or $$(x - a)(x - 5a)^2 = 0.$$

The solutions of (i) and (ii) give the points $(a, \pm\sqrt{\tfrac{8}{3}}a)$ and $(5a, \pm 4a)$, but only the latter are on the curve. The equation may therefore be written

$$3(6y^2 - x^2 - 14ax - a^2)^2 - (x - 5a)^3(3x + a) = 0,$$

hence, if $$x = 5a + \xi, \quad y = \pm 4a + \eta,$$

we obtain $$\pm\eta = \tfrac{1}{2}\xi + \tfrac{1}{12}(3a)^{-\frac{1}{2}}\xi^{\frac{3}{2}};$$

near $(-a, 0)$, $$27ay^2 + 8\xi^3 = 0.$$

For the rectilinear asymptotes the first approximation is $3y^2 = x^2$, the second is obtained from

$$9(3y^2 - x^2)y^2 - 9 . 14axy^2 + 32ax^3 = 0;$$

PLATE
VIII.

and the rectilinear asymptotes are $\pm\sqrt{3}y - x - \tfrac{5}{3}a = 0$.

Fig. 1.

The guiding asymptote is $-9y^2 + 32ax = 0$, the proper asymptote being $y^2 = \tfrac{32}{9}(x - \tfrac{1}{3}a)$.

Observe that two of the cusps lie within the loops formed by the asymptotes.

Note. This tricusped curve is the locus of a point through which if the three maximum or minimum chords be drawn in a parabola $y^2 = 4ax$, two of the three chords coincide; it was given to me by J. Wolstenholme, who observed that the equation may be written

$$(x - 5a)^{-\frac{1}{2}} + (4x - 6y + 4a)^{-\frac{1}{2}} + (4x + 6y + 4a)^{-\frac{1}{2}} = 0.$$

If (α, β) be any point through which chords are drawn, writing $\alpha + lr$, $\beta + mr$, where $l^2 + m^2 = 1$, for x and y in the equation of the parabola, the values of r for the direction (l, m) are given by $(\beta + mr)^2 = 4a(\alpha + lr)$, and, if r_1, r_2 be the roots of this equation,

$$(r_1 \sim r_2)^2 = 16am^{-4}(al^2 - \beta lm + \alpha m^2) = 16af(l, m),$$

and the chord is a maximum or minimum when $f(l, m)$ is greater or less than $f(l + \lambda, m + \mu)$ for all small values of λ and μ, such that $$l\lambda + m\mu = 0. \quad\dots\dots\dots\dots\dots\dots(i)$$

PLATE
VIII.

Let $f(l+\lambda,\ m+\mu)-f(l,\ m)=L\lambda+M\mu+$ terms in λ^2, etc.
This must be of the same sign for all small values of λ, μ,
which can only be the case when $L\lambda+M\mu=0$.

Hence, by (i), $Lm-Ml=0$; where $L=m^{-4}(2al-\beta m)$
and $M=m^{-4}(-\beta l+2\alpha m)-4m^{-5}(al^2-\beta lm+\alpha m^2)$,
$\therefore (2alm-\beta m^2)m-\{2\alpha m^2-\beta lm-4(al^2-\beta lm+\alpha m^2)\}l=0$,
and the directions of the three chords are given by

$$4al^3-3\beta l^2m+2(a+\alpha)lm^2-\beta m^3=0.$$

If two of these directions coincide

$$6al^2-3\beta lm+(a+\alpha)m^2=0,$$

and $$3\beta l^2-4(a+\alpha)lm+3\beta m^2=0,$$

whence by eliminating $l:m$ the locus of $(\alpha,\ \beta)$ is found.

DIVISION INTO COMPARTMENTS.

164. A great assistance in selecting the proper mode of
making the junction of isolated parts of a curve, which may
have been already determined, is acquired by observing
that, if $f(x,\ y)=0$ be an equation which does not represent
separate curves, an even number of which coincide, when a
variable point moves so as to cross the curve, every time
that it so crosses, the value of the function $f(x,\ y)$, obtained
by substituting the coordinates of the point for x and y,
will change sign. This does not require any proof.

165. Suppose the equation of a curve to be put in the
form $tu+vw=0$, where $t=0$, $u=0$, $v=0$, $w=0$, represent
four curves; and take two points P and Q on opposite sides
of $t=0$, so that a line joining PQ crosses $t=0$, but does not
cross any of the other three lines; it follows that the values
of t for the coordinates of P and Q are of opposite signs,
while u, v, and w retain the same sign, therefore P and Q
cannot both be points on the curve. The only path by which
the curve can cross $t=0$ is through the point of intersection
of t, v, or t, w, unless $t=0$ represents an even number of
coincident curves.

PLATE
VIII.

166. We are thus enabled to name certain compartments within which the curve cannot lie, when one point has been determined, and the general form of the curves, with equations of high degree, can be frequently obtained with very little calculation.

Any of the examples which have been given of homogeneous curves will serve to illustrate this in a simple way.

The following curves will shew how to choose the compartments, and how to obtain the direction of the curve in passing from one to another compartment; in these it will be seen that by rearranging the equation of the curve in different forms, different sets of compartments may be mapped down, and so assistance given in determining doubtful cases.

Ex. 1. $xy(x^2 - y^2) + ra^2(x^2 + y^2 - a^2) = 0.$

Fig. 2.   The four asymptotes are represented in the figure, viz. yOy', xOx', AOA', BOB', and the circle $x^2 + y^2 - a^2 = 0$ by $ab \ldots d'$.

The intersections of the asymptotes with the circle, a, b, etc., are all points in the curve.

The tangent at $(0, a)$ is $x - 2r\eta = 0$; if, therefore, r be positive, this shews two compartments dOc and $ycbA$ in which the curve must lie, and since none of the five lines mentioned above can be crossed separately without a change of sign, the compartments bOc, dOa', $b'Oc'$, $d'Oa$, and $xabA$, $ycdB$, $x'a'b'A'$, $y'c'd'B'$ must be empty; whence the curve may be readily drawn.

The figure represents the three principal forms which the curve can assume according as $r <$, $=$, or > 1, denoted by the letters β, α, γ respectively.

To find the value of r, in order that there may be a multiple point, the following three equations must be satisfied simultaneously:

$$3yx^2 - y^3 + 2a^2rx = 0, \quad \ldots\ldots\ldots\ldots\ldots\ldots(i)$$
$$-3xy^2 + x^3 + 2a^2ry = 0, \quad \ldots\ldots\ldots\ldots\ldots\ldots(ii)$$
and $$2(x^2 + y^2) - 4a^2 = 0 \quad (Art.\ \textbf{162}).\ \ldots\ldots(iii)$$

PLATE
VIII.

From (i) and (ii), $\qquad 6x^2y^2 = x^4 + y^4,$

$$\therefore (x^2-y^2)^2 = 4x^2y^2 \quad \text{and} \quad (x^2+y^2)^2 = 8x^2y^2.$$

Hence $\qquad\qquad x^2-y^2 = \pm 2xy,$ ....(iv)

and, using (iii), $\qquad 2x^2y^2 = a^4.$ ....(v)

Again, by (i) and (ii),

$$3xy(x^2-y^2) + xy(x^2-y^2) + 2ra^2(x^2+y^2) = 0,$$

from which, by (iii),

$$xy(x^2-y^2) + a^4r = 0,$$

and, by (iv) and (v), $\qquad r = \pm 1.$

Also, since (iv) may be written

$$y = (\pm\sqrt{2}\mp1)x,$$

two of the radii from O to the four multiple points are inclined to Ox, and two to Oy at angles $\tfrac{1}{8}\pi$.

Ex. 2. $\qquad \mathbf{xy(x^2 - y^2) + a(x - c)(x^2 + y^2 - a^2) = 0.}$

All the points of intersection of $x = 0, y = 0, x \pm y = 0$ with $x = c$ and $x^2 + y^2 = a^2$, are points in this curve.

The asymptotes are $y + a = 0$, which meets the curve where $cx = a^2$; $x = 0$, the next approximation to which is $x = -ac/y$; also $x - y + a = 0$, and $x + y - a = 0$.

The only difficulty which arises with these data in tracing the curve is settled by fixing on which side of the asymptote $x + y - a = 0$ the curve lies, and the next approximation giving $x+y = a - \tfrac{1}{2}(a-2c)a/y$, the curve is below the asymptote in $x'Oy$, when $c < \tfrac{1}{2}a$; and above, when $c > \tfrac{1}{2}a$.

When $c = \tfrac{1}{2}a$, since the three points $(a, 0), (\tfrac{1}{2}a, \tfrac{1}{2}a), (0, a)$ all lie in the line $x + y = a$, taking into account the two points at an infinite distance, this straight line would meet the curve in one more point than the degree, which shews that the curve, for this value of c, contains the complete line $x + y - a = 0$. That this is the case is made obvious by writing the equation in the form

$$xy\{(x-a)^2 - y^2\} + a(x - \tfrac{1}{2}a)\{(x+y)^2 - a^2\} = 0,$$

the other part of the curve having for its equation

$$xy(x-y) + ax^2 + \tfrac{1}{2}a^2(x-y) - \tfrac{1}{2}a^3 = 0,$$

or $\qquad\qquad (y+a)(x^2 - \tfrac{1}{2}a^2) - x(y^2 - \tfrac{1}{2}a^2) = 0.$

PLATE
VIII.

Fig. 3.

The figure represents three forms of the curve, α denoting the case in which the curve divides into two, is drawn with stronger lines, and β, γ are cases in which $c < \frac{1}{2}a$, and $\frac{a}{2} < c < a$.

Fig. 4.

The next figure is for $c > a$.

Ex. 3. $\qquad x^6 - y^6 + a^3(x^3 + y^3 - 3axy) = 0.$

The curve $x^3 + y^3 - 3axy = 0$ (Pl. V. fig. 2), and the asymptotes $x \pm y = 0$, make separate compartments, which are alternately occupied by the curve.

Near $(-a, 0)$, $\quad y = \xi$; near $(0, a)$, $\quad x + \eta = 0$.

The dividing lines are dotted.

PLATE
IX.

Fig. 1.

Note. The equation might be arranged
$$(x^3 + y^3)(x^3 - y^3 + a^3) - 3a^4 xy = 0,$$
and the form would be obtained perhaps more easily if the point $x = y = \frac{3}{2}a$ were noticed to be on the curve.

Ex. 4. $\qquad x^6 - y^6 + a^2(x-a)(x^3 + y^3 - 3axy) = 0.$

Here $x - a = 0$ is a line in addition to those of Ex. 3, for obtaining empty compartments, and since $x^3 + a^2 x - a^3 = 0$

Fig. 2.

has only one root which is positive, and, near $(0, -a)$, $3\eta = 4x$, the curve is easily drawn.

Ex. 5.

$$(y - 2x + 2a)(x - 2y + 2a)(x^2 + y^2)xy + b^3(x^3 + y^3 - a^3) = 0.$$

Near $(0, a)$, $\qquad x^2 a^2 + b^3 \eta = 0$;

this, with the symmetry with respect to $x = y$, is sufficient to determine the compartments within which the curve must lie, and therefore the sides of the asymptotes at which the curve comes into sight from an infinite distance.

Fig. 3.

The lines determining the compartments are dotted, except the axes.

Ex. 6. $\qquad (y^2 - ax)^2(x-a)^2 - a^2 xy(x^2 + y^2 - a^2) = 0.$

The circle and the axes determine the compartments, and two points coincide where any one of the three meet the curve.

PLATE
IX.

The asymptotes are $(x-a)^2 = 0$, and $(y^2 - ax)^2 = 0$.

Near (a, ∞), $(x-a)^2 = a^3/y$;

near (∞, ∞), $(ax - y^2)^2 = a^2xy = ay^3$,

near $(0, 0)$, $x + y = 0$,   and $a^2x + y^3 = 0$,

near $(a, 0)$, $a^4\xi^2 - (2a\xi + y^2)a^3y = 0$;

or $\xi - 2y = 0$,   and $2a\xi + y^2 = 0$.

It may be seen by the compartments necessarily empty Fig. 4.
that when x is positive the curve is without the circle
when y is positive, and within when y is negative.

Ex. 7. $(x^2 - y^2)(x - a)y^3 - a^2(x^2 + y^2 - a^2)(x^2 + y^2 - 4a^2) = 0$.

Three of the dividing lines $x^2 - y^2 = 0$, and $x - a = 0$ are
asymptotes. It is easily seen by the triangle, that $y^3 - a^2x = 0$
is a parabolic asymptote, or, still nearer, taking in the next
term $-ax^2y^3$, $y^3 = a^2(x+a)$.

If $x = 0$, $y^5 - a(y^2 - a^2)(y^2 - 4a^2) = 0$,
the only root of which is a little less than a, being the
ordinate common to

$$y^2 = ax \quad \text{and} \quad (y-a)x^2 + 5a^2x - 4a^3 = 0.$$

It requires great care to determine in what direction Fig. 5.
certain elements of the curve should be joined; for instance,
whether P, P' should be joined with Q, Q', and R, R' with
S, S', or P, P' with R, R', and Q, Q' with S, S'.

For this purpose it will be sufficient to examine where
the curve is intersected by the two lines $x + 2a = 0$, and
$y + 2a = 0$.

It is easily shewn that the first meets the curve where

$$y^2(3y^3 - ay^2 - 12a^2y - 3a^3) = 0,$$

$y^2 = 0$ giving the two coincident points in the circle, radius $2a$.
The other factor gives one positive root near $\frac{7}{3}a$, and two
negative, one small, the other near $-\frac{7}{4}a$, the small root
arising from the curve bending from $(-2a, 0)$ in the same
direction as the circle. These are found from the intersection of $y^2 = ax$ with the hyperbola $(3y - a)(x - 4a) = 7a^2$.

The other line $y + 2a = 0$ meets the curve where

$$x^4 + 8ax^3 - 5a^2x^2 - 32a^3x + 32a^4 = 0.$$

PLATE
IX.

If $x^2 = 4a\eta$, we have $(\eta - a)(\eta + 2x - \frac{1}{4}a) = -\frac{7}{4}a^2$. The axis of this hyperbola is $\eta - a = -\frac{1}{2}(\sqrt{5}-1)(x + \frac{3}{8}a)$, giving for one vertex $(a, \frac{1}{8}a)$ very nearly. If the two curves be drawn carefully it will be seen that they very nearly intersect, and that they are very near, where $x = \frac{5}{4}a$; when $x = (\frac{5}{4} + \alpha)a$, α being very small,

for the hyperbola $\quad \dfrac{\eta}{a} = \frac{3}{8} - \frac{7}{128} + \frac{5}{8}\alpha - \frac{105}{128}\alpha^2,$

for the parabola $\quad \dfrac{\eta'}{a} = \frac{3}{8} + \frac{1}{64} + \frac{5}{8}\alpha + \frac{1}{4}\alpha^2;$

therefore $\quad \dfrac{(\eta' - \eta)}{a} = \frac{1}{64} + \frac{7}{128} + \frac{137}{128}\alpha^2,$

which shews that $\frac{1}{64} + \frac{7}{128}$ is a minimum value of $(\eta' - \eta)/a$ and that the curves do not intersect in the quadrant xOy' so that the branches at P and Q must join and also those at R and S.

The two negative values of x are $-\frac{5}{2}(1 - \frac{1}{20})a$ and $-8a$ nearly.

In the figure the asymptote $y^3 = a(x + a)$ is drawn, for want of room, so as to recede from the axis of x more rapidly than it ought to do, seeing that when $y = -2a$, $x = -9a$.

For the sake of testing the direction of the curve at any point (α, β) as well as the direction of its flexure, I give the equation which determines the form near this point, viz.

$$A\eta + B\xi + C\eta^2 + D\eta\xi + E\xi^2 = 0,$$

where

$A = \beta^2(a - \alpha)(5\beta^2 - 3\alpha^2) - 2a^2(2\alpha^2 + 2\beta^2 - 5a^2)\beta,$

$B = \beta^3(\alpha^2 - \beta^2) - 2\alpha\beta^3(a - \alpha) - 2a^2(2\alpha^2 + 2\beta^2 - 5a^2)\alpha,$

$C = (10\beta^2 - 3\alpha^2)(a - \alpha)\beta - a^2(2\alpha^2 + 6\beta^2 - 5a^2),$

$D = 3\beta^2(\alpha^2 - \beta^2) - 6\beta^2\alpha(a - \alpha) - 2\beta^4 - 8\alpha\beta a^2,$

$E = 2\alpha\beta^3 - (a - \alpha)\beta^3 - a^2(6\alpha^2 + 2\beta^2 - 5a^2).$

Thus it can be shewn that the curve bends upwards at P, and downwards at Q'. A further confirmation of the form drawn in the figure can be found by examining where the straight lines $y = \frac{2}{3}x$ and $y = -\frac{4}{3}x$ meet the curve.

ISOLATED PORTIONS.

167. In order to find whether there is an isolated closed portion of the curve, which does not cut either of the axes, the existence of which might be suspected on account of some compartments being empty which might have contained a portion of the curve, or for any other reason, several methods may be practically useful.

Since the curve is closed there must be two pairs of real points at which the curve is parallel to the axes. The points where it runs parallel to one of the axes will very often be able to be found, and the oval being once known to exist its nature can be examined by other processes.

168. Another plan is to draw a straight line from some point in the curve, a multiple point if there be one, and determine its direction when two of the other points of intersection become coincident, which would be feasible, *e.g.* for a curve of the fifth degree with a triple point; since the intersections of $y = mx$ with the curve would be given by a quadratic, if the origin were the triple point.

The directions so found would include those of all tangents drawn from the multiple point, and the curve being supposed traced with the exception of the oval, the two directions of the tangents to the oval could be selected.

Or, without seeking for the tangents, if any line parallel to one of the axes or to an asymptote, or drawn through a multiple point, could give, by assigning particular positions, two real points among the points of intersection, which do not coincide with any points previously determined, the oval would be detected.

In the following curve, the symmetry and the compartments which can be occupied shew where we should have to look for an isolated oval, if any existed:

$$(y - 2x + 2a)(x - 2y + 2a)x^2y^2 + b(x^5 + y^5 + 2a^3xy) = 0.$$

The asymptotes are $2x^2 = by$, and $2y^2 = bx$,

$$y - 2x + 2a - \tfrac{11}{4}b = 0, \quad \text{and} \quad x - 2y + 2a - \tfrac{11}{4}b = 0.$$

PLATE
X.

The compartments are defined by the curve (cf. Pl. V. fig. 20)

$$x^5 + y^5 + 2a^3xy = 0, \quad \ldots\ldots\ldots\ldots\ldots(\text{A})$$

and the two lines parallel to the rectilinear asymptotes,

$$y - 2x + 2a = 0, \quad \text{and} \quad x - 2y + 2a = 0,$$

and it is to be observed that $x^2 = 0$, and $y^2 = 0$ do not influence the division into compartments since x^2 and y^2 are of invariable sign.

The forms at the origin are given by

$$2a^3bx = -by^4 - 4a^2x^2y \quad \text{for the given curve,}$$

and

$$2a^3x = -y^4 - \frac{x^5}{y} \quad \text{for the curve (A),}$$

so that the curve lies nearer to Oy' and Ox', and further from Oy and Ox than the curve (A) which defines the compartments; this determines the compartments which can be occupied by the curve.

If $y = x$, $\qquad (x - 2a)^2x^2 + 2b(x^3 + a^3) = 0,$

the roots of which are the abscissæ of the points of intersection of

$$x^2y + 2a^3 = 0, \quad \ldots\ldots\ldots\ldots\ldots\ldots(\text{i})$$

$$(x - 2a)^2 = b(y - 2x). \quad \ldots\ldots\ldots\ldots\ldots(\text{ii})$$

Of these (i) is a fixed curve for all values of b, and (ii) is a parabola, which changes its shape and position with the value of b, the vertex being $(2a - b, 4a - b)$, and the latus rectum b. The vertex lies in the straight line $y - x = 2a$.

Fig. 1. The figure is drawn for three positions of the parabola, marked α, β, and γ, the values of b corresponding to β and γ being a and $6a$. The case α belongs to the value of b which makes (i) and (ii) touch one another, and is therefore the case of a multiple point; β, γ belonging to cases in which (ii) intersects $x'Ox$ in no point, or two distinct points.

Fig. 2. The curve corresponding to β is drawn completely. The part of the curve α is drawn only to shew the position of the multiple point, and of γ to shew how the curve runs near $(-4a, -4a)$; the asymptotes being too distant to be represented in the figures.

PLATE
X.

I find no isolated oval, after trying several search-lights such as where the curve intersects the line $x = c$ for different values of c.

169. The following curve affords an example of an outlying oval, whose existence might not have been suspected :

$$xy^3 - 4x^3y + ay^3 + 3a^2xy + a^3x = 0.$$

The asymptotes are $y = 0$, $x + a = 0$, and $y \mp 2x \pm a = 0$.

Near $(0, 0)$, $\qquad y^3 + a^2x = 0$.

Writing the equation

$$(x + a)y^3 - 4xy(x^2 - a^2) - a^2x(y - a) = 0,$$

we see that the form near $(-a, a)$ is

$$\xi - 4 \times 2\xi + \eta = 0, \quad \text{or} \quad \eta = 7\xi.$$

The equations of the asymptotes lead us to put the equation of the curve in the form

$$(y - 2x + a)(y + 2x - a)(x + a)y + a^3(y + x) = 0.$$ Fig. 3.

The curve cuts the asymptotes where $x = 0$, $y = a$, $-\tfrac{1}{3}a$, $-a$, respectively, there being three points in each at an infinite distance.

(a) The curve is parallel to Oy where

$$4x(\tfrac{4}{3}x^2 - a^2)^3 = a^6(x + a),$$

whose real solutions are the common abscissæ of

$$x^2 = \tfrac{3}{4}a(y + a), \quad \text{and} \quad 4xy^3 = a^3(x + a),$$

which gives roughly $x = -\tfrac{3}{5}a$, $-\tfrac{1}{4}a$, and $\tfrac{7}{8}a$.

(b) Or, the curve is parallel to Ox at the points of intersection of the two curves

$$y^3 + 3a^2y - 12x^2y + a^3 = 0, \quad 8x^3 + ay^2 = 0.$$

The five points at which the curve runs parallel to Ox Fig. 4. are denoted by a, b, c, d, and e, of which a, b belong to the isolated portion.

(c) Or, trying $x = -\tfrac{1}{2}a$, $\quad y^3 - 2a^2y - a^3 = 0$,

whence $\qquad y = -a$, or $\tfrac{1}{2}(\pm\sqrt{5} + 1)a$.

PLATE
X.

SPECIAL CURVE OF THE FOURTH DEGREE.

170. I shall conclude this chapter by shewing how the methods which have been explained work when applied to some equations selected by A. Beer, in a paper* on symmetrical curves of the fourth order, which serve excellently to illustrate the varieties which the general equation may produce. It will be found that all the peculiarities of the curves can be determined without any great difficulty.

The equations are

$$(y^2 \mp x^2)\{(\tfrac{1}{2}y-1)^2 \mp x^2\} + \mu(y+a) = 0,$$

the ambiguous signs allowing the equation to represent a curve with four, two, or no asymptotes.

171. $(\mathbf{y}^2 - \mathbf{x}^2)\{(\tfrac{1}{2}\mathbf{y}-1)^2 - \mathbf{x}^2\} + \mu(\mathbf{y}+\mathbf{a}) = 0.$

The curve being symmetrical with respect to Oy, we need only examine on which side of two of the asymptotes the curve lies; this is given by

$$y - x = 2\mu/3x^2, \quad \text{and} \quad \tfrac{1}{2}y - x - 1 = -\mu/3x^2.$$

The compartments, formed by the four asymptotes and the line $y + a = 0$, within which the curve can lie, are thus determined for the cases μ positive and negative.

Where the curve meets Ox,

$$x^2 = \tfrac{1}{2}\{1 \pm \sqrt{(1-4\mu a)}\}, \quad \dots\dots\dots\dots\dots\dots(i)$$

so that, if $4\mu a$ be positive and not greater than 1, or negative, it is cut in four points, two on each side of Oy.

Where the curve intersects Oy,

$$y^2(\tfrac{1}{2}y-1)^2 + \mu(y+a) = 0,$$

the solutions of which are the common ordinates of

$$(y-1)^2 = x+1, \quad \dots\dots\dots\dots\dots\dots\dots(ii)$$
and
$$x^2 + 4\mu(y+a) = 0. \quad \dots\dots\dots\dots\dots\dots(iii)$$

If $(0, \beta)$ be one of these points, the above equation for y may be of one of the forms

$$(y-\beta)f(y) = 0, \quad (y-\beta)^2\phi(y) = 0,$$
or
$$\tfrac{1}{4}(y-\beta)^3(y-\alpha) = 0.$$

* Bonn, 1852.

PLATE
X.

Writing $y = \beta + \eta$, we see that the shape of the curve near $(0, \beta)$ is given in these three cases by

$$\{\beta^2 + (\tfrac{1}{2}\beta - 1)^2\}x^2 = \eta f(\beta),$$

or
$$= \eta^2 \phi(\beta),$$

or
$$= \tfrac{1}{4}\eta^3(\beta - \alpha),$$

so that it is generally parabolic, but in critical cases a double point or a cusp. The values of the constant, in order that there may be a cusp on Oy, may be found by equating coefficients of the powers of y in

$$(y - \beta)^3(y - \alpha) \quad \text{and} \quad (y^2 - 2y)^2 + 4\mu(y + a).$$

Thus $\mu = \pm \tfrac{2}{9}\sqrt{3}$, $a = -1 \mp \tfrac{1}{2}\sqrt{3}$, $\beta = 1 \pm \tfrac{1}{3}\sqrt{3}$, $\alpha = 1 \mp \sqrt{3}$.

Writing the equation of the curve in the form

$$[x^2 - \tfrac{1}{2}\{y^2 + (\tfrac{1}{2}y - 1)^2\}]^2 - \tfrac{1}{4}\{y^2 - (\tfrac{1}{2}y - 1)^2\}^2 + \mu(y + a) = 0,$$

we see that there are two equal values of x^2, or the curve is parallel to Ox, except in the case of a singular point, where

$$\{y^2 - (\tfrac{1}{2}y - 1)^2\}^2 = 4\mu(y + a).$$

The ordinates of such points are the common ordinates of

$$y^2 - (\tfrac{1}{2}y - 1)^2 = x,$$

or
$$(y + \tfrac{2}{3})^2 = \tfrac{4}{3}(x + \tfrac{4}{3}), \quad \dots\dots\dots\dots\dots\text{(iv)}$$

and
$$x^2 = 4\mu(y + a). \quad \dots\dots\dots\dots\dots\text{(v)}$$

The points themselves lie on the hyperbola

$$2x^2 = y^2 + (\tfrac{1}{2}y - 1)^2,$$

or
$$\frac{x^2}{\tfrac{2}{5}} - \frac{(y - \tfrac{2}{5})^2}{(\tfrac{4}{5})^2} = 1. \quad \dots\dots\dots\dots\dots\text{(vi)}$$

The tangents to the curve which are parallel to Ox, are lines which pass through the intersections of (ii) and (iii), or of (iv) and (v); the points of contact of the former being on Oy, in critical cases the parabolic form is replaced by a double point or cusp; the latter tangents touch the curve where they meet the hyperbola (vi), the critical cases being when two or three of the lines coincide, in which case there is a multiple point or cusp which touches the hyperbola.

The two parabolas (ii) and (iv), and the hyperbola (vi) are independent of the values of μ and a, and it may be observed, that the hyperbola passes through those four points

Fig. 5.

PLATE
X.

of intersection of the asymptotes of the curve which do not
lie on Oy, viz. $(\pm 2, -2)$ and $(\pm \frac{2}{3}, \frac{2}{3})$.

For any value of μ and a, the parabolas (iii) and (v) are
equal, but are turned in opposite directions.

172. These considerations are sufficient to distinguish the
general shapes for all values of a and μ.

Suppose a figure carefully drawn of the three fixed curves,
(ii), (iv) and (vi), and that for any value of a the system of
curves corresponding to different values of μ is to be drawn.

If μ be positive the singular point on $y'Oy$ is first
determined by the point of contact of the parabola (iii),
whose axis is measured downwards, with (ii). It will be
in Oy', if the vertex be in Oy', and in OB, if the vertex be
either in OB or By.

The singular points which do not lie in $y'Oy$ are then
determined by means of the points of contact of the parabola (v), whose axis is measured upwards, with (iv) and, if
KC, HD be parallel to Ox, they lie in the lowest part of the
portion ED of the hyperbola (vi) if the vertex be in Hy' or
OH, and in CF if the vertex be in Ky.

If the curves corresponding to these critical values of μ
be constructed, they serve as guides to determine the directions in which the curves run for other values of μ. It is
also to be noticed that, as μ diminishes and ultimately
vanishes, the curve coincides with the asymptotes, and
therefore when μ is very small bends towards them.

We have thus the system for different values of a drawn
with tolerable accuracy without determining the exact angles
at which the curves cross at particular points.

Similarly, if μ be negative, we may find the singular
points and draw the curves.

173. This method of tracing the system of curves, which
correspond to any value of a, may be illustrated by taking
$a = 1$.

Corresponding to some large positive values of μ, the
parabola (iii) touches (ii) and gives two equal ordinates,

PLATE
X.

indicating a multiple point on Oy; these are the only points in which these parabolas meet.

The parabola (v) in the opposite direction meets (iv) in the quadrants $x'Oy'$ and xOy, giving two points at which the curve is parallel to Ox, one in ED, the other in CF.

If a smaller value of μ than this be chosen, (iii) does not meet (ii) and there is no point in Oy, but (v) meets (iv) in two points, giving points on CED and CF nearer to C than the former.

If a larger value of μ be taken, (ii) and (iii) intersect in two points, giving points on Oy', one on each side of the multiple point which corresponds to the case when the parabolas (ii) and (iii) touch.

If μ be negative, the critical case is when (ii) and (iii) touch, which they do at a point not far from the vertex of (ii), giving a conjugate point on Oy. The other points of intersection give a point on Oy' near O and a point at some distance on Oy beyond B. The reversed parabola (v) gives two points on CED and DG near D.

If a less value of μ be chosen, (ii) and (iii) give two values on OB, one on each side of the conjugate point; (iv) and (v) give two points on CED and DG nearer to D.

If a greater value of μ be taken, (ii) and (iii) give only two points on Oy' and Oy further from O than in the last case; (iv) and (v) give two points in CED and DG further from D.

The figure represents by a darker line the critical cases, denoted by α and α', for μ positive and negative respectively, and by lighter lines the other cases in order denoted by β, γ and β', γ'; β and β' being the curves which approach towards the asymptotes.

Fig. 6.

The dotted curve is the hyperbola (vi) on which lie all the points of contact of tangents to the different curves of the system, which are parallel to Ox and have not their points of contact on yOy'. The dotted straight lines are the asymptotes common to all curves.

PLATE
X.

174. It can be seen from the figure of the fixed curves that when a is negative, a parabola (iii) can be drawn with some small value of a, which, if μ be negative, will touch the parabola (ii), and cut it in two other points, and that, for a particular value of a, the particular parabola which touches (ii) will meet it in three consecutive points, the corresponding point of the curve being a cusp on Oy.

Fig. 7.

The figure represents the central part of three curves belonging to different values of μ, one of which corresponds to the cusp, one is small, and the third is large. The corresponding curves are denoted by α, β, γ respectively, and it should be noted how the curve β approaches the asymptotes.

175. There will also be a cusp for some negative value of a, less than 2, and a positive value of μ; and for this value

PLATE
XI.

of a, some value of μ will give contact between the parabolas (iv) and (v), and therefore a multiple point.

Fig. 1.

In the figure the curves marked α and ω are the cases of cusp and multiple point respectively, β denotes the curve which approaches the asymptotes, γ that which corresponds to a large value of μ, making (iv) and (v) intersect in two points, and therefore indicating four points at which the curve is parallel to Ox, situated on the dotted curve which is the hyperbola (vi).

A fourth curve, denoted by δ, bends towards the cusp α and the multiple point ω.

176. For the purpose of accurate drawing, we may find the directions of the curve at the principal points as follows:

At a point $(\alpha, 0)$ where the curve intersects Ox we have
$$\alpha^4 - \alpha^2 + \mu a = 0. \quad \dots\dots\dots\dots\dots\dots(\text{A})$$
Writing the equation of the curve
$$x^4 - x^2 + \mu a + (x^2 + \mu)y + \text{terms in } y^3 = 0,$$
and substituting for μa from (A), we obtain
$$x^4 - \alpha^4 - (x^2 - \alpha^2) + (x^2 + \mu)y + \dots = 0,$$
whence $\qquad 4\alpha^3\xi - 2\alpha\xi + (\alpha^2 + \mu)y = 0$
gives the tangent at $(\alpha, 0)$ for any value of α.

Near $(a, -a)$,
$$2a(\xi+\eta)\{a^2-(\tfrac{1}{2}a+1)^2\}+\mu\eta=0,$$
near $(-a, -a)$,
$$-2a(\xi-\eta)\{a^2-(\tfrac{1}{2}a+1)^2\}+\mu\eta=0,$$
near $(\tfrac{1}{2}a+1, -a)$,
$$-\{a^2-(\tfrac{1}{2}a+1)^2\}(a+2)(\tfrac{1}{2}\eta+\xi)+\mu\eta=0,$$
near $(-\tfrac{1}{2}a-1, -a)$,
$$-\{a^2-(\tfrac{1}{2}a+1)^2\}(a+2)(\tfrac{1}{2}\eta-\xi)+\mu\eta=0.$$

At a point $(0, \beta)$ where the curve crosses Oy
$$\beta^2(\tfrac{1}{2}\beta-1)^2+\mu(\beta+a)=0.$$

If $(0, \beta)$ is an ordinary point, the form there is given by
$$\{\beta^2+(\tfrac{1}{2}\beta-1)^2\}x^2-\{\beta(\beta-1)(\beta-2)+\mu\}\eta=0.$$

If $(0, \beta)$ is a multiple or conjugate point, the form is given by
$$\{\beta^2+(\tfrac{1}{2}\beta-1)^2\}x^2-\{3(\beta-1)^2-1\}\eta^2=0,$$
and hence we have a multiple point if $(\beta-1)^2>\tfrac{1}{3}$ and a conjugate point if $(\beta-1)^2<\tfrac{1}{3}$.

If $(0, \beta)$ is a cusp, the form is given by
$$\{\beta^2+(\tfrac{1}{2}\beta-1)^2\}x^2-6(\beta-1)\eta^3=0,$$
and hence the cusp points upwards or downwards according as $\beta<$ or >1.

The values of a, μ, and β for a cusp on Oy may be determined at once by the three equations
$$3(\beta-1)^2=1,\quad (\beta-1)^3-(\beta-1)+\mu=0,$$
and
$$\{(\beta-1)^2-1\}^2+4\mu(\beta-1+a+1)=0;$$
whence
$$\beta-1=\pm\tfrac{1}{3}\sqrt{3}=\pm\tfrac{4}{7}\text{ nearly,}$$
$$\mu=\pm\tfrac{2}{9}\sqrt{3}=\pm\tfrac{8}{21}\text{ nearly,}$$
and
$$a+1=\mp\tfrac{1}{2}\sqrt{3}=\mp\tfrac{7}{8}\text{ nearly, as in Art. }\mathbf{171.}$$

177. The algebraical determination of the singular points is as follows:

The equations to be satisfied besides that of the curve are
$$2y\{(\tfrac{1}{2}y-1)^2-x^2\}+(\tfrac{1}{2}y-1)(y^2-x^2)+\mu=0,$$
or
$$y(y-1)(y-2)-(\tfrac{5}{2}y-1)x^2+\mu=0,$$
and
$$x\{2x^2-y^2-(\tfrac{1}{2}y-1)^2\}=0;$$

PLATE
XI.

and μ is to be determined so that these equations and the equations of the curve are simultaneously satisfied.

(a) If $x=0$, $y(y-1)(y-2)+\mu=0$,

and $y^2(\tfrac{1}{2}y-1)^2+\mu(y+a)=0$;

therefore $y(y-2)-4(y-1)(y+a)=0$,

so that when a is given, the last equation gives the values of y, and the first gives the corresponding values of μ. The last equation gives

$$y=\tfrac{1}{3}[-2a+1\pm\sqrt{\{4(a+1)^2-3\}}],$$

and $4(a+1)^2=3$ for a cusp.

(b) If $2x^2-y^2-(\tfrac{1}{2}y-1)^2=0$,

$$y^2-x^2=-\{(\tfrac{1}{2}y-1)^2-x^2\}=\tfrac{1}{2}\{y^2-(\tfrac{1}{2}y-1)^2\} ;$$

therefore $\tfrac{1}{2}(\tfrac{3}{2}y+1)(\tfrac{3}{4}y^2+y-1)=\mu$;

and from the equation of the curve,

$$\tfrac{1}{4}(\tfrac{3}{4}y^2+y-1)^2=\mu(y+a) ;$$

therefore $\tfrac{3}{4}y^2+y-1=(3y+2)(y+a)$,

and $y=\tfrac{2}{9}[-(3a+1)\pm\sqrt{\{(3a-2)^2-12\}}]$,

which gives the position of the singular point for any value of a.

In the particular case of the cusp

$3a-2=\pm2\sqrt{3}$,   or $a=\tfrac{11}{6}$,   or $-\tfrac{1}{2}$ nearly ;

whence $y=\tfrac{2}{9}(-3\mp2\sqrt{3})=-\tfrac{2}{3}\mp\tfrac{7}{9}$ nearly.

Again, $3y+2=\mp\tfrac{4}{3}\sqrt{3}$,

so $9y^2+12y+4=\tfrac{16}{3}$,   or $\tfrac{3}{4}y^2+y-1=-\tfrac{8}{9}$;

therefore $\mu=\pm\tfrac{8}{27}\sqrt{3}=\pm\tfrac{14}{27}$ nearly.

Figs. 2, 3. **178.** The figures represent the systems of curves which can be drawn for different values of μ, both positive and negative, in the two cases in which a cusp occurs which is not in the axis Oy, viz. when $a=\tfrac{2}{3}(\pm\sqrt{3}+1)$.

The multiple point in Oy' belongs to the positive value of μ, the conjugate point in Oy to the negative value.

179. The only other case which need be considered is the case of $a=\infty$. Here μ is indefinitely small and μa finite if we wish to bring the curve within sight.

PLATE
XI.

The equation thus becomes

$$(y^2-x^2)\{(\tfrac{1}{2}y-1)^2-x^2\} = \pm c^2. \quad \ldots\ldots\ldots\ldots(A)$$

When $y=0$, $\qquad x^2 = \tfrac{1}{2}\{1 \pm \sqrt{(1 \pm 4c^2)}\}$,

when $x=0$,

$\qquad y = 1 \pm \sqrt{(1 \pm 2c)}$, with the upper sign of (A);

with the lower sign y is impossible.

Two values of x^2 are equal each to $\tfrac{1}{2}\{y^2+(\tfrac{1}{2}y-1)^2\}$, if

$\qquad y^2 - (\tfrac{1}{2}y-1)^2 = \pm 2c$, with the lower sign of (A),

or $\qquad\qquad y = \tfrac{2}{3}\{-1 \pm \sqrt{(4 \pm 6c)}\}$.

The figure is drawn for three values of c, both for the upper and lower sign; the dark lines and conjugate point α correspond to the upper, with a value $c=\tfrac{1}{2}$, the dark lines and conjugate point β to the lower, with a value $c=\tfrac{2}{3}$.

Fig. 4.

180. The case of two asymptotes is given by the equation

$$(\mathbf{y}^2+\mathbf{x}^2)\{(\tfrac{1}{2}\mathbf{y}-1)^2-\mathbf{x}^2\}+\mu(\mathbf{y}+\mathbf{a})=0.$$

The side of the asymptotes on which the curve lies is given by $\tfrac{1}{2}y \pm x - 1 = -\mu/5x^2$.

Where the curve meets Ox,

$$x^2 = \tfrac{1}{2}\{1 \pm \sqrt{(1+4\mu a)}\}. \quad \ldots\ldots\ldots\ldots\ldots(i)$$

The curve meets Ox in two points if $4\mu a$ be positive, in four points if it be negative and > -1, and in no point if it be < -1.

Where it meets Oy,

$$y^2(\tfrac{1}{2}y-1)^2+\mu(y+a)=0,$$

the ordinates, as before, are the common ordinates of

$$(y-1)^2 = x+1, \quad \ldots\ldots\ldots,\ldots\ldots\ldots(ii)$$

and $\qquad\qquad x^2+4\mu(y+a)=0. \quad \ldots\ldots\ldots\ldots\ldots(iii)$

Writing the equation in the form

$$[x^2+\tfrac{1}{2}\{y^2-(\tfrac{1}{2}y-1)^2\}]^2-\tfrac{1}{4}\{y^2+(\tfrac{1}{2}y-1)^2\}^2-\mu(y+a)=0,$$

we see that x^2 has equal values, or the curve is parallel to Ox, or else has a singular point, where

$$\{y^2+(\tfrac{1}{2}y-1)^2\}^2+4\mu(y+a)=0 ;$$

PLATE
XII.

therefore the ordinates of such points are the common ordinates of $y^2+(\tfrac{1}{2}y-1)^2=x$,

or $\qquad\qquad (y-\tfrac{2}{5})^2=\tfrac{4}{5}(x-\tfrac{4}{5}),$ ....(iv)

and $\qquad\qquad x^2+4\mu(y+a)=0,$ ....(v)

the points themselves are on the ellipse

$$2x^2+\tfrac{3}{4}y^2+y-1=0,$$

or $\qquad\qquad \dfrac{x^2}{\tfrac{2}{3}}+\dfrac{(y+\tfrac{2}{3})^2}{(\tfrac{4}{3})^2}=1.$ ....(vi)

Fig. 1. **181.** The fixed parabolas (ii) and (iv) and the ellipse (vi) are represented in the figure, the parabolas touch one another at the point $(8, -2)$. The parabolas (iii) and (v), which vary with μ and determine the points of intersection of the curve with Oy and the points where the curve is parallel to Ox, are in this example identical. In the last example they were of the same magnitude but turned in opposite directions.

It will be sufficient to shew in three cases, viz. when a is 1, -3, and ∞, how to form the systems of curves corresponding to different values of μ.

182. When $a=1$, the variable parabola has four critical magnitudes, when it touches (iv) in some points P and U, and (ii) in some points S and T; lines parallel to Ox through these points determine p, u, on the ellipse (vi) which are multiple points, and s, t, on the axis of y which are conjugate Fig. 2. points. The curves corresponding to the two values of μ which make the parabolas (iv) and (v) touch, are drawn with a dark line, the conjugate points are marked s and t.

The curves which belong to other values of μ bend towards the asymptotes or the dark curves, the points where the curves cross the dotted line spu are the points of contact of tangents parallel to Ox.

Fig. 1. **183.** When $a=-3$, the critical magnitudes, μ being positive, are where the parabolas touch at some points Q and Fig. 3. R, determining the multiple point q and conjugate point r. There is also a multiple point on Oy corresponding to

contact with the upper branch of (ii). The dotted line rq
is the ellipse which contains the points at which the curves
are parallel to Ox.

184. The case of $a = \infty$ may be found from the equation
$$(y^2+x^2)\{(\tfrac{1}{2}y-1)^2-x^2\} = \pm c^2. \quad \dots\dots\dots\dots(A)$$
When $y=0$, $x^2 = \tfrac{1}{2}\{1 \pm \sqrt{(1 \mp 4c^2)}\}$;
with the upper sign of (A), when $x=0$, $y = 1 \pm \sqrt{(1 \pm 2c)}$.

With the upper sign of (A), if two values of x^2 are equal,
they are given by
$$x^2 = \tfrac{1}{2}\{(\tfrac{1}{2}y-1)^2-y^2\}. \quad \dots\dots\dots\dots\dots(B)$$
The corresponding values of y are given by
$$y^2+(\tfrac{1}{2}y-1)^2 = 2c,$$
or $y = \tfrac{2}{5}\{1 \pm \sqrt{(10c-4)}\}, \quad \dots\dots\dots\dots\dots(C)$
so that when the upper sign is taken, the curve does not
meet Ox unless $2c =$ or < 1, and if $2c = 1$, there is a conjugate
point at $(0, 1)$.

There is a multiple point when $5c = 2$ at a point near
$(\tfrac{1}{2}, \tfrac{2}{5})$.

When $c = 4$, and $x=0$, $y = -2$ or 4; near $(0, -2)$,
$x^4 = -24\eta$, near $(0, 4)$, $5x^2 = 8\eta$, and since in this case the
values of y obtained from (C) are -2 and $\tfrac{14}{5}$, the values of
x^2 obtained from (B) are one zero and the other negative, so
that the curve is not parallel to Ox at any point out of $y'Oy$.

The figure represents the principal varieties, the critical   Fig. 4.
cases of $c = \tfrac{1}{2}$ and $\tfrac{2}{5}$ being marked α and β.

When the lower sign is taken there is no singular point,
the curve running along the asymptotes like a hyperbola.

185. The remaining case of no asymptote is given by
$$(\mathbf{y}^2+\mathbf{x}^2)\{(\tfrac{1}{2}\mathbf{y}-1)^2+\mathbf{x}^2\} + \mu(\mathbf{y}+\mathbf{a}) = 0.$$
The points of intersection with Ox are given by
$$x^2 = \tfrac{1}{2}\{-1 \pm \sqrt{(1-4\mu a)}\}. \quad \dots\dots\dots\dots(i)$$
The values of x^2 are only possible for values of y which
make $y^2(y-2)^2+4\mu(y+a)$ negative, $= -\alpha^2$ suppose, and if
β be given by $\alpha^2+4\mu(\beta+a)=0$, these values of y will

PLATE
XII.

satisfy $y^2(y-2)^2+4\mu(y-\beta)=0$, and be the common ordinates of the parabolas,

$$x^2+4\mu(y-\beta)=0, \quad\dotsfill\text{(ii)}$$

and
$$(y-1)^2=x+1. \quad\dotsfill\text{(iii)}$$

With these values

$$x^2=\tfrac{1}{2}\sqrt{[\alpha^2+\{y^2+(\tfrac{1}{2}y-1)^2\}^2]}-\tfrac{1}{2}\{y^2+(\tfrac{1}{2}y-1)^2\}$$
$$=\tfrac{1}{2}\{\sqrt{(\alpha^2+\xi^2)}-\xi\}, \quad\dotsfill\text{(iv)}$$

if
$$(y-\tfrac{9}{5})^2=\tfrac{4}{5}(\xi-\tfrac{4}{5}). \quad\dotsfill\text{(v)}$$

186. The parabola (iii) is fixed for all values of a and μ; the parabola (ii) for particular values of a and μ commences in the position where its vertex is at $(0, -a)$, and moving in the direction of its axis, gives, by its intersections with (iii), successive values of y which give real values of x; the initial position giving the points where the curve meets the axis of y.

No values of y give equal values of x differing from zero, so that the curve is never parallel to Ox, except where it meets the axis of y.

The equation giving the points where the tangent to the curve is parallel to Oy is of too high an order to solve approximately except in particular cases.

187. The equations (iv) and (v) give means of determining by construction the value of x corresponding to any value of y.

Fig. 5.

Construct the parabolas (iii), (v), and (ii), the last for two positions, viz. when $\beta=-a$, and when β has a general value.

If P be one of the points of intersection of (ii) and (iii), let PMQ parallel to Ox meet (v) in Q and Oy in M, so that $MQ=\xi$, and let βR, the tangent at β, the vertex of (ii), intersect the parabola (ii) in its first position, viz. aR, in R. Take S in aM such that $MS=\beta R=\alpha$, and T in PM, so that $QT=QS=\sqrt{(\alpha^2+\xi^2)}$; then, by (iv), $x^2=\tfrac{1}{2}TM$ corresponds to $y=OM$; and x is the ordinate UN to the abscissa $AN=\tfrac{1}{2}TM$ in the parabola (iii).

PLATE
XIII.

Fig. 1.

188. To shew how to trace the curve we will take the case in which the parabola (ii) in its first position, when $\beta = -a$, touches (iii) as at A, and cuts it in B, C, μ being negative. Aa, Bb, Cc determine points where the curve cuts the axis of y, of which a is a multiple point. As (ii) moves upwards it cuts (iii) in P, Q, R, S; as (ii) continues to move upwards, P and Q move away from A in opposite directions, and R and S from B and C towards O and D. When (ii) touches (iii), R and P meet as at T, the figure traced out by the points which correspond to them being $aprb$ and the symmetrical half loop; similarly Q and S meet when (ii) touches (iii) with the last contact as at U, and they produce the top loop asc.

It may be seen, from the last article, that the maximum value of x in the top loop is very nearly opposite to the point of last contact, on account of the large value of ξ.

189. The system of curves which have μ for their parameter when a is a given positive quantity are readily traced, a guide to the general direction being the fact that, as $-\mu$ increases from 0 to the value which corresponds to the figure of eight, called a lemniscate, which has just been formed, the curve changes from two conjugate points at O and D to the lemniscate.

When μ is negative and small, the points in which the initial position of (ii) meets (iii) are two pairs of points, one on each side of and near both O and B, giving rise to two small ovals surrounding the conjugate points.

As $-\mu$ approaches the value for the lemniscate, the ovals terminate near c, a, and b.

When $-\mu$ is greater than this value, the initial position of (ii) meets (iii) in only two points R' and S', joining points on Oy below b and above c. As (ii) moves upwards, R' moves towards O until (ii) and (iii) touch, which they may do if μ be not too great. The two points P, Q then come into existence, at first coincident, and then P meeting R, Q meeting S as before.

PLATE
XIII.

Fig. 2.

The figure represents two of the ovals, the lemniscate, and two curves beyond.

The case of μ positive is the conjugate point and oval marked $+$ in the figure.

190. The case of a cusp on the axis of y occurs when $a = -1 \pm \frac{1}{2}\sqrt{3}$ or $-\frac{1}{8}$, and $-\frac{15}{8}$ nearly, as shewn in Art. **171.**

Fig. 3.
The figure is drawn for the case of $a = -1 + \frac{1}{2}\sqrt{3}$, shewing the systems for negative and positive values of μ.

The figures are somewhat similar for $a = -1 - \frac{1}{2}\sqrt{3}$, differing principally in the breadth, and in the position where it is greatest.

191. When a is between $-1 \pm \frac{1}{2}\sqrt{3}$, the systems for μ positive and negative are each a conjugate point and a Fig. 4. series of ovals.

192. The case of $a = \infty$ is given by

$$(y^2 + x^2)\{(\tfrac{1}{2}y - 1)^2 + x^2\} = c^2.$$

If $y = 0$, $x^2 = \frac{1}{2}\{-1 + \sqrt{(1 + 4c^2)}\} = \alpha^2$, suppose,

if $x = 0$, $y^2 - 2y = \pm 2c$, or $y = 1 \pm \sqrt{(1 \pm 2c)}$.

Near $(\alpha, 0)$, $\quad -\alpha^2 y + (4\alpha^3 + 2\alpha)\xi = 0$,

near $(0, 1)$, when $2c = 1$, $\frac{5}{2}x^2 - \eta^2 = 0$, or $\eta = \pm \frac{8}{5}x$ nearly.

In this case we can construct for the points where the curve is parallel to Oy by means of the equations

$$4(5y - 2)^2 c^2 = y(2 - y)(3y^2 + 4y - 4)^2, \quad \ldots\ldots\ldots(1)$$

and $\quad (5y - 2)x^2 + 2y(y - 1)(y - 2) = 0, \quad \ldots\ldots\ldots\ldots(2)$

which are easily obtained from the condition.

The solutions of equation (1) are the common ordinates of the hyperbola

$$x(5y - 2) = 3y^2 + 4y - 4,$$

or $\quad (5y - 2)(x - \tfrac{3}{5}y - \tfrac{26}{25}) = -\tfrac{48}{25}, \quad \ldots\ldots\ldots\ldots(3)$

and the curve $\quad x^2 y(2 - y) = 4c^2. \quad \ldots\ldots\ldots\ldots\ldots(4)$

Lines drawn parallel to Ox through the points of intersection of (3) and (4) meet the curve (2) in points where the tangents to the given curve are parallel to Oy.

PLATE
XIII.

Fig. 5.

The figure contains portions of the branches of the hyperbola (3), the curve (2), viz. Oqu and $astp$, and the curve (4) traced for $c = \frac{1}{2}$ and $\frac{3}{8}$, viz. PAQ and $P'Q'$.

When $2c = 1$, the curve has a lemniscate form, and the points where it is parallel to Oy are p, q corresponding to the intersections P, Q; the point a corresponds to A, and, being the node of the lemniscate, the condition of equal values of y is satisfied.

When $c = \frac{3}{8}$; p', q' are the points at which the curve is parallel to Oy, corresponding to the points of intersection P' and Q', the third point giving no point on the curve.

When $c > \frac{1}{2}$, the curves (3) and (4) first intersect in R and S and the lower branch, and, as c increases, they touch in T, and afterwards give only one value in the branch QU. The corresponding points in the given curve are r, s, t, u, there being a point of inflexion at t.

The complete system is drawn with the letters r, s, ...   Fig. 6.

Note. The curve (4) is easily drawn for different values of c, since, by transposing the origin to $(0, 1)$, the equation is $4c^2 = (1 - y^2)x^2$. If then $y = \sin\theta$, $x = 2c\sec\theta$.

Examples X.

1.
$$(x^2 - a^2)^2 y = (y^2 - b^2)^2 x.$$

Find the multiple points, and trace the curve.
Shew that each branch has a point of inflexion at each multiple point.

2.
$$ay(x - a) = x^3(x + a).$$

Shew that $(-\cdot 26a, \cdot 01a)$ is a point of inflexion.

3. Apply the method of compartments to draw the curves:

(a)
$$xy^3 = c^2(x^2 + y^2 - a^2).$$

Shew that, in order that there may be a singular point, $4c^2 = 3\sqrt{3}\,a^2$, and that the two branches are inclined to Ox at angles $\frac{1}{12}\pi$ and $\frac{7}{12}\pi$.

(b)
$$x^4 - y^4 = ax(x^2 + y^2 - c^2).$$

Trace the curve for the two cases $c = \frac{2}{3}a$ and $c = a\sqrt{2}$.
Shew that when $c = 2a$, the curve cuts Ox where $x = -\frac{4}{3}a$ nearly.

(c)
$$x^4 - y^4 - xy(x^2 + y^2 - c^2) = 0.$$

Trace the curve in the quadrant xOy and shew that the rest follows by symmetry.

PLATE
XIII.

(d) $2\{x^2-(y-a)^2\}\{4x^2-(y-2a)^2\}+9y^2\{x^2+a(y-a)\}=0.$

Find the two multiple points and shew that one of the branches in each has a point of inflexion.

Prove that there are two loops in the acute angle between the dividing lines, and that at the points where the loops are parallel to Ox, $y=-\frac{2}{3}a$ nearly.

4. $(y-x)(y^2+x^2)=a(y+x-a)(y+x-4a).$

Shade the compartments unoccupied by the curve, and shew that it cuts Ox and Oy at distances nearly $3a$ and a from the origin.

5. $(3x^2-y^2-2ax)y^3-4a^2x(x^2+y^2-\frac{5}{2}a^2)=0.$

Use the method of compartments, and find the direction of the tangents at the points where the circle and hyperbola intersect.

6. $(x^2-y^2)(x^4+y^4)=a^2(x^2+y^2-a^2)(x^2+y^2-4a^2).$

Shew that at the two points where the curve cuts the asymptote in the quadrant xOy, it is equally inclined to the asymptote.

7. $(y-x-a)y^3-(y-ma)bx^2=0,$

or $x(y-ma)(y^2+bx)-y^2(y^2-ay-max)=0.$

Use the method of compartments derived from these two forms, to limit the space within which the curve can lie, and compare with Plate VI. figs. 15, 16, 17.

8. Draw the systems of curves corresponding to different values of μ in the equations

$$(x^2\pm y^2)\{x^2\pm(\tfrac{1}{2}y-1)^2\}=\mu(y+3) \quad \text{and} \quad \mu y.$$

CHAPTER XI.

SYSTEMATIC TRACING OF CURVES.
REPEATING CURVES.

PLATE XIV.

193. In the preceding chapters, when giving examples of the particular points upon which I was engaged, I thought it would be more interesting to the student to see how the part under examination fitted into the rest of the curve considered, and I therefore have given throughout a number of elements of the curves, which have frequently been sufficient to determine the entire shape. At the same time, I have generally expected the student only to examine the figure, in order to see how the elements were combined. I shall now give a few rules for the systematic treatment of the equation of a curve, only recommending them as convenient plans to adopt, and leaving to the ingenuity of the student such modifications as particular forms of equations may suggest.

194. The discussion of those equations which can be readily solved with respect to either of the coordinates, or in which the coordinates may be separated from each other, can be conveniently arranged in the following order:

i. The statement of any symmetry which may be observed in the equation of the kinds mentioned in Art. **7.**

Any fresh arrangement of the terms of the equation which may from the form suggest properties of the curve, for instance, if it could be arranged in the form $u^2 + vw = 0$, in which case $v = 0$ and $w = 0$ would be curves which would touch the required curve at their points of intersection with

$u = 0$; or any arrangement which would give distinct compartments within which the curve must lie.

ii. The tabulation of particular points such as those which lie on the axes, or which the form of the solution of the equation may suggest.

iii. The form of the curve at all the points at a *finite* distance which may seem to be most important.

iv. The position of the asymptotes, rectilinear or parabolic, when the fact of the curve going off to infinity in any direction has been established in the course of tabulation. If not obvious for other reasons, the side of the asymptote on which the curve lies must be investigated.

v. If more than the general form be looked for, it may be necessary to find such points as where the curve is parallel to the axes, and other peculiar points which would not be required in a rough determination of the locus.

195. The following curves, selected on account of special difficulties, will illustrate the application of these rules, commencing with the curve, some of the properties of which are discussed, without tracing it, in page 44, Ex. 4.

Ex. 1. $\qquad y(b^2 - y^2) = x^2(a - x).$

i. There is no symmetry, but the lines $y = 0$ or $\pm b$, and $x = a$ determine compartments within which the curve must lie.

ii. If $x = 0$ or a, $\qquad y = 0$ or $\pm b$,

if $x = \infty$, $\qquad y = \infty$.

iii. Near $(0, 0)$, $\qquad b^2 y = ax^2$,

near $(0, \pm b)$, $\qquad -2b^2\eta = ax^2$,

near $(a, 0)$, $\qquad b^2 y = -a^2\xi$,

near $(a, \pm b)$, $\qquad 2b^2\eta = a^2\xi$.

iv. Near (∞, ∞), $\qquad y - x + \frac{1}{3}a = 0$.

The asymptote meets the curve at a finite distance, where

$$-\tfrac{1}{3}a(y^2 + xy + x^2) + ax^2 - b^2y = 0,$$

or $\qquad a(y^2+xy-2x^2)+3b^2y=0,$

or $\qquad a^2(y+2x)-9b^2y=0,$

or $\qquad (9b^2-a^2)y=2a^2x.$

The three points of intersection are at an infinite distance if this equation is $y=x$, that is if $3b^2=a^2$.

v. The curve is parallel to Ox, or else there is a singular point, where $2ax-3x^2=0$.

It is parallel to Oy, or there is a singular point, where $b^2-3y^2=0$.

The singular point occurs when $(2a/3\pm b/\sqrt{3})$ is a point on the curve, in which case $2a^3=\pm3\sqrt{3}b^3$.

The figures are drawn for the cases of $b=a$, $b\sqrt{3}=a$, and $\quad$ Fig. 1. $2a^3=3\sqrt{3}b^3$, which are denoted by β, γ, and α respectively.

Ex. 2. $\qquad \mathbf{x^4y^3=a^2(a-x)^3(a-2x)^2}.$

The compartments are determined by $x=a$ and $y=0$. The lines $x^2=0$ and $(a-2x)^2=0$, being double lines, do not affect the division into compartments.

If $x=0,$	$y=\infty,$
if $x=a,$	$y=0,$
if $x=\frac{1}{2}a,$	$y=0,$
if $x=\infty,$	$y=\infty.$
Near $(a,0),$	$y^3=-\xi^3,$
near $(\frac{1}{2}a,0),$	$y^3=8a\xi^2,$
near $(0,\infty),$	$x^4=a^7y^{-3},$
near $(\infty,\infty),$	$y^3=-4a^2x.$

The curve is parallel to Ox where $x=\frac{5}{8}a$, or $-\frac{25}{8}a$, nearly. $\quad$ Fig. 2.

Ex. 3. $\qquad \mathbf{(x^2-a^2)^2+(y^2-b^2)^2=a^4}.$

The equation may be written

$$(y^2-b^2)^2=(2a^2-x^2)x^2.$$

The curve is symmetrical with respect to both axes.

If $x=0$ or $a\sqrt{2},$	$y=b$, two values,
if $y=0,$	$x^2=a^2\pm\sqrt{(a^4-b^4)},$
if $y^2=b^2\pm a^2,$	$x=a$, two values.

PLATE
XIV.

Near $(0, b)$, $4b^2\eta^2 = 2a^2x^2$,

near $(a\sqrt{2}, b)$, $4b^2\eta^2 = 2a^2(-2\sqrt{2}\,a\xi)$.

Fig. 3.   The figures are drawn for the cases $a = b$, $b\sqrt{2}$, and $a\sqrt{2} = b$, denoted by α, β, and γ, the case $a = b$ giving two ellipses whose major axes are inclined to Ox at angles $\pm\pi/4$.

Ex. 4. $a^2y^2(x-b)^2 = (a^2-x^2)(bx-a^2)^2$.

The curve is symmetrical with respect to the axis of x.

When $x = 0$, $y = a^2/b$,

$\qquad x = a^2/b$, $y = 0$,

$\qquad x = a$, $y = 0$,

$\qquad x = b$, $y = \infty$.

If y is real, we must have $-a < x < a$.   But $(a^2/b, 0)$ is a multiple point, and therefore must be a double point or conjugate point, according as $b >$ or $< a$.

When $b = a$, the curve divides into two coincident straight lines and a circle.

Near $(0, a^2/b)$, $y = a^2/b - (1 - a^2/b^2)x$,

near $(a^2/b, 0)$, $(1 - a^2/b^2)y^2 = \xi^2$,

near $(\pm a, 0)$, $y^2 = \mp 2a\xi$,

near (b, ∞), $x - b = (a^2 - b^2)^{\frac{3}{2}}/ay$.

Fig. 4.   The dark lines correspond to $b = a$, the curves marked α and β correspond to $b >$ and $< a$.

Ex. 5. $(a^3y - x^4)^2 - a^4(x - 2a)^2(x^2 - a^2) = 0$.

There can be no value of x between a and $-a$.

If $x = \pm a$, $y = a$, two values,

$\qquad x = 2a$, $y = 2^4a$, two values,

$\qquad x = \infty$, $y = \infty$,

and $y = 0$ gives no real values of x.

Near $(\pm a, a)$, $\eta^2 = \pm 2a\xi$,

near $(2a, 2^4a)$, $(a^3\eta - 4 \cdot 2^3a^3\xi)^2 - 3a^6\xi^2 = 0$,

or $\eta = (2^5 \pm \sqrt{3})\xi$.

Near (∞, ∞), $a^3y - x^4 = \pm a^2x^2$.

PLATE
XIV.
Fig. 5.

There is, therefore, a multiple point $(2a, 2^4a)$ on the parabolic asymptote $a^3y = x^4$, from which the curve runs off on both sides of the asymptote.

Ex. 6. $(x^2 - 4)^2 - y^2(y + 16) = 0.$

The curve is symmetrical with respect to Oy; therefore, considering only positive values of x,

if $y = 0$ or -16, $x = 2$, two values,

if $x = 0$, $y^3 + 16y^2 = 16$,

whence $y = 1 - \frac{1}{35}$, $-(1 + \frac{1}{29})$, $-(16 - \frac{1}{16})$ nearly;

if $y = \infty$, $x = \infty$.

Near $(2, 0)$, $(4\xi)^2 - 16y^2 = 0$,

near $(2, -16)$, $(4\xi)^2 - 16^2\eta = 0$.

If β be one of the values of y when $x = 0$,

near $(0, \beta)$, $-8x^2 - (3\beta^2 + 32\beta)\eta = 0$,

hence $4x^2 + 17\eta = 0$,

                           $4x^2 - 15\eta = 0$,

and $x^2 + 32\eta = 0$ nearly.

Near (∞, ∞), $x^4 - y^3 = 0$.

It may be shewn that the curve is parallel to Oy, where $y = -\frac{32}{3}$ and $x = \frac{16}{3}$ nearly.

Fig. 6.

196. In the case of equations which cannot be solved with respect to either of the coordinates, or which, if capable of solution, would lead to clumsy results, no order of proceeding can be laid down as being generally the best; but it must be good, in the first place, to look for symmetry in an equation, and to examine whether the equation can be rearranged so as to exhibit properties, or whether a change of coordinate axes would simplify it; in the second place, to find whether the curve cuts the axes and where, and to discover whether the curve passes off to infinity, either directly, or, if there be many terms or any doubt exists, by means of the Analytical Triangle. It will generally be best to find next some of the most important forms

PLATE
XIV.
of the curve near such particular points as may have turned up, and the side of the asymptotes on which the curve lies at each end, or, instead of this, the points where the curve cuts the asymptotes at a finite distance; it will then be seen whether it is necessary to go into the question of the points where the curve is parallel to the axes or whether there are any singular points.

197. The example given at the end of the last chapter is a good illustration of the methods of meeting difficulties, but a few more examples, which have been selected with a view of meeting as many difficulties as possible in a short space, will not be useless.

Ex. 1. $\qquad (y^2 - ax)^2 + (x^2 - ay)^2 = a^4.$

The curve is symmetrical with respect to $x = y$.

When $x = 0,\quad y^2 = \frac{1}{2}(\sqrt{5} - 1)a^2 = \frac{5}{8}a^2$ nearly,

$$\therefore\ y = \tfrac{9}{16}a\sqrt{2} = \tfrac{4}{5}a \text{ nearly.}$$

Where $x = y$ cuts the curve,

$$x = y = \tfrac{1}{2}\{1 \pm \sqrt{(2\sqrt{2} + 1)}\}a = \tfrac{3}{2}a \quad \text{or} \quad -\tfrac{1}{2}a \text{ roughly.}$$

If $x^2 - ay = \pm a^2,\quad (y^2 - ax)^2 = 0$;

the first parabola, therefore, touches the curve where

$$y^4 - a^3 y \mp a^4 = 0.$$

The lower sign gives no solution; but with the upper sign

$$y = -\tfrac{3}{4}a \quad \text{and} \quad \tfrac{6}{5}a \text{ nearly,}$$

$$x = \quad \tfrac{1}{2}a \quad \text{and} \quad \tfrac{3}{2}a \text{ nearly,}$$

where $x^2 = a(y + a)$ touches the curve.

Near $(0, \alpha),\quad -2a\alpha^2 x + 4\alpha^3 \eta + 2a^2\alpha\eta = 0$;

and as $\qquad \alpha = \pm \tfrac{4}{5}a$ nearly, $\quad \therefore\ \eta = \pm \tfrac{1}{3}x$ nearly.

Fig. 7. In the figure the parabola AB is drawn touching the curve at P and Q where $y^2 = ax$ meets it.

Ex. 2. $\qquad axy^3 - (x - a)^3 y^2 + a^4 x = 0.$

Fig. 8. Placing the equation on the triangle, we have at the origin $y^2 + ax = 0$.

PLATE
XIV.

Near $(0, \infty)$, $\qquad xy + a^2 = 0$,

near $(\infty, 0)$, $\qquad x^2y^2 - a^4 = 0$,

near (∞, ∞), $\qquad ay - x^2 + 3ax - 3a^2 = 0$,

or $\qquad\qquad (x - \tfrac{3}{2}a)^2 = a(y - \tfrac{3}{4}a)$,

near $(a, -a)$, $\qquad 3a^2\eta - \xi^3 = 0$.

The curve is parallel to Ox where

$$a(y^3 + a^3) - 3(x - a)^2 y^2 = 0,$$

or $\qquad\qquad (y^3 + a^3)\{3x - (x - a)\} = 0 ;$

whence $\qquad\qquad y = -a, \quad x = a,$

and $\qquad x = -\tfrac{1}{2}a, \quad y = 6{\cdot}7a, \ {\cdot}40a, \ -{\cdot}37a$, nearly.

Fig. 9.

Ex. 3. $\mathbf{a^3(y - x) - 2a^2(y^2 - x^2) + a(y^3 + x^3) - x^2y^2 = 0.}$

The equation may be arranged

$$ay(y - a)^2 + ax(x^2 + 2ax - a^2) - x^2y^2 = 0.$$

If $x = 0$, $\qquad y = 0$, or a, two values,

if $y = a$, $\qquad x = 0$, or $\tfrac{1}{2}(\pm\sqrt{5} - 1)a = \alpha$, say,

if $y = 0$, $\qquad x = (\pm\sqrt{2} - 1)a$,

if $x = (\pm\sqrt{2} - 1)a$,

$$y = 0, \quad \text{and} \quad (y - a)^2 - (3 \mp 2\sqrt{2})ay = 0,$$

whence $y = \tfrac{3}{2}a$ and $\tfrac{2}{3}a$ nearly for the upper sign, and $y = \tfrac{1}{8}a$ and $(8 - \tfrac{2}{7})a$ nearly for the lower sign.

The lines $y = \pm x$ meet the curve where

$$x = y = 2a, \quad \text{and} \quad -x = y = a\sqrt[3]{2} = 1{\cdot}26a.$$

When $x = \pm a$, $\qquad y^3 - 3ay^2 + a^2y + 2a^3 = 0$,

whence $\qquad\qquad y = 2a$, or $\tfrac{1}{2}(\pm\sqrt{5} + 1)a$.

Near $(0, 0)$, $\qquad y - x + 2x^3/a^2 = 0$,

near $(0, a)$, $\qquad \eta^2 - ax = 0$,

near (α, a), $\qquad (3\alpha^2 + 2a\alpha - a^2)\xi - 2\alpha^2\eta = 0$,

or $\qquad\qquad (2\alpha + a)\xi - 2\alpha\eta = 0$,

so that if $\alpha = \tfrac{5}{8}a$, $\qquad 9\xi = 5\eta$,

and if $\alpha = -\tfrac{13}{8}a$, $\qquad 9\xi = 13\eta$.

PLATE
XIV.

Near (∞, ∞), $x^2 = a(y - 2a)$, and $y^2 = a(x + 2a)$.

The last parabolic asymptote meets the curve where

$$y^3 - 3ay^2 + a^2y + 2a^3 = 0,$$

that is at the same distance from Ox as it meets the lines $x = \pm a$, so the curve has the property that the parabolic asymptote $y^2 = a(x + 2a)$ and the two lines $x = \pm a$ intersect the curve in nine points, three and three in the straight lines $y = 2a$, and $y = \frac{1}{2}(\pm\sqrt{5} + 1)a$.

Fig. 10.

Ex. 4. $(\mathbf{y}^2 - \mathbf{a}\mathbf{x})(\mathbf{y}^2 - \mathbf{b}\mathbf{x}) + \mathbf{x}^4 = \pm \mathbf{c}^4$.

The equation may be written

$$\{y^2 - \tfrac{1}{2}(a+b)x\}^2 = \pm c^4 + \tfrac{1}{64}(a-b)^4 - \{x^2 - \tfrac{1}{8}(a-b)^2\}^2.$$

When $y = 0$, $x^2 = -\tfrac{1}{2}ab + \sqrt{(\tfrac{1}{4}a^2b^2 \pm c^4)}$.

The curve is symmetrical with respect to Ox, and two values of y^2 are equal where

$$x^2 = \tfrac{1}{8}(a-b)^2 \pm \sqrt{\{\tfrac{1}{64}(a-b)^4 \pm c^4\}}.$$

i. Taking the positive sign in the equation of the curve, the compartments within which the curve lies are given by the two parabolas $y^2 = ax$, $y^2 = bx$, and the two lines $x = \pm c$, and the curve is parallel to Oy where it meets the parabola $y^2 = \tfrac{1}{2}(a+b)x$.

Fig. 11.

The three parabolas are dotted in the figure.

ii. Taking the negative sign, $y^2 = ax$, $y^2 = bx$ are the only dividing lines, between which the curve must lie.

In order that the curve may be possible, $c^4 < \tfrac{1}{64}(a-b)^4$.

Let $c^4 = \tfrac{1}{64}(1 - n^2)(a-b)^4 = (1 - n^2)f^4$,

then, where the curve is parallel to Oy,

$$x^2 = (1 \pm n)f^2,$$

and its equation may be written

$$\{y^2 - \tfrac{1}{2}(a+b)x\}^2 - \{x^2 - (1-n)f^2\}\{(1+n)f^2 - x^2\} = 0,$$

therefore x^2 lies between $(1-n)f^2$, and $(1+n)f^2$.

If $n = 0$, $\{y^2 - \tfrac{1}{2}(a+b)x\}^2 + (x^2 - f^2)^2 = 0$, shewing that

Fig. 12. there are two conjugate points.

PLATE
XIV.

Ex. 5. $y^2(x+y)^2(x-y)-2a(x+y)x^2y-4a^2x^3=0.$

Near the origin the triangle shews that $y^5+4a^2x^3=0.$
When x is infinite and y is finite,

$$y^2-2ay-4a^2=0,$$

whence $y=(1\pm\sqrt{5})a.$

Near (∞,∞),

$$2(x+y)^2+2a(x+y)-4a^2=0,$$

or $x+y=-2a,$ or $a,$

and $x-y-a=0.$

The asymptote $x+y+2a=0$ meets the curve at a finite
distance where

$$4a^2y^2(x-y)+4a^2x^2y-4a^2x^3=0,$$

or $-(x+y)(x-y)^2=2a(x-y)^2=0\,;$

therefore this asymptote touches the curve at $(-a,-a)$.

The asymptote $x+y-a=0$ meets it where

$y^2(x-y)-2x^2y-4x^3=0,$ or $-y^2+2xy-4x^2=0,$

the roots of which are impossible.

The asymptote $x-y=a$ meets the curve where

$$y^2(x+y)^2-2y(x+y)x^2-4ax^3=0,$$

or $y(x+y)(y^2+xy-2x^2)-4ax^3=0,$

or $y(x+y)(y+2x)+4x^3=0.$

To solve, write $y=zx$, then

$$z^3+3z^2+2z+4=0,$$

so that if $z^2=2u,$ $(u+1)(z+3)=1.$

The hyperbola and parabola which represent these equations
intersect where $z=-3+\frac{2}{11}$ nearly.   Fig. 13.

Note. The asymptotes parallel to Ox have each two
points of the curve at a finite distance, and three points at
an infinite distance, one of which is due to the point in
which the parallel lines meet, so that in each case the curve
lies on opposite sides of the asymptote at an infinite
distance.

PLATE
XIV.

Ex. 6. $x^5 = (x - y)^2 (x + y)(x - 2y).$

When $x = 1$, $y = 0$, or $2y^3 - 3y^2 - y + 3 = 0$, whose only real root is nearly equal to $-\cdot 9$.

Near $(0, 0)$, $(x - y)^2 = -\frac{1}{2}x^3$, giving a ceratoid cusp,

or $x + y = \frac{1}{12}x^2$,

or $x - 2y = \frac{8}{3}x^2$.

Near (∞, ∞), $x^5 + 2y^4 = 0$.

The curve is parallel to Oy, where $3x^2 + xy - 8y^2 = 0$,

or, nearly, $x = \frac{3}{2}y = -\frac{5}{81}$,   and $x = -\frac{11}{6}y = \frac{25}{11}$.

Fig. 14.   It is parallel to Ox, where $x = 5y$ and $x^2 = 2y^2$.

Ex. 7. $x^6 + a^2y^4 + a^2x^3y + a^3xy^2 = 0.$

Fig. 15.   Placing the equation on the triangle, the forms at the origin are $y^2 + ax = 0$, $x^2 + ay = 0$, and $x^3 + a^2y = 0$.

Where $x = y$, $x^3 + 2a^2x + a^3 = 0$, or $x = -\frac{7}{15}a$, the only value.

The line $x = -y$ meets the curve where $x = -y = -a$, near which point $\eta = 2\xi$. Also, $y = -\frac{1}{7}x$ nearly represents

Fig. 16.   the tangent to the loop in xOy'.

Ex. 8. $4y^2(x + y - a)^3 = (x - y - b)^5.$

The equation may be put into a simpler form by making the lines $x + y - a = 0$ and $x - y - b = 0$ axes of coordinates, thus if $x + y - a = y'\sqrt{2}$, and $x - y - b = x'\sqrt{2}$, the equation becomes $y'^3(y' - x' + \alpha)^2 = x'^5.$ ....(i)

The lines parallel to the asymptote through the new origin are $y'^3(y' - x')^2 = x'^5$.

If $x' = zy'$, $z^5 = (z - 1)^2$, and the values of z in this equation are the abscissæ of the points of intersection of $x^3 = y^2$ and $y^2x^2 = (x - 1)^2$, the latter of which is the two rectangular hyperbolas $(1 \pm y)x = 1$. These only intersect in two points,

Fig. 17.   whose common abscissa is nearly $\frac{2}{3}$; if m be this value, let

$$z^5 - (z - 1)^2 \equiv (z - m)\phi(z),$$

write $z = m + \zeta$, and equate coefficients of ζ, then

$$\phi(m) = 5m^4 + 2(1 - m).$$

PLATE
XIV.

The equation of the asymptote is, by (i),

$$x' - my' = 2\alpha(1-m)/\phi(m), \quad \text{or} \quad x' - \tfrac{2}{3}y' = \tfrac{2}{5}\alpha,$$

and when $\qquad\qquad x' = \alpha, \quad y' = \tfrac{9}{10}\alpha.$

Near the origin, $\qquad \alpha^2 y'^3 = x'^5,$

near $(0, -\alpha),\qquad \eta - x' = (-x'^5/\alpha^3)^{\frac{1}{2}},$

near $(\alpha, \alpha),\qquad$ if $x' = \alpha + \xi, \quad y' = \alpha + \eta,$

$$(\alpha + \eta)^3 (\alpha + \eta - \xi)^2 = (\alpha + \xi)^5,$$

therefore $\qquad 3\eta + 2(\eta - \xi) = 5\xi, \quad \text{or} \quad 5\eta = 7\xi.$

Where the curve meets the original axis of y,

$$4y^2(y-a)^3 = (-y-b)^5,$$

therefore y is the common ordinate of

$$b^2(y-a) + x^2(y+b) = 0, \quad \text{and} \quad b(y+b)^2 = 2x(y^2 - ay),$$

whence if $a = \tfrac{1}{2}b, \; y = \tfrac{5}{4}b, \; \tfrac{1}{11}b$ or $-\tfrac{1}{15}b$ nearly.

Fig. 18.

REPEATING CURVES.

198. I shall conclude this Chapter by shewing how to trace a large class of curves, whose equations involve trigonometrical functions of the coordinates in the place of the coordinates themselves. The loci of such curves, from the nature of a trigonometrical function, are made up of patterns continually repeated in every direction.

This symmetrical arrangement frequently gives very elegant figures, where the original curve has nothing to recommend it from this point of view, trigonometrical functions acting in fact as a kind of kaleidoscope.

The following is the method I have adopted for tracing such curves.

199. If $f(x, y) = 0$ be the equation of any curve, and we write for y any trigonometrical function of x, and for x any trigonometrical function of y, a new equation will be formed of the kind which was spoken of; and it will be easy to see how any other functions can be treated, if we take the particular functions $\sin x$ and $\sin y$, and give constructions for the corresponding locus.

PLATE XV.

200. Take the equation of the curve to be

$$f(\sin y,\ \sin x) = 0, \quad\dots\dots\dots\dots\dots\text{(i)}$$

and construct the curve

$$f(\xi,\ \eta) = 0, \quad\dots\dots\dots\dots\dots\text{(ii)}$$

and the two curves of sines

$$\eta = \sin x, \quad\dots\dots\dots\dots\dots\dots\text{(iii)}$$

and

$$\xi = \sin y. \quad\dots\dots\dots\dots\dots\dots\text{(iv)}$$

Fig. 1.

Let p be a point in the locus of (ii), which, by (iii) and (iv), must lie within a square whose sides AC, BC are parallel to the axes at the unit distance from them.

Let pr parallel to Ox meet (iii) in r, and ps parallel to Oy meet (iv) in s.

Draw sN, rM perpendicular to Oy, Ox, and let them intersect in P, then P will be the point in the locus of (i) which corresponds to p.

For

$$\eta = rM, \quad \therefore OM = x, \quad\dots\dots\dots\dots\text{by (iii)}$$

$$\xi = sN, \quad \therefore ON = y. \quad\dots\dots\dots\dots\text{by (iv)}$$

Hence we have the following construction for the point P of (i) which corresponds to p of (ii).

Draw pr, ps, parallel to Ox, Oy respectively, meeting the curves (iii) and (iv) in r and s, and the point P will be at the angle of the rectangle $prPs$, which is opposite to p.

Observing that each of the lines Pr, Ps will meet their respective curves in an infinite number of such points as r, s, for each point p of (ii) there will be an infinite number of corresponding points, arranged in pairs symmetrically with respect to lines whose distances from the axes are odd multiples of $\frac{1}{2}\pi$.

201. In order to facilitate the tracing of any curve, such as (i), by constructing a sufficient number of points, the following properties should be noticed.

Fig. 1.

(1) When ps is a tangent to (ii), sP will be a tangent to (i); for, if p' be an adjacent point on ps, P' the corresponding point will be adjacent to P on sN.

PLATE
XV.

And similarly, if pr be a tangent at p, PM will be a tangent at P.

(2) Since ξ and η have no values beyond 1 and -1, the portion of the locus of (ii) which lies within the squares, whose sides are given by $x = \pm 1$ and $y = \pm 1$, is the only portion which gives any part of the curve (i).

(3) If q be a point of (ii) which lies on the side of the square $x = 1$, and q' be an adjacent point, by considering where lines through q and q' parallel to Oy meet the curve (iv), it is seen that the points corresponding to q and q' are Q, and the pair of points Q', Q'', and the portion of (i) which corresponds to qq' is $Q'QQ''$ touching the line through Q parallel to Oy; except when (ii) touches AC.

(4) From the first of the properties given above, it follows that, if the curve (ii) touch Ox at the origin, the curve (i) will touch Oy at the origin.

202. It is easy to see that similar constructions hold for the loci of equations in which $\sin mx$, $\tan mx$, etc., and $\sin ny$, $\tan ny$, etc., take the place of $\sin x$ and $\sin y$. The method of dealing with all these cases will be sufficiently shewn by a few illustrations.

Ex. 1. Take the curve whose equation is

$$\sin^3 y + \sin^3 x - 3a \sin x \sin y = 0, \quad \ldots\ldots\ldots\ldots(\text{A})$$

derived from $\quad x^3 + y^3 - 3axy = 0, \quad \ldots\ldots\ldots\ldots\ldots(\text{B})$

which has been traced in page 89.

i. Consider first the case in which a is small enough to allow the whole of the loop to lie within the square which limits the values of $\sin x$ and $\sin y$.

Fig. 2.

Draw the curve (B), and suppose it the dotted curve apO in the figure; the curve being symmetrical with respect to the line $y = x$, it will be only necessary to construct the part of the curve (A) corresponding to the portion $abpOc$ of (B).

PLATE
XV.

The principal points to be considered are a in the line $y = x$; b where the curve is parallel to Oy; the origin; and c where it is cut off by the limiting square.

The corresponding points are A, also in $y = x$; B where the curve (A) is parallel to Ox; the origin, at which the branch corresponding to Op touches Oy; and C where the curve (A) is parallel to Oy.

The construction of Art. **200** is made in the figure for the points P, Q which correspond to two points p, q, in a line parallel to Ox and meeting the curve $y = \sin x$ in r, while ps and qt, parallel to Oy, meet the curve $x = \sin y$ in s and t, and $Pspr$ and $Qtqr$ are the rectangles spoken of in Art. **200**. The shape of half the curve may then be drawn, and the other half by symmetry.

Fig. 4.   The manner in which the curve repeats itself is given in another figure.

ii. Consider next the case in which the loop of (B) intersects two sides of the limiting square.

Fig. 3.   The points of (B) to be principally considered are a in $y = x$; b, d where it meets the side $x = 1$; the origin; and c in $x = -1$.

The corresponding points are A in Oa; B and D where the curve (A) is parallel to Oy; the origin O, where it touches Oy; and C where it is parallel to Oy. The construction is given for two points p, q taken as before.

Fig. 4.   The manner of repetition is given in another figure.

iii. The intermediate case, in which the loop touches the two sides of the square, is represented in the figure, without any construction, being given by a darker line, the previous cases by lighter lines.

Fig. 3.   *Note.* The isolated portion AB reduces to a conjugate point A' when the loop passes through the point $(1, 1)$.

203. The different effects obtained by introducing a tangent instead of one of the sines will be illustrated in the most striking manner by taking the same auxiliary equation.

PLATE
XV.

Thus to trace the curve

$$\sin^3 x + \tan^3 y - 3a \sin x \tan y = 0.$$

The auxiliary equation is

$$\eta^3 + \xi^3 - 3a\eta\xi = 0.$$

In this case the curve will not be symmetrical with respect to the line $y = x$, although the auxiliary curve is so; it will therefore be necessary to examine the positions of corresponding points for the whole of that part of the curve which is limited by the lines $y = \pm 1$.

The principal points to be considered are a in $y = x$; b, c Fig. 5.
where the curve is parallel to the axes; the origin; and d, e
on the limiting lines. The corresponding points are $A, B,$
$C, O, D, E.$

To shew how other points lie, p, q, r are points in a line parallel t Ox, and P, Q, R are the corresponding points lying in a line parallel to Oy, drawn through the point where pqr meets the curve of sines.

The figure, which is derived from the case in which the   Fig. 6.
loop cuts the line $y = 1$ in two points, is given without
naming the construction.

PLATE
XVI.

The manner of repetition is given in another figure, the
dark line corresponding to the critical case in which the line   Fig. 1.
$y = 1$ is a tangent to the loop, in which case the two points
on $y = 1$ coincide and give rise to the double point.

204. The figure is given without any construction for   Fig. 2.
the curve $\tan^3 x + \tan^3 y - 3a \tan x \tan y = 0.$

To assist in the tracing, it is easily shewn that the tangent
at the point $(\frac{1}{2}\pi, -\frac{1}{2}\pi)$ is $\xi + \eta = 0.$

205. The curve

$$\sin^3 x + \sec^3 y - 3a \sin x \sec y = 0$$

is more difficult to trace, and I have given three figures.

Fig. 3, in which $OA = 1$, $OB = \frac{1}{2}\pi$, represents for different   Fig. 3.
values of a, those parts of the curves, which are generated

PLATE
XVI.

from the portions of the auxiliary curve $\eta^3 + \xi^3 - 3a\eta\xi = 0$ lying between $y = 0$, $y = 1$, and beyond $x = 1$; the guiding curves $\eta = \sin x$ and $\xi = \sec y$ are dotted.

The Lemniscate form L, drawn with a dark line, is derived from the case in which the loop of the auxiliary curve passes through $(1, 1)$, viz., when $a = \frac{2}{3}$.

The portion of the auxiliary curve which corresponds to this Lemniscate form, viz. that which lies beyond $x = 1$, is given in the figure, a and c being the points where it meets $x = 1$, and b the point at which the tangent is parallel to Oy. The constructions for d, e, B, the points which correspond to a, b, and c, are indicated in the figure.

The point b lies in the line $x = \sqrt[3]{2}y$, which contains the points in each auxiliary curve obtained by giving different values to a, at which the tangent is parallel to Oy, the tangents at the corresponding points being parallel to OAB.

The conjugate point C corresponds to the point of contact when the auxiliary curve touches $x = 1$, where it meets Ob.

The small oval surrounding the conjugate point is derived from a particular auxiliary curve which passes between those which produce the Lemniscate form and the conjugate point.

The curve like a Cartesian oval is constructed from the case in which a is little greater than $\frac{2}{3}$.

The outside curve corresponds to very large values of a.

Fig. 4. **206.** Fig. 4 represents part of the curve which corresponds to the branches of the auxiliary curve which run from the origin along the asymptote, for the particular case in which $a = \frac{2}{3}$, the same value which gave rise to the Lemniscate of Fig. 3.

The portions d are generated from the part of the branch which lies between $x = -1$ and $x = -\frac{1}{2}\pi$;

a from the part between $y = \pi \mp 1$,

c from the part between $y = -(\pi \mp 1)$,

b from the part between $y = -(2\pi \mp 1)$.

PLATE
XVI.

Each time that the asymptotic branches intersect the curve $\xi = \sec y$, a line such as a, b, c is generated, as where the auxiliary curve lies between $y = n\pi \pm 1$ or $y = -(n\pi \pm 1)$, these lines lying nearer to the asymptotes of $\xi = \sec y$ as n increases.

The conjugate points at B and B' belong to the particular case $a = 0$, when the auxiliary equation becomes $\xi + \eta = 0$, in which case there are two points, $(-1, 1)$ and $(1, -1)$, which generate isolated points in the curve. In this case, the part of the line $\xi + \eta = 0$, which lies between $y = \pi \mp 1$, generates the fine line e above the dark line a, and similarly for other portions between $y = n\pi \mp 1$, n being a positive or negative integer.

Note. To assist in drawing the lines a, b, c, etc., I recom- mend the student to shade the spaces in any part of which no part of the auxiliary curve can generate any portion of the curve to be drawn; as between $x \pm 1 = 0$, and between $y = 1$ and $\pi - 1$ or $y = \pi + 1$ and $2\pi - 1$.

Fig. 5.

207. Fig. 5 is drawn to shew the manner of repetition, and in order to save confusion, the curves corresponding to only two of the auxiliary curves are given, viz., that which generates the dark lined curves of figs. 3 and 4, and that for which $a = 0$, generating the conjugate points B and B'.

208. By way of further illustration of the kaleidoscope property, I have given the patterns of the figures which correspond to three substitutions of trigonometrical func- tions in another equation $a(\xi + \eta)^2 = \eta(\xi^2 + \eta^2)$, the dark lines corresponding to the case in which $a = \frac{1}{2}$, for which the auxiliary curve is parallel to Ox at the point $(1, 1)$.

(1) $\qquad a(\sin y + \sin x)^2 = \sin x(\sin^2 x + \sin^2 y).$ Fig. 6.

(2) $\qquad a(\sin y + \tan x)^2 = \tan x(\sin^2 y + \tan^2 x).$ Fig. 7.

(3) $\qquad a(\tan y + \sin x)^2 = \sin x(\tan^2 y + \sin^2 x).$ Fig. 8.

Examples XI.

1. $\qquad 2y^2(a^2+x^2)-4ay(a^2-x^2)+(a^2-x^2)^2=0.$

Prove that there are two cusps, the tangents to which cut the curve at a distance $\frac{4}{5}a$ from Ox, also that the curvatures at the points where the curve crosses Oy are very nearly in the ratio $1:16$.

2. $\qquad x^2(3y^2-4a^2)+y^4-6a^2y^2+4a^4=0.$

Shew that the radius of curvature where the curve crosses Ox is $\frac{1}{2}a$. If it cross Oy at B and C, prove that OB, OC are the radii of curvature at C, B.

3. $\qquad x^5=(x^2-y^2)(x^2-4y^2).$

Shew that the two loops on the negative side of yOy' run parallel to Oy near points $(-\frac{9}{16}, \frac{7}{16})$ and $(-\frac{9}{16}, -\frac{7}{16})$.

Shew also what parts of the curve are cut by the guiding asymptote $x^5=4y^4$.

4. $\qquad x^6=(x^2-y^2)(x^2-4y^2).$

Shew that the semi-cubical parabolas which are the guiding asymptotes cut the loops where $x=\pm\frac{2}{5}$ nearly.

5. $\qquad (x^2+y^2)^2-6axy^2+2ax^3=0.$

Shew that there are three loops, and that the tangents are parallel to Ox where $x+\frac{5}{4}a=0$ and $x=\frac{7}{8}a$ nearly.

6. $\qquad x^5=(x^2-y^2)(2x^2-5xy+2y^2).$

Prove that the lines joining the origin with the points of contact of tangents to the three loops which are parallel to Oy are $x+2y=0$, $3x=2y$, $3x=4y$ roughly.

7. $\qquad (y-x^2)(y-x^3)-y^2x=0.$

Examine the forms which correspond to the sides of the quadrilateral on the triangle. Shew on which side of the two guiding parabolic asymptotes the curve lies at the four ends.

8. $\qquad x^5y-ax^2y^3+\frac{1}{2}\sqrt{2}\,a^2y^4+a^4xy-\frac{1}{2}a^4x^2=0.$

Using the sides of the pentagon formed on the analytical triangle, shew that the guiding parabolic asymptote cuts the curve where $x=\frac{7}{20}a$ nearly, and that the semi-cubical parabolic asymptote cuts the curve in the quadrant xOy'.

9. $\qquad x^7+y^7-3a^2(x^5+y^5)+4a^3x^2y^2=0.$

Shew that there are two cusps and a double point; that the radius of curvature at the points where the curve meets the axes is $\frac{9}{4}a$; and that the branches of the double point make equal angles with $y=x$, each being $\tan^{-1}(\frac{1}{13}\sqrt{39})$.

PLATE
XVI.

10. $x^3y^2 = (y-x^2)(y-2x^2)(y-3x^2).$

Shew by the triangle and by compartments that there are two curvilinear asymptotes, and two very small loops ending near the points $(\frac{1}{6}, \frac{1}{24})$ and $(-\frac{3}{50}, \frac{9}{1000})$.

11. $(y^3-x)^2x^2 = (x^2-1)(x^2-4),$

or $y^3x^2(y^3-2x) = 4-5x^2.$

Use the method of compartments from the second form, and observe from the first form that x^2 cannot lie between 1 and 4.

12. $\sin^2 x = \cos y.$

Trace the curve, and shew that the radius of curvature at $(\frac{1}{4}\pi, \frac{1}{3}\pi)$ is nearly $\frac{14}{3}$.

13. $\sin^2 x + \cos^2 y = a\cos y.$

Trace the pattern corresponding to $a = \frac{1}{2}$ and 1.

14. $\tan^2 x + \sec^2 y - \tan x - \sec y = a^2 - \frac{1}{2}.$

Trace the pattern corresponding to the auxiliary circles inscribed in and circumscribed about the squares whose sides are $x = \pm 1$ and $y = \pm 1$, and $x = \pm\frac{1}{2}\pi$, $y = \pm\frac{1}{2}\pi$.

15. $(\cos^2 y + \sin^2 x)^2 - 6a\cos y\sin^2 x + 2a\cos^3 y = 0.$

Draw the repeating curve in the two cases in which the auxiliary curve of example 5 lies entirely within, and where part lies without the square formed by $y = \pm 1$ and $x = \pm 1$.

CHAPTER XII.

INVERSE PROCESS. A CURVE BEING GIVEN, TO FIND ITS EQUATION.

PLATE
XVII.

209. I propose in this last chapter to say a few words on methods of discovering equations which will represent the general form of a traced curve, at all events when it is known that the curve is capable of representation by means of an algebraical equation.

Of course there are difficulties which are unavoidable in the way of the exact determination of all the coefficients of the terms of an equation, some of which it will be well to point out, so that too much may not be expected from the treatment of this kind of problem.

210. If a curve could be supposed to be so accurately drawn that it would stand the test of measurement in every part, we could theoretically obtain equations for determining all the constants which would appear in the general equation of any degree which we might judge the curve to require. But in the case of curves which run off to infinity, the observations which I have made in Art. **27**, are sufficient to explain the impossibility of such accuracy in some of the most important parts of the curve. Again, it is impossible, except by some sort of convention as to drawing, to distinguish the degrees of closeness of contact of such parabolic forms as are given by $y^2 = ax$, $y^4 = ax^3$, $y^4 = a^3x$, and the misappreciation of the order of contact would affect the degree of the equation to be tried.

Such difficulties might be met by a verbal statement of the nature of the asymptotes and the forms at particular

PLATE XVII.

important points, at the same time that the curve is given in its general features.

If such statement be not made we must make the best approximation to which our experience in the direct treatment of curves may guide us.

211. The impossibility of the representation of a given curve by an algebraical equation would manifest itself in a variety of ways. A breach of continuity, for example, might exhibit itself by the curve passing off to an infinite distance by one branch without returning by another; for the continuity involved in an algebraical equation requires that, when a curve disappears along one branch of a rectilinear or parabolic asymptote, it should reappear either at the same or the opposite end, just as much as that the curve should not stop short at a finite distance; this could only be represented by the introduction of discontinuous functions.

212. In spite of the uncertainty which the difficulties mentioned above introduce, I think this exercise in the highest degree profitable, as an illustration of the manner in which, in physical subjects, difficulties arising from uncertain data and imperfect measurements are met and theories formed, which, as science advances, become nearer and nearer representations of the results given by experiments.

This must be my excuse for making this attempt, however imperfect, to shew how to deal with a problem which is in its nature not very precise.

213. The most obvious step towards this inverse process is to find as nearly as possible the degree of the curve. A lower limit to the degree is given at once by finding the greatest number, n, of points in which a straight line, drawn in the most favourable position, can be made to intersect the curve, since, in any position, there may be imaginary points of intersection, the degree of the equation may be $n + 2m$ where m is any positive integer.

PLATE
XVII.

For example, a curve whose equation is $x^4+y^4=c^4$ can only be cut by a straight line in two distinct points. Such a curve might be distinguished from a circle by its flatness where it meets the axes, but it would be hard to distinguish it from the curve $x^8+y^8=c^8$.

However, there will very often be some position of an intersecting line which will give as many real points of intersection as are exactly equal to the degree of the curve; at all events, it would be advisable to make the first attempt with such a degree.

214. The next necessary step is to select favourable positions for the coordinate axes to which it is intended to refer the curve. In this choice we are guided by many considerations, among which are symmetry, relations to the directions of asymptotes, contact of the axes with branches of multiple points, or, if we observe that there is one direction parallel to which all straight lines cut the curve in a smaller number of points than in any other direction, it may be advisable to take one of the axes, as that of x, in that direction, since, if there were no imaginary values, the highest power of x which would then appear in the equation would be less than for any other direction, and there would be a consequent diminution of the number of terms of the general equation which would have to be introduced.

The advantage of having the origin at a multiple point or cusp is obvious.

215. The terms involving the highest powers of one or both coordinates can be found from the first approximations to the asymptotic branches, if there be any, and those of the lowest powers from the forms near the origin; at the same time there might be imaginary branches which would not be revealed by the figure, and yet the corresponding factors would raise the indices of the highest powers; the fact of their existence could then be detected by the impossibility of representing the given form by the tentative equation.

PLATE XVII.

We must then adjust the intermediate terms so as to satisfy the conditions of magnitude and other peculiarities presented by the curve.

If, when a sufficient number of conditions have been taken into consideration to determine these intermediate terms, it should be found that other conditions are not satisfied, this would shew that an equation of a higher degree ought to have been tried, or that some error of magnitude has been made.

When the curve has not many special points, these tentative methods will be generally sufficient for the purpose.

In more complicated curves other processes will be required, but before proceeding to these I shall give a few examples of what I have been observing.

Ex. 1. Take the curve fig. 28, Plate III.

The principal features which have to be represented are the following :

It is at least of the fourth degree.

It is symmetrical with respect to a line which should be chosen as the axis of x.

It has no asymptotes.

Its shape near the origin is that of two parabolas, one of which has a smaller curvature than the other.

It has a multiple point on the x-axis, with its branches equally inclined to the axis.

It touches at two points a line perpendicular to the axis.

Assuming that it is of the fourth degree, there can be no odd powers of y; the terms of the highest powers must give imaginary results.

The equation which represents the form near the origin must be of the form

$$(y^2 - ax)(y^2 - bx) = 0,$$

so that the coefficients of y^2 in the complete equation must be of the form $\alpha x + \beta x^2$.

PLATE
XVII.

Where $y = 0$, the equation reduces to
$$\gamma^2 x^2 (x - c)^2 = 0.$$

To satisfy these conditions it is sufficient to assume the equation to be
$$y^4 + y^2(\alpha x + \beta x^2) + \gamma^2 x^2 (x - c)^2 = 0.$$

To determine the constants, measure the ordinate where $x = c$, and it will be found that $y = \tfrac{7}{4}c$, or $y^2 = 3c^2$ nearly, therefore
$$3c^2 + \alpha c + \beta c^2 = 0,$$
or
$$\alpha + \beta c = -3c. \qquad\qquad\ldots\ldots\ldots\ldots\ldots\ldots(A)$$

The greatest value of x is $\tfrac{9}{4}c$ nearly, and since
$$\{y^2 + \tfrac{1}{2}(\alpha x + \beta x^2)\}^2 = \tfrac{1}{4}x^2\{(\alpha + \beta x)^2 - 4\gamma^2(x - c)^2\},$$
we have $\qquad (\alpha + \beta x)^2 - 4\gamma^2(x - c)^2 = \delta^2(\tfrac{9}{4}c - x),$

hence $\qquad\qquad \beta^2 = 4\gamma^2, \quad \alpha^2 - \beta^2 c^2 = \tfrac{9}{4}c\delta^2,$

and $\qquad\qquad 2\beta(\alpha + \beta c) = -\delta^2; \qquad\ldots\ldots\ldots\ldots\ldots\ldots(B)$

therefore $\qquad\qquad \alpha - \beta c = -\tfrac{9}{2}\beta c,$

and by (A) $\qquad \tfrac{1}{7}\alpha = -\tfrac{1}{2}\beta c = -\tfrac{3}{5}c.$

The resulting equation is
$$y^4 - \tfrac{3}{5}(7c - 2x)xy^2 + \tfrac{9}{25}x^2(x - c)^2 = 0,$$
whence at the multiple point $y = \pm\tfrac{7}{20}\xi$ nearly, and near the origin $(y^2 - \tfrac{41}{10}cx)(y^2 - \tfrac{1}{10}cx) = 0.$

This does not coincide with the equation in the text, but sufficiently represents the general features, the discrepancy arising from a misappreciation of the magnitudes involved. With good drawing and accurate measurements as near an approximation as we like could be made.

Ex. 2. Take the curve fig. 28, Pl. IV.

This curve appears to be of the fifth degree.

Choosing the axes as in the figure, the form at the origin may be represented by $x^3 = ma^2 y.$

For any value of x there are only two values of y.

The asymptotes can be represented by $x = a$, $-a$, and $2a$ and $y = \pm a$.

The equation of the curve may therefore be written
$$(x^2 - a^2)(x - 2a)y^2 - a^2 x^3 + ma^4 y = 0.$$

PLATE
XVII.

When $x=0$, $y=-2a$, therefore $m=4$; this solution gives $(2a, 2a)$ as a point in the curve, and it is easily seen that the curve lies on the proper sides of the asymptotes.

The equation deduced is the same as that given in the text.

Ex. 3. Take fig. 17, Pl. III.

The curve may be of the fourth degree.

By observing the direction in which the branches at the triple point run, their equations, near that point, are reducible to

$$y-2x=a^2x^2, \quad y-x=-\beta^2x^2, \quad \text{and} \quad y+x=\gamma^2x^2;$$

the parabolic form at an infinite distance might be represented by $\quad y^2=\delta^2x, \quad \text{or} \quad y^4=\delta^3x, \quad \text{or} \quad \delta x^3,$

of these the last should be chosen, as representing a curve spreading more rapidly than the others.

The form of the curve as it crosses the axis of y appears to be given by $y-a+2x=-\epsilon^2x^2$.

These conditions are all satisfied by

$$a(y-2x)(y^2-x^2)=y^4,$$

which is the equation given in the text.

Of course, there being other conditions, such as the size of the loops, to be considered, it would be merely accidental if a curve of the fourth degree could represent all the conditions, since the arbitrary constants have been all exhausted.

Ex. 4. Take fig. 26, Pl. III.

Observe that in the form near the origin $y \infty x^2$ and $y^2 \infty x^3$, both are represented by the equation

$$2\delta y^3+\alpha x^3y+\beta x^5=0.$$

For the infinite branches $x=2$ and $y=\delta x^2$.

To fulfil these four conditions the equation may be written in the form

$$(x-2)(y-\delta x^2)y^2+\alpha x^3y+\beta x^5=0.$$

Since there is a multiple point near $(1, 1)$, the equation for determining y when $x=1$, viz.

$$y^3-\delta y^2-\alpha y-\beta=0,$$

PLATE
XVII.
must be $$(y-1)^2(y-\beta)=0;$$
$$\therefore \ \delta=\beta+2, \quad -\alpha=2\beta+1.$$

The equation now becomes

$$(x-2)(y-\delta x^2)y^2+(3-2\delta)x^3y-(2-\delta)x^5=0.$$

When $x=1$, $y=-\frac{3}{2}$ nearly, by the figure;

therefore $\qquad -\frac{3}{2}=\delta-2$ and $\delta=\frac{1}{2}$.

We have now arrived at the final equation

$$(x-2)(y-\tfrac{1}{2}x^2)y^2+2x^3y-\tfrac{3}{2}x^5=0.$$

It only remains to test the equation by some properties not yet used.

Near $(2, \infty)$, $x-2+16y^{-2}=0$, so that the curve lies to the left of the asymptote at both ends.

Near $(1, 1)$, let $\quad x=1+\xi, \quad y=1+\eta,$

since $\qquad y^3-\tfrac{1}{2}y^2-2y+\tfrac{3}{2} \equiv (y-1)^2(y+\tfrac{3}{2}),$

$$[(x-1)y-\tfrac{1}{2}\{(x-1)^2x-(x-1)\}]y^2+2(x^3-1)y-\tfrac{3}{2}(x^5-1)$$
$$=(y-1)^2(y+\tfrac{3}{2}),$$

whence $\qquad -(9+\tfrac{1}{2})\xi^2+10\xi\eta=\tfrac{5}{2}\eta^2;$

therefore $\ (\eta-2\xi)^2=\tfrac{1}{5}\xi^2$, and $\ \eta=\tfrac{2\cdot 2}{9}\xi$, or $\ \tfrac{1\cdot 4}{9}\xi$,

giving a proper result.

When $x=2$, $y=3$, while, according to the figure, y ought to be nearer to 2.

The equation differs altogether from the one given in the text, the divergence arising from the entirely different forms of the parabolic asymptotes. It is curious, however, to see how nearly the forms of the curves agree in all the essential points.

216. In more difficult cases it will be advisable to save trouble by making use of the properties of the analytical triangle, by means of which, when the terms which give the directions of infinite branches and branches of multiple points and cusps at the origin have been determined, it is seen exactly what intermediate terms may be introduced without affecting these directions.

METHOD BY THE TRIANGLE.

217. The arrangement of terms corresponding to infinite branches and multiple points is made easy by considering the property proved in Art. **145**, i., that all parallel lines containing circles which indicate terms of an equation give, when such are equated to zero, the same relation between x and y as far as degree is concerned; so that, if there be, for example, a point of inflexion at the origin, the branch touching one of the axes, an equation giving such a form would be $y^r = Ax^s$, where r and s are different odd numbers, and the same relation would be given for all parallel lines; the polygon must, therefore, have one of its lower sides parallel to the line $x/r + y/s = 1$.

218. If the form of the curve, whose equation is required, be represented in the neighbourhood of the origin by the two equations $x^r \infty y^s$ and $x^{r'} \infty y^{s'}$, in which $r/s < r'/s'$, let Ox, Oy be the sides of the triangle, intersected by AB, $A'B'$, where $OA = r$, $OB = s$, etc. Complete the parallelogram $B'OAF$, in Ox take $A'C = B'F = OA$, and in Oy take $BD = AF = OB'$, then DF, FC will contain circles which correspond to terms in the equation giving the required forms near the origin, if we take care that no circles lie between DFC and the right angle of the triangle. Thus the equation which would give the two forms might be $\alpha x^{r+r'} + \beta x^r y^{s'} + \gamma y^{s+s'} = 0$; thus, if we neglect $y^{s+s'}$, $x^{r'} \infty y^{s'}$, and the term was properly neglected if γy^s vanished compared with βx^r, or $x^{r'/s'}$ compared with $x^{r/s}$, which is the case, since $r/s < r'/s'$.

219. A similar argument holds for asymptotes with respect to the upper sides of the polygon.

If there be a rectilinear asymptote, one of the sides of the polygon must be parallel to the hypotenuse of the triangle.

If the asymptote pass through the origin, there is generally no circle at those angles which the side first encounters, when moved parallel to itself towards the right angle, the exception being when the same factor which gives the asymptote is also a factor of the terms of dimensions lower by unity.

If the curve cut one of the axes, we must take care that circles are placed on the corresponding side of the triangle, sufficient to give as many solutions as there are points of intersection.

220 Having thus selected convenient axes, and determined the direction of lines corresponding to tangents to the branches through the origin, as well as the equations representing first approximations to the asymptotic branches, a polygon must be drawn whose sides shall be parallel to these and contain no re-entering angles, the upper sides corresponding to the asymptotic branches, and, if the axes of coordinates intersect the curve, two of the sides being coincident with the sides of the triangle.

It will be seen that the sides of the polygon may often be made to cover less ground by the introduction of additional sides, taking care that the corresponding equations give imaginary solutions.

221. When the polygon is completed, circles indicating terms must be placed in the interior, so as to satisfy the other conditions of magnitude and position presented by the curve. We must then trust to our ingenuity, or, if we can rely on the correctness of the drawing, to our measurements, to determine suitable coefficients for the terms.

222. The advantage gained by this use of the triangle may be seen at once by trying to reproduce the equation of the curve given, Pl. VI. figs. 25 and 26, which may be of the seventh degree, the general equation of which would contain thirty-six terms.

The forms at the origin are given by $x - y^2 = 0$, $x^2 + y^3 = 0$, and $y^2 - x^4 = 0$; by the method of Art. **218**, these are represented by the simple equation

$$xy^5 - y^7 + x^3y^2 - x^7 = 0,$$

PLATE
XVII.

which also gives the line corresponding to the asymptote, so that the four sides of the polygon drawn in fig. 24 are given by this equation. If they had not been sufficient to represent the form of the curve in other respects, any of the six terms between x^7 and y^7 might have been inserted, having taken care that there was no real solution but $x+y=0$. One term x^5y might have been introduced between x^7 and x^3y^2, which would have had the effect of making the latera recta of the parabolic forms different, and only three terms more could have appeared, viz. x^2y^4, x^3y^3, x^4y^2. Even if every possible additional term had been introduced, the reduction of terms to be tried would have been very great.

223. Both in the direct and inverse process Des Cartes' rule of signs is invaluable as a test of correctness; thus, when x and y are both positive or both negative, there are only two changes of sign for a given value of x, so that in the quadrants xOy and $x'Oy'$, any line parallel to Oy meets the curve in two points or more, as in the fig. 25, Plate VI.; when x and y have opposite signs, x positive gives three changes, and y has either three negative values or one, x negative gives only one change, and y has only one positive value as in the figure.

224. I shall give a small number of examples of the manner in which, when the directions of the sides of the polygon are determined, they may be placed end to end, without attempting in every case to complete the equation in other respects.

225. **Ex. 1.** In the curve represented in the figure, if we make the point A the origin, and the tangent at the point of inflexion the axis of y, the forms at the origin could be represented by $y^3 = -a^2x$ and $x^3 = by^2$, giving directions ab, cd of the two lower sides of the polygon.

When $y=0$, $x+c=0$, so that one side of the polygon is on a side of the triangle.

Fig. 1.

Fig. 2.

PLATE
XVII.

$x^3 = d^2 y$ will apparently represent the infinite branches, and an upper side must be parallel to *ed*.

The polygon $\alpha\beta\gamma\delta\epsilon$ satisfies these conditions, with one side $\gamma\delta$ which we must take care to make correspond with an equation having imaginary solutions.

The equation

$$\alpha xy^2 + \beta y^5 - \gamma x^3 y^4 - \delta x^5 - \epsilon x^4 = 0$$

represents all the above forms which correspond to the sides of the polygon, the coefficients being chosen so as to identify the terms with the corresponding circles in the angles of the polygon; and it must be remembered that all the Greek letters are positive, that $\epsilon = c\delta$, and that the equation corresponding to $\gamma\delta$ gives an imaginary parabolic asymptote.

Again, since the form at B would be given by $y^3 = e^2(x+c)$, the coefficients of y and y^2 must vanish when $x = -c$. These conditions are satisfied by the introduction of terms involving $x^2 y^2$ and $x^3 y^3$, and the simplest equation to be tried is therefore

$$y^5 - \gamma x^3 y^4 - \zeta x^3 y^3 + \alpha(x+c)xy^2 - \delta(x+c)x^4 = 0.$$

Applying Des Cartes' rule of signs:

$$x > 0, \quad y+ \text{ gives } + - - + -,$$
$$y- \text{ gives } - - + + -,$$

consistent with one or more $+$, two $-$ values of y,

$$-c < x < 0, \quad y+ \text{ gives } + + + - -,$$
$$x- \text{ gives } - + - - -,$$

consistent with one $+$, one or more $-$ value of y,

$$-\infty < x < -c, \quad y+ \text{ gives } + + + + +,$$
$$y- \text{ gives } - + - + +,$$

consistent with no $+$, one $-$ value of y.

So also for the values x for any given value of y.

This form of the equation will therefore represent the curve with tolerable accuracy.

PLATE
XVII.

Fig. 3.
Fig. 4.

Ex. 2. The curve represented in fig. 3 may be of the sixth degree; the shapes near the origin appear to be $x+y=0$, and $y^2 = Ax$, corresponding to the sides $\alpha\beta$, $\beta\gamma$ of the polygon.

Near $(0, \infty)$, $xy^2 = B$ corresponding to $\gamma\delta$,

near (∞, ∞), $(x-y)^2 = 0$, „ „ $\delta\epsilon$,

near (∞, a), $y^3 - a^3 = 0$, „ „ $\epsilon\zeta$,

near $(2a, 0)$, $x - 2a = 0$, „ „ $\zeta\alpha$.

As far then as terms which correspond only to the perimeter of the polygon the equation would be

$$xy^3(x-y)^2 - a^3x^3 - sa^3y^3 + 2a^4x(x+y) = 0.$$

To determine what terms correspond to circles within the polygon, we must examine the effects of still nearer approximations.

Since the asymptote is met by the curve on both sides at the positive end, $(x-y)^2 = k^2/x$, so that there can be no term of the fourth degree, and the most general equation would be of the form

$$xy^3(x-y)^2 - a^3x^3 - sa^3y^3 + ra^3xy^2 + ta^3x^2y + 2a^4x(x+y) = 0.$$

Near $(2a, 0)$, $(t+1)y = x - 2a$,

therefore, according as we consider the tangent to be $y = x - 2a$ or $y = 2(x-2a)$, $t = 0$ or $-\frac{1}{2}$.

Apparently the bisectors of the angles between the axes meet the curve where

$$x = y = 2a, \quad \text{whence } s - r = 1 + t;$$

$$x = -y = a, \quad \text{whence } s + r = 5 + t;$$

$$\therefore r = 2, \quad \text{and} \quad s = 3 \text{ or } \tfrac{5}{2}, \quad \text{as} \quad t = 0 \text{ or } -\tfrac{1}{2}.$$

The complete equations are therefore on the two suppositions

$$xy^3(x-y)^2 - a^3x^3 + 2a^4x(x+y) + 2a^3xy^2 = 3a^3y^3, \ldots\ldots(i)$$

or $$= \tfrac{5}{2}a^3y^3 + \tfrac{1}{2}a^3x^2y. \ldots\ldots\ldots\ldots\ldots\ldots(ii)$$

It only remains to see which equation will best represent other apparent properties. Near $(0, \infty)$, $x = 3a^3/y^2$ and $\tfrac{5}{2}a^3/y^2$

PLATE
XVII.

in the two cases; when $x = 2a$, $y = 0$, and $2a$ in both cases, and the third value is given by

$$2y^2(y - 2a) - a^2(3y + 2a) = 0,$$

or $\qquad 2y^2(y - 2a) - a^2(\tfrac{5}{2}y + a) = 0,$

one giving y a little greater and the other a little less than $\tfrac{8}{3}a$, the other roots are impossible.

Near (∞, a), (i) gives $y = a - a^3/x^2$, whereas (ii) gives $y = a + \tfrac{1}{6}a^2/x$; hence (i) is alone admissible since the curve is below the asymptote at both ends.

To shew that (i) satisfies the conditions fairly we observe that the tangent at $(2a, 0)$ intersects the curve at $(\tfrac{3}{2}a, -\tfrac{1}{2}a)$ and $(a, -a)$, and that the next approximation to the tangent is $y = \xi - \xi^2/2a$, or that the curve bends downwards at $(2a, 0)$.

Near $(\tfrac{3}{2}a, -\tfrac{1}{2}a)$, $\qquad \eta = \tfrac{5}{6}\xi$;

near $(a, -a)$, $\qquad\qquad \eta = \tfrac{7}{5}\xi$;

these agree with the double bend in passing from $(2a, 0)$ to $(0, -\infty)$.

Again, the curve represented by (i) cuts the asymptote $y = a$, where $x = \tfrac{3}{5}a$.

Also, if $x = -my$, y is known from the equation

$$m(m + 1)^2 y^4 - (m^3 - 2m - 3)a^3 y - 2m(m - 1)a^4 = 0;$$

to obtain some idea of the size of the loop, let $m = \tfrac{1}{2}$, then

$$9y^4 + 31a^3 y + 4a^4 = 0,$$

whence $y = -\tfrac{3}{2}a$ and $-\tfrac{2}{15}a$ nearly, so that the loop is smaller than in the figure.

If we assign values to y and apply the rule of signs to the resulting equations in x, we find that the results agree with the figure, and similarly if we assign values to x.

Fig. 5. **Ex.** 3. The curve in the figure is apparently of the fourth degree, the form near the origin is represented by $(y - x)^2 = A^2 x^3$; near $(0, \infty)$, by $xy = B^2$; near (∞, a), by $x^2(y - a) = -C^2$; also near $(-a, 0)$, which is a point of the curve, $x + a + y = 0$.

PLATE XVII.

Fig. 6.

The bounding polygon contains the circles corresponding to the following terms

$$a^2(x-y)^2-(y-a)x^3-\gamma xy^3-\delta x^2y^2,$$

where γ is $+$, and $x^2+\delta xy+\gamma y^2=0$ has no real root.

The most general equation which can represent the curve, supposed of the fourth degree, is of the form

$$a^2(x-y)^2-(y-a)x^3-\alpha yx^2-\beta y^2x-\gamma xy^3-\delta x^2y^2=0.$$

Since near (∞, a) there is no term in x^{-1}, $a^2-\alpha a-\delta a^2=0$.

Near $(-a, 0)$,

$$ax^2(x+a)-2a^2xy-x^3y-\alpha x^2y=0,$$

which becomes $x+a+y=0$, if $\alpha=2a$, whence $\delta=-1$; β and γ can be determined by the apparent values of y when $x=-a$, viz., $y^2+3ay+2a^2=0$, and $y=0$. The equation so far obtained gives $y=0$, and

$$a(y+2a)+a^2-2a^2+\beta y+\gamma y^2+ay=0,$$

or

$$\gamma y^2+(\beta+2a)y+a^2=0 ;$$

$$\therefore\ 2\gamma=1,\quad 2\beta+4a=3a,\quad \beta=-\tfrac{1}{2}a,\quad \gamma=\tfrac{1}{2},$$

and the equation of the curve is

$$a^2(y-x)^2-(y-a)x^3-2ayx^2+\tfrac{1}{2}axy^2-\tfrac{1}{2}xy^3+x^2y^2=0.$$

It only remains to see how far this agrees with the given curve.

When $y=a$, $\qquad (x-a)^2-2x^2+x^2=0,$

$$\therefore\ x=\tfrac{1}{2}a, \text{ almost exact.}$$

When $y=x$, $\qquad x^3(x+a)=0,$

so that the tangent at O cuts the curve at $(-a, -a)$.

The equation corresponding to the upper side of the polygon is $x^2-xy+\tfrac{1}{2}y^2=0$, whose roots are imaginary.

Near (∞, a), $\qquad y-a=-2a^3x^{-2}$.

The tangent at $(-a, 0)$, viz., $y+x+a=0$, meets the curve where $a^2y^2-(2axy+x^2y)(x+a)+\tfrac{1}{2}xy^2(2a+3x)=0$ or $y^2=0$ and $a^2+3ax+\tfrac{5}{2}x^2=0$, whose roots are impossible, so that all the conditions are satisfied.

PLATE
XVII.

METHOD BY PARTIAL CURVES.

226. It is frequently possible to discover, from the form of the curve, simple partial curves, from which the given curve may be supposed to have degenerated. If we then form a single equation which will represent these partial curves, we may obtain at once terms which will form the required equation, by a proper alteration of the coefficients, or by the introduction of such terms as will prevent the equation from being split into simpler equations.

227. A simple case of the application of this method is to the curve represented in fig. 15, Pl. II., which may be supposed to be degenerated from a circle and two straight

Fig. 7.   lines, as in the figure.

The equation representing the partial curve is

$$(x^2 - y^2)(x^2 + y^2 - c^2) = 0,$$

from which we obtain an equation

$$x^4 - y^4 - a^2x^2 + b^2y^2 = 0,$$

which, if a be a little greater than b, would give the required curve.

Fig. 8.   **228.** The curve represented (Pl. XVII. fig. 8) can be conceived to have degenerated from the three dotted circles, whose equation is

$$\{(x^2 + y^2)^2 - 4a^2x^2\}(x^2 + y^2 - 4a^2) = 0,$$

and, considering the compartments within which the curve lies, the equation may be written

$$\{(x^2 + y^2)^2 - 4a^2x^2\}(x^2 + y^2 - 4a^2) + \alpha a^6 = 0.$$

When $x = 0$, one value of y is $\frac{2}{3}a$, by the figure; whence $\alpha = \frac{32}{45}(1 - \frac{1}{81})$, and the other value of y^2 is approximately

$$4a^2 - \alpha a^2/16 = 4a^2 - 2a^2/45, \quad \therefore \quad y = 2a - a/90.$$

Thus the curve is properly represented by this value of α.

If there were a conjugate point at the origin, we might write $a^4(\alpha x^2 + \beta y^2)$ for αa^6.

PLATE
XVII.

Fig. 9.

The curve (Pl. XVII. fig. 9) may be obtained from the partial curves whose equation is

$$(x^2 + y^2 - a^2)(x^2 - b^2)(y + c) = 0.$$

Assuming the equation of the curve to be

$$(x^2 + y^2 - a^2)(x^2 - b^2)(y + c) + ca^2 b^2 \gamma^2 = 0,$$

where γ is small compared with a, b, and c, the curve cuts Ox where $x^2 = a^2 - a^2 b^2 \gamma^2/(a^2 - b^2)$ or $b^2 + a^2 b^2 \gamma^2/(a^2 - b^2)$ nearly, which accounts for the two side loops, part of the darker curve.

If $x = 0$, $(y^2 - a^2)(y + c) = ca^2 \gamma^2,$

$\therefore$ $y = \pm a\{1 + \tfrac{1}{2} c\gamma^2/(c \pm a)\}$ and $-c\{1 - a^2 \gamma^2/(c^2 - a^2)\}$

which account for the position of the lower loop, and the upper infinite branch.

It will be found that the curvature at the first and second points on Oy is in the same direction and nearly equal to that of the guiding circle, and that at the third point the curvature is very small.

If $-\gamma^2$ be written for γ^2 we obtain the light curve.

Note. The side loops degenerate each into a very small oval touching the axis of x where $x^2 = \tfrac{1}{2}(a^2 + b^2)$, if

$$2a^2 b^2 \gamma^2 = (a^2 - b^2)^2.$$

In the figure $13b = 8a$ and $6c = 13a$ nearly.

229. The following examples will shew how the use of compartments may be combined with that of partial curves to obtain the equation of some curves.

230. Fig. 10 and fig. 11 represent curves which can plainly be derived from an ellipse and straight line as given by the dotted lines.

The equation of the curve in fig. 10 is of the form   Fig. 10.

$$(ax^2 + by^2 - 1)(y - c) + \alpha^2 = 0,$$

where α is a small quantity compared with those employed in the partial equations; for in the case of the oval $ax^2 + by^2 - 1$ is negative, and $y - c$ positive, and *vice versâ* for the remaining portion of the curve.

PLATE
XVII.

Fig. 11. To find the equation of the curve in fig. 11 we have to contrive that the partial curves shall be cut by the given curve in the three points A, B, C; as these points are placed in the figure they would lie in a parabola, and the equation of the curve would be of the form

$$(ax^2+by^2-1)(y-c)+\alpha^2(y^2-bx)=0.$$

If B had been in the line AC, the equation would have been

$$(ax^2+by^2-1)(y-c)-\alpha^2(x-d)=0.$$

231. The curves given in fig. 12 and fig. 13 are clearly derivable from a circle, and three lines forming an inscribed triangle.

Fig. 12. The equation of the curve in fig. 12 is of the form

$$(x^2+y^2-2cx)(y^2-m^2x^2)\{(1+m^2)x-2c\}+\alpha^2=0\ ;$$

Fig. 13. and since the curve in fig. 13 crosses the partial lines in A, B, C, D, E which lie in a line, the equation is of the form

$$(x^2+y^2-2cx)(y^2-m^2x^2)\{(1+m^2)x-2c\}$$
$$-\alpha^2(ax+by-1)=0.$$

Examples XII.

As examples the equations of the figs. 14–19 and each of the two curves in fig. 20 may be found ; fig. 19 represents half of the curve, whose equation is to be discovered, the curve being symmetrical with respect to $x'Ox$; the partial curves are indicated by dotted lines.

For general examples of this chapter, equations may be investigated to represent the curves 1, 2, 6, 9, 13, 15–18, 20, 21, 25, 28 traced in Pl. V.

CLASSIFIED LIST OF THE CURVES DISCUSSED.

CUBIC CURVES.

Figure (Plate, number)	Equation	Analysis (Page)
I. 8	$y = x(x^2 - 1)$	6
II. 5	$y = x^2 + x^3$	21
II. 6	$y = x(x^2 - 1)$	23
II. 7, 8, 9, 10	$cy^2 = x(x^2 + ax + b)$	23
II. 11	$y = \dfrac{a(x-a)(x-3a)}{x(x-2a)}$	24
II. 13	$(y^2 - 1)y = (x^2 - 4)x$	25
IV. 16	$x(y-x)^2 - b^2 y = 0$	73
IV. 18	$x(y-x)^2 - a^3 = 0$	76
IV. 22	$(x-a)y^2 - a^2 x = 0$	82
V. 1	$x^2(y+b) = y^2(x+a)$	88
V. 2	$x^3 + y^3 - 3axy = 0$	89
V. 3	$x(y-x)^2 = ay^2$	93
V. 6	$(x+2y)(x-y)^2 - 6a^2(x+y) = 0$	96
V. 8	$2x(x-y)^2 - 3a(x^2-y^2) + 4a^2 y = 0$	96
V. 9	$x(x+1)y = (x^2+x+1)(x-2)$	97
V. 10	$(x-a)y^2 = c^3$	98
V. 11	$(x-a)(x-b)y = c^3$	98
V. 15	$(y-x)(y-4x)(y+2x) = a^3$	100
V. 16	$(y-x)(y-4x)(y+2x) = 2a^2 x$	100
V. 17	$(y-x)(y-4x)(y+2x) = 8ax^2$	101
V. 30	$x^2 y - y^2 x = a(x-b)^2 - b(y-a)^2$	105
VII. 28	$xy^2 + 2a^2 y - ax^2 - 3a^2 x - 3a^3 = 0$	140
XIV. 1	$y(b^2 - y^2) = x^2(a-x)$	168

QUARTIC CURVES.

Figure (Plate, number)	Equation	Analysis (Page)
I. 9	$x^4 - 3axy^2 + 2ay^3 = 0$	6
I. 10	$x^4 - a^2xy + b^2y^2 = 0$	7
I. 12	$x^4 + a^2xy - y^4 = 0$	8
II. 12	$y^2 = \dfrac{a^2(x-a)(x-3a)}{x(x-2a)}$	25
II. 14	$y(y-1)(y-2) = x(x^2-1)(x-2)$	26
II. 15	$y^4 - 96a^2y^2 + 100a^2x^2 - x^4 = 0$	26
III. 1	$y = x(x-1)(x^2-1)$	32
III. 5	$a^3(y+x) - 2a^2x(y+x) + x^4 = 0$	45
III. 7	$y^4 - 2a^2y^2 + 2a^2x^2 - 3ax^3 + x^4 = 0$	47
III. 9	$a^2(x^2 - y^2) + x^4 + y^4 = 0$	48
III. 10	$a^2(x+2y)(y-2x) - a(y-2x)x^2 + y^4 = 0$	49
III. 13	$(ax - by)^2 - ax^2y - y^4 = 0$	51
III. 14	$(x-y)^2 - (x-y)x^2 - \frac{1}{3}x^4 - \frac{1}{9}y^4 = 0$	52
III. 16	$a^2(x^2+y^2) - 2a(x-y)^3 + (x^4+y^4) = 0$	53
III. 17	$a(y^2 - x^2)(y - 2x) - y^4 = 0$	55
III. 18	$a(y-x)(x^2+y^2) + x^4 = 0$	55
III. 19	$a(y-x)^2(y+x) - y^4 - x^4 = 0$	55
III. 22	$x^4 - axy^2 + y^4 = 0$	59
III. 23	$ax(y-x)^2 - y^4 = 0$	62
III. 24	$x^4 - a^2xy - b^2y^2 = 0$	62
III. 28	$(y^2+x^2)^2 - 6axy^2 - 2ax^3 + a^2x^2 = 0$	63
III. 29	$y^4 - 2axy^2 - 3a^2x^2 + x^4 = 0$	63
IV. 6	$x^4 - axy^2 - a^3y = 0$	65
IV. 7	$x^4 - axy^2 - ay^3 = 0$	65
IV. 8	$x^4 - a^2xy - ay^3 = 0$	65
IV. 9	$x^4 + ax^2y - ay^3 = 0$	65
IV. 10	$x^4 - axy^2 - a^2y^2 + by^3 = 0$	65
IV. 17	$y(y-x)^2(y-2x) + 3a(y-x)x^2 - 2a^2x^2 = 0$	75
IV. 21	$y^2(x^2 - y^2) - 2ay^3 + 2a^3x = 0$	77
IV. 20	$(x-a)y^3 = (y-b)x^3$	77
IV. 23	$(x-a)(x-b)y^2 - a^2x^2 = 0$	83
IV. 24	$y^2x(y-x) - ay^3 - byx^2 + a(a+b)x^2 = 0$	83
IV. 25, 26, 27	$(x-a)y^3 = (y-b)^2x^2$	84

FIGURE (Plate, number)	EQUATION	ANALYSIS (Page)
IV. 29, 30	$(xy - ab)^2 = b^2 d(c - y)$	86
IV. 32, 33	$x^2y^2 - 2a^2xy - b^2y^2 + 2a^2b^2 - b^4 = 0$	86
V. 4	$y(y - x)^2(y + 2x) = 9cx^3$	94
V. 5	$y(y - x)^2(y + 2x) = 3c^2x^2$	96
V. 7	$(x + 2y)^2(x - y)^2 - a^3(x + y) = 0$	96
V. 18	$(y - x)^2(y + x)(y + 2x) = 16a^4$	101
V. 19	$(y - x)^2(y + x)(y + 2x) = 6ax^3$	101
V. 26	$(x^2 - y^2)^2 - 4y^2 + y = 0$	104
V. 27	$y(y - x)^2(y - 2x) + 3a(y - x)x^2 - 2a^2x^2 = 0$	104
V. 28	$y^2x(y - x) - ay^3 - byx^2 + c^2x^2 = 0$	105
VI. 6	$a^3(y + x) - 2a^2x(y + x) + x^4 = 0$	111
VI. 7	$y^4 - 2(3x - 4a)ay^2 + a^2x^2 = 0$	112
VI. 8	$x^4 - 3ax^2y + 2a^2y^2 - ay^3 = 0$	112
VI. 12	$ay^2(y - a) - x^2(y^2 - a^2) + 2axy^2 - x^4 = 0$	113
VI. 14	$yx^2(y - x) - ay^3 - byx^2 + c^2x^2 = 0$	114
VI. 15, 16, 17	$(y - x - a)y^3 - byx^2 + mabx^2 = 0$	114
VII. 2	$(y^2 - x^2)^2 + 2axy^2 - 5ax^3 = 0$	124
VII. 22, 23	$y(y - \alpha)(y - \beta)(y - \gamma) = ax(x - \delta)(x - \epsilon)$	135
VII. 27	$(y^2 - x^2)(x - 1)(x - \tfrac{3}{2}) = 2(y^2 + x^2 - 2x)^2$	139
VII. 29	$(y^2 - x^2)^2 + 6axy^2 - 7ax^3 - 4a^2y^2$ $+ 18a^2x^2 - 20a^3x + 8a^4 = 0$	141
VIII. 1	$27y^4 - 9y^2(x^2 + 14ax + a^2) + 32a(a + x)^3 = 0$ or $(x - 5a)^{-\frac{1}{2}} + (4x - 6y + 4a)^{-\frac{1}{2}}$ $+ (4x + 6y + 4a)^{-\frac{1}{2}} = 0$	141
VIII. 2	$xy(x^2 - y^2) + ra^2(x^2 + y^2 - a^2) = 0$	144
VIII. 3, 4	$xy(x^2 - y^2) + a(x - c)(x^2 + y^2 - a^2) = 0$	145
X. 3	$xy^3 - 4x^3y + ay^3 + 3a^2xy + a^3x = 0$	151
X. 6, 7 XI. 1, 2, 3	$(y^2 - x^2)\{(\tfrac{1}{2}y - 1)^2 - x^2\} + \mu(y + a) = 0$	152
XI. 4	$(y^2 - x^2)\{(\tfrac{1}{2}y - 1)^2 - x^2\} = \pm c^2$	159
XII. 2, 3	$(y^2 + x^2)\{(\tfrac{1}{2}y - 1)^2 - x^2\} + \mu(y + a) = 0$	159
XII. 4	$(y^2 + x^2)\{(\tfrac{1}{2}y - 1)^2 - x^2\} = \pm c^2$	161
XIII. 2, 3, 4	$(y^2 + x^2)(\tfrac{1}{2}y - 1)^2 + x^2\} + \mu(y + a) = 0$	161
XIII. 5, 6	$(y^2 + x^2)\{(\tfrac{1}{2}y - 1)^2 + x^2\} = \pm c^2$	164
XIV. 3	$(x^2 - a^2)^2 + (y^2 - b^2)^2 = a^4$	169
XIV. 4	$a^2y^2(x - b)^2 = (a^2 - x^2)(bx - a^2)^2$	170

Figure (Plate, number)	Equation	Analysis (Page)
XIV. 6	$(x^2-4)^2 - y^2(y+16) = 0$	171
XIV. 7	$(y^2-ax)^2 + (x^2-ay)^2 = a^4$	172
XIV. 10	$a^3(y-x) - 2a^2(y^2-x^2) + a(y^3+x^3) - x^2y^2 = 0$	173
XIV. 11, 12	$(y^2-ax)(y^2-bx) + x^4 = \pm c^4$	174

CURVES OF THE FIFTH DEGREE.

I. 11	$x^5 - 2a^3x^2 + 5a^3xy - 2a^3y^2 + y^5 = 0$	8
III. 11	$a^3(y^2-x^2) - 2a^2(y^3+x^3) + ay^4 + x^5 = 0$	50
III. 20	$a^2(y-x)^3 - 2ax^4 + ay^4 - x^5 = 0$	55
III. 21	$2a^2(y-x)^2(y+x) - 4ax^3(y-x) + 2x^5 - x^4y = 0$	55
III. 25	$x^5 - a^2(x^3+y^3) + a^3xy = 0$	62
III. 26	$x^5 - 3bx^3y - bxy^3 + 4b^2y^3 = 0$	62
III. 27	$x^5 - ax^3y - axy^3 + a^2y^3 = 0$	63
IV. 1	$x^5 - ax^3y - 2a^2xy^2 + a^2y^3 = 0$	64
IV. 11	$x^5 - a^3xy - a^2y^3 = 0$	66
IV. 12	$x^5 - a^3xy - ay^4 = 0$	66
IV. 13	$x^3y^2 - ax^4 + a^2y^3 = 0$	66
IV. 14	$x^3y^2 - a^3x^2 + ay^4 = 0$	66
IV. 15	$x^5 - ax^4 - a^3xy + ay^4 = 0$	66
IV. 19	$x^5 + y^5 - 5ax^3y = 0$	76
IV. 28	$(x^2-a^2)(x-2a)y^2 - a^2x^3 + 4a^4y = 0$	85
IV. 31	$x^3y^2 - 2a^2x^2y + a^4x - b^5 = 0$	86
V. 12, 13, 14	$x^5 - ax^3y - bx^2y^2 + y^5 = 0$	98
V. 20	$x^5 - 2a^3xy + y^5 = 0$	102
V. 21	$x^5 - 5ax^2y^2 + y^5 = 0$	102
V. 22	$x^5 - a^2x^2y - b^2xy^2 + y^5 = 0$	102
V. 23	$y^2(3x-4y)^3 - a^4x = 0$	102
V. 25	$4a^2(y-x)^2(y+x) - 8ax^3(y-x) + x^5 + y^5 = 0$	103
VI. 2	$x^2(y-x)^3 - ay^4 = 0$	109
VI. 4	$axy^3 - (x-a)^4y + a^5 = 0$	111
VI. 5	$axy^3 - (x-a)^3y^2 + a^5 = 0$	111
VI. 28	$x(x^2-ay)^2 - y^5 = 0$	123
VII. 18, 19	$x(x^2-ay)^2 - y^4(y-c) = 0$	128
XIV. 9	$axy^3 - (x-a)^3y^2 + a^4x = 0$	172
XIV. 13	$y^2(x+y)^2(x-y) - 2a(x+y)x^2y - 4a^2x^3 = 0$	175

FIGURE (Plate, number)	EQUATION	ANALYSIS (Page)
XIV. 14	$x^5 = (x-y)^2(x+y)(x-2y)$	176
XIV. 18	$4y^2(x+y-a)^3 = (x-y-b)^5$	176

CURVES OF THE SIXTH DEGREE.

III. 15	$2(x-y-\frac{2}{3}x^2)^2 + (x+y)y^4 - y^6 - x^6 = 0$	53
IV. 2, 3, 4	$x^6 + ax^4y - cx^2y^2 + dxy^3 \pm ey^4 = 0$	64
IV. 5	$x^6 + a^2y^4 + a^2x^3y + a^3xy^2 = 0$	64
VI. 1	$x^6 + 2a^2x^3y - b^3y^3 = 0$	108
VI. 3	$a(x^5+y^5) - x^3y^3 = 0$	110
VI. 10	$a(x^5+y^5) - a^2x^3y + x^2y^4 = 0$	113
VI. 13	$c^6y^2 - (a+b)c^3x^3y + abx^6 - c^3x^3y^2 = 0$	114
VI. 23	$x^6 + 2a^2x^3y - b^3y^3 = 0$	122
VII. 4	$x^6 - 2bx^3y^2 - 2abx^4 + b^2y^4 - 2ab^2xy^2 + a^2b^2x^2 = 0$	124
VII. 24, 25	$y^6 + x^6 - ay^5 + a(ay-cx)x^3 = 0$	137
VII. 26	$(y^2-a^2)^3 + x^4(2x+3a)^2 = 0$	138
IX. 1	$x^6 - y^6 + a^3(x^3+y^3 - 3axy) = 0$	146
IX. 2	$x^6 - y^6 + a^2(x-a)(x^3+y^3 - 3axy) = 0$	146
IX. 3	$(y-2x+2a)(x-2y+2a)(x^2+y^2)xy$ $+ b^3(x^3+y^3-a^3) = 0$	146
IX. 4	$(y^2-ax)^2(x-a)^2 - a^2xy(x^2+y^2-a^2) = 0$	146
IX. 5	$(x^2-y^2)(x-a)y^3$ $- a^2(x^2+y^2-a^2)(x^2+y^2-4a^2) = 0$	147
X. 2	$(y-2x+2a)(x-2y+2a)x^2y^2$ $+ b(x^5+y^5+2a^3xy) = 0$	149
XIV. 16	$x^6 + a^2y^4 + a^2x^3y + a^3xy^2 = 0$	176

CURVES OF THE SEVENTH DEGREE.

V. 24	$\{x(y-x)-a^2\}^2y^3 = a^7$	102
V. 29	$x^7 - x^3y^4 + a^4y^3 - ax^2y^4 = 0$	105
VI. 9	$x^7 - x^4y^3 + a^3y^4 - axy^5 = 0$	112
VI. 11	$x^7 - a^3x^2y(x-y) + a^5(x-y)^2 = 0$	113
VI. 25	$x^3y^2 + xy^5 - y^7 - x^7 = 0$	60, 122
VII. 6, 7	$x^3y^4 + ax^2y^3 + by^2 + cx^4y + dx = 0$	125
VII. 11	$(y-a)^3x^4 - 2a^4(y-a)x^2 + a^4(x-a)y^2 = 0$	127
VII. 21	$6x^7 - 2x^5y^2 - a^3x^2y^2 + 4a^3x^3y$ $+ 2a^5x^2 - 3a^5xy + a^5y^2 = 0$	130
XIV. 2	$x^4y^3 = a^2(a-x)^3(a-2x)^2$	169

CURVES OF THE EIGHTH DEGREE.

FIGURE (Plate, number)	EQUATION	ANALYSIS (Page)
VII. 9	$a^3y^5 + x^2y^6 - x^5y^3 + ax^6y - a^6x^2 = 0$	126
XIV. 5	$(a^3y - x^4)^2 - a^4(x - 2a)^2(x^2 - a^2) = 0$	170

CURVES WITH EQUATIONS INVOLVING TRIGONOMETRICAL FUNCTIONS.

XV. 4	$\sin^3 x + \sin^3 y - 3a \sin x \sin y = 0$	179
XVI. 1	$\sin^3 x + \tan^3 y - 3a \sin x \tan y = 0$	181
XVI. 2	$\tan^3 x + \tan^3 y - 3a \tan x \tan y = 0$	181
XVI. 3, 4, 5	$\sin^3 x + \sec^3 y - 3a \sin x \sec y = 0$	181
XVI. 6	$a(\sin x + \sin y)^2 = \sin x(\sin^2 x + \sin^2 y)$	183
XVI. 7	$a(\sin y + \tan x)^2 = \tan x(\sin^2 y + \tan^2 x)$	183
XVI. 8	$a(\sin x + \tan y)^2 = \sin x(\sin^2 x + \tan^2 y)$	183

INDEX.

The numbers refer to pages.

Analytical Triangle, 117-122, 171, 193.
Approximation, rules for, 33.
  examples of, 34.
  to asymptotes, 79-82, 88-95.
  to tangents, 15, 39, 44.
  at multiple point, 45, 49, 51, 54.
  at point of inflexion, 42, 48, 49.
Asymptotes, 5, 23, 68, 69, 193.
  curvilinear, 107, 108.
  inflexional, 72.
  parabolic, 64, 65, 93, 108.
  parallel, 95, 98.
  parallel to axes, 80.
  not parallel to axes, 88-92.
  quasi-, 69, 108.
  determination of, 74.
  determination by approximation, 79-82.
  how curve approaches, 81, 91, 92.
Auxiliary equation, 29.

Beer, A., 152.

Change of origin, 3, 137.
Compartments, method of, 143.
Conjugate points, 5, 51, 53, 135.
Cubic equation, graphical solution of, 32.
Curvature, 17, 40.
  circle of, 18, 41, 43.
  conic of, 40, 41.
  diameter of, 18, 41, 44.
  at multiple point, 54.
Curvilinear asymptotes, 5, 69, 93, 107.
Cusp, 5, 15, 135.
  ramphoid, 5, 16, 51.
  keratoid, 5, 13, 16, 51.

Degeneration of curves, 24, 83, 135.
Degree of a curve, 23.
De Gua's Analytical Triangle, 58, 61, 117.
Des Cartes' Rule of Signs, 195, 196.
Double points, 45, 85.
  at infinity, 95, 98.

Guiding asymptote, 5, 62, 69, 108.

Homogeneous curves, 100.
  asymptotes to, 100.

Inflexion, point of, 5, 15, 22, 30, 31, 42, 48, 49.
  at infinity, 72, 97.
Isolated portions of a curve, 149.

Keratoid cusp, 5, 13, 16, 51.

Method of compartments, 143.
  of partial curves, 200.
Multiple points, 5, 45, 54, 134.
  at infinity, 72, 80, 95, 98.
  determination of, 85, 137.

Newton's Lemmas, 16.
  Parallelogram, 58, 117.
  Principia, 1.

Orders of quantities, 9, 58, 79.
Origin, change of, 3, 137.
  shape of curve near, 39, 45, 58.
Osculating branches of curve, 55.

Parabola, semicubical, 21, 24, 64, 65, 108.
Parabolic asymptotes, 64, 65, 93, 108.
  curves, 12, 20.

The numbers refer to pages.

Point, conjugate, 5, 51, 53, 135.
    double, 45, 85, 95, 98.
    multiple, 5, 45, 54, 134.
    of inflexion, 5, 15, 22, 30, 31, 42, 48, 49.
    of osculation, 5.
    singular, 5, 137.
Points of intersection at infinity, 69, 80, 97.

Quarterly Journal, 135.
Quartic equation, graphical solution of, 33.
Quasi-asymptote, 69, 108.

Ramphoid cusp, 5, 16, 51.
Repeating curves, 177.

Tangents, 15, 16, 39.
    approximations to, 15, 39, 44.

Theory of equations, 29.
Triangle, the Analytical, 117-122, 171, 193.
Trigonometric functions, graphs of, 28.
    curves whose equations involve, 177.

Semicubical parabola, 21, 24, 64, 65, 108.
Singular points, 5, 137.
Solution of equations, 32.
    of tan $x = x$, 35.
Special curve of fourth degree, 152.
Symmetry, 7, 133.

Walker and Walton, 135.
Wolstenholme, J., 142.